FAO
FOOD AND
NUTRITION
PAPER

52
Add. 5

Compendium of food additive specifications

Addendum 5

**Joint FAO/WHO Expert Committee
on Food Additives
49th session**
Rome, 17-26 June 1997

WORLD
HEALTH
ORGANIZATION

Food
and
Agriculture
Organization
of
the
United
Nations

Rome, 1997

M-84
ISBN 92-5-104023-0

INTRODUCTION

This volume contains specifications of identity and purity prepared at the forty-ninth meeting of the Joint FAO/WHO Expert Committee on Food Additives (JECFA), held in Rome, 17-26 June 1997. These specifications should be considered only in conjunction with the Report of the above meeting which will be printed in the WHO Technical Report Series. Toxicological monographs of the substances considered at the 49th meeting of JECFA will be published in the WHO Food Additives Series as No. 40.

The general principles applied in the elaboration of specifications established at the earlier JECFA sessions have been published in the Principles for the Safety Assessment of Food Additives and Contaminants in Food, WHO Environmental Health Criteria, No. 70, 1987. The specifications of identity and purity of food additives established by JECFA are meant to identify the substance that has been subject to biological testing, to ensure that the substance is of adequate degree of purity for safe use in food, and to reflect and encourage good manufacturing practices. These principles were last reaffirmed by the 39th session of JECFA in 1992.

The specifications are mainly established for the use of toxicologists and others concerned with the identity and purity of the substance. As agreed by JECFA at its twenty-sixth meeting, specifications may also be established prior to the eventual completion of toxicological evaluation, in certain cases, when the available toxicological data are inadequate or incomplete, and do not permit the establishment of full or temporary acceptable daily intakes (ADIs). References are made in individual specifications to some of the criteria that may be of interest in commerce, but they do not necessarily include all the requirements of interest to the commercial user. These specifications are not more stringent than is necessary to accomplish their purpose and should easily be attainable by the producing industries. The report of the twenty-third session gives the reasons why certain specifications are designated as "tentative".

There were a total of 204 specifications prepared at the 49th session of which 158 were new. Thirty-four specifications were designated as tentative. Specifications for anoxomer were withdrawn because the substance is no longer a product of commerce. Specifications for turmeric were withdrawn, because the Committee considered the substance as food. Specifications for enzyme-treated starches were included in the revised specifications for modified starches.

Comments and suggestions regarding this Volume are encouraged. Please send to Chief, Food Quality and Standards Service, Food and Nutrition Division, FAO, Via delle Terme di Caracalla, 00100 Rome, Italy.

NOTE: Use of *italics* in specifications refers to General Methods (Guide to JECFA Specifications), FAO Food and Nutrition Paper 5/Rev. 2 (1991), unless otherwise indicated or evident.

CONTENTS

SECTION A. Food additives (uses other than as flavouring agent)

Additive	**Page**

SECTION B. Flavouring agents

SECTION B. Flavouring agents

TENTATIVE	**ALPHA-ACETOLACTATE DECARBOXYLASE FROM BACILLUS BREVIS EXPRESSED IN BACILLUS SUBTILIS**

Prepared at the 49th JECFA (1997)

These specifications are designated tentative because Appendix B "General Considerations and Specifications for Enzymes from Genetically Manipulated Microorganisms" of Annex 1 of the Compendium of Food Additive Specifications, FNP 52, Rome 1992, is tentative.

SYNONYMS

ALDC

SOURCE

Produced extracellularly by submerged fermentation of *Bacillus subtilis* UW193 (a *dal*-transformant strain of ToC46) which through rDNA techniques contains the gene for α-decarboxylase from *Bacillus brevis* ATCC 11031 in plasmid pUW235. When fermentation is complete, the broth is filtered then stabilised with glutaraldehyde before further filtration.

ACTIVE PRINCIPLE

α-Acetolactate decarboxylase

SYSTEMATIC NAME AND NUMBER

(S)-2-Hydroxy-2-methyl-oxobutanoate carboxy-lyase
EC 4.1.1.5

REACTIONS CATALYSED

Decarboxylation of α-acetolactate to acetoin

DESCRIPTION

Commercial preparations are brown liquids containing the active enzyme. These preparations are standardised with glycerol and lactic acid and preserved with 0.2% potassium sorbate

FUNCTIONAL USES

Enzyme preparation
Processing aid in the brewing of beer and fermentation step of alcohol production

GENERAL SPECIFICATIONS

Must conform to the "General Specifications for Enzyme Preparations Used in Food Processing" in Annex 1 of the Compendium of Food Additive Specifications, FAO Food and Nutrition Paper 52, Rome 1992.

CHARACTERISTICS

IDENTIFICATION

α-Acetolactate decarboxylase activity

The sample shows α-acetolactate decarboxylase activity
See description under TESTS

TESTS
α-Acetolactate decarboxylase activity

PRINCIPLE

The enzyme α-acetolactate decarboxylase (ALDC) decarboxylates α-acetolactate to produce acetoin. The resultant acetoin can be reacted with a mixture of naphthol and creatine, resulting in quantitative formation of a characteristic red colour.

APPARATUS

1. Spectrophotometer or equivalent capable of measuring optical density (absorbance) at 522 nm
2. Water bath, held at 30±1°, containing test tube rack
3. Volumetric glassware

REAGENTS

1. MES buffer, 0.05M (pH = 6.0).
Dissolve 9.76 g of MES (2-(N-morpholino) ethanesulphonic acid) in approximately 900 ml of deionised water. Adjust pH to 6.0 ± 0.5 with 1 N NaOH. Transfer to a 1-litre volumetric flask and make to volume with deionised water. This solution may be kept for two weeks at room temperature.

2. Brij 35 solution, 15% w/v.
Dissolve 15.0 g of Brij 35 (polyoxyethylene lauryl ether, Atlas Chemie, BDH, or equivalent) in approximately 70 ml of deionised water, heating to 60° to aid dissolution. After cooling, transfer to a 100-ml volumetric flask and make to volume with deionised water. This solution should be stored in a refrigerator, and can be kept for up to two months.

3. MES/Brij 35/NaCl solution.
Dissolve 48.8 g of MES and 175.32 g of NaCl (AR grade) in approximately 4.5 litres of deionised water. Add 17 ml of 15% Brij 35 solution (see 2. above). Adjust pH to 6.0 ± 0.5 with 1 N NaOH. Transfer to a 5-litre volumetric flask and make to volume with deionised water. This solution may be kept for two weeks at room temperature.

4. α-Acetolactate substrate, 0.2% v/v.
Pipette 100 μl of ethyl-2-acetoxy-2-methylacetolactate into a 50 ml volumetric flask. Add 6.0 ml of 0.5 N NaOH to the flask and stir for 20 minutes. Add MES buffer (see 1. above) to bring the volume to approximately 40 ml. Adjust pH to 6.0 ± 0.5 with 0.5 N HCl. Make to volume with MES buffer (see 1. above). This substrate should be made just before use.

5. Naphthol/Creatine colour reagent.
Dissolve 5.00 g of 1-naphthol and 0.50 g of creatine in 1 N NaOH, make to volume with 1 N NaOH in a 500-ml volumetric flask. This colour reagent should be made fresh just before use and shielded from light as much as possible.

6. Acetoin stock solution, 1000 mg/l.
Dissolve 0.100 g of acetoin (3-hydroxy-2-butanone) in deionised water in a 100-ml volumetric flask. Make to volume with deionised water.

7. Acetoin standards.
Dilute 0, 1.0, 2.0, 4.0, 6.0, and 8.0 ml of stock acetoin solution (see 6. above) to volume with deionised water in 100-ml volumetric flasks to give standard solutions of 0, 10, 20, 40, 60, and 80 mg/l of acetoin. These solution may be kept for two weeks stored in a refrigerator.

8.   Enzyme solutions.

Test samples of the enzyme α-acetolactate decarboxylase (ALDC) are diluted with MES/Brij 35/NaCl solution (see 3. above). The exact dilution will need to be determined by experience and experimentation to give an enzyme concentration which produces a result within the range of the acetoin standards (see 7. above) under the conditions of the test.

PROCEDURE

Preparation of standard curve

Prepare a standard curve by treating the acetoin standards (7.) in the following manner:

Pipette 400 μl of the acetoin standard solutions into 10-ml plastic test tubes. Add 4.6 ml of colour reagent (5.) to each test tube, mix, and let the test tube stand at room temperature for exactly 40 minutes. At the end of this 40 minute period, place 0 mg/l acetoin standard in the spectrophotometer set to read absorbance at 522 nm and adjust absorbance reading to zero. Measure the absorbance of the remaining acetoin standards at 522 nm.

Determination of enzyme activity

Preheat enzyme solutions (see 8. above), MES buffer (see 1. above), and the substrate (see 4. above) in a water bath at 30± 1°C for approximately 10 minutes.

Four solutions must be prepared for each analysis:

1. Enzyme blank (B1). Pipette 200 μl of enzyme solution (8.) and 200 μl of MES buffer (1.) into a 10 ml plastic test tube. Mix, and immediately place the test tube back into the water bath.

2. Sample value (H1). Pipette 200 μl of enzyme solution (8.) and 200 μl of substrate (4.) into a 10 ml plastic test tube. Mix, and immediately place the test tube into the water bath.

3. Buffer blank (B2). Pipette 200 μl of MES buffer (1.) and 200 μl of MES/Brij 35/NaCl solution (3.) into a 10 ml plastic test tube. Mix, and immediately place the test tube into the water bath.

4. Buffer value (H2). Pipette 200 μl of MES/Brij 35/NaCl solution (3.) and 200 μl of substrate (4.) into a 10 ml plastic test tube. Mix, and immediately place the test tube into the water bath.

For each enzyme determination the test tubes, are prepared in the order: B1, H1, B2, H2.

Exactly 20 minutes after mixing of each of solutions B1, H1, B2, and H2, remove from water bath, add 4.6 ml of colour reagent (5.), mix and leave at room temperature for exactly 40 minutes. At the end of this 40 minute period measure the absorbance of the solutions at 522 nm on a spectrophotometer or equivalent. previously adjusted so that the 0 mg/l acetoin standard gives an absorbance reading of zero.

CALCULATION

The activity of the ALDC enzyme is defined in terms of activity units where:

1 ADU (α-Acetolactate Decarboxylase Unit) = the amount of enzyme which, by decarboxylation of α-acetolactate produces 1 μmol of acetoin per minute under the test reaction conditions.

Plot optical density values at 522 nm for the acetoin standards against acetoin concentration (in mg acetoin/l) of the standard and generate a standard curve. Use the standard curve to convert the optical density measurements for solutions H1, B1, H2, and B2 to mg acetoin/l.

Activity of enzyme (in ADU/g) = $\dfrac{\{([H1] - [B1]) - ([H2] - [B2])\} \times 0.0011351 \times F}{W}$

Where.:

$[H1]$, $[B1]$, $[H2]$, $[B2]$	are the concentrations of acetoin in the respective solutions in mg/l
F	is the final volume of enzyme solution, after dilutions, in millilitres
W	is the weight of enzyme in volume F, in grams

The factor 0.0011351 contains:

• the conversion from mg acetoin/l to μmol acetoin/min
• the conversion for the actual volumes of substrate and enzyme solution used in the analysis.

AGAR

Prepared at the 49th JECFA (1997)
superseding specifications prepared at the 44th JECFA (1995),
published in FNP 52 Addendum 3 (1995)

SYNONYMS   Agar-agar; gelose; Japan agar; Bengal, Ceylon, Chinese or Japanese isinglass; Layor Carang; INS No. 406

DEFINITION   Agar is the dried hydrophilic, colloidal substance extracted from certain marine algae of the class *Rhodophyceae*. It is a polysaccharide, consisting primarily of D- and L-galactose units. About every tenth D-galactopyranose unit contains a sulfate ester group. Calcium, magnesium, potassium or sodium cations are also associated with the polysaccharide.

C.A.S. number   9002-18-0

Assay   Not higher than 0.25% for threshold gel concentration

DESCRIPTION   Agar is odourless or has a slight characteristic odour. Unground agar usually occurs in bundles consisting of thin, membranous, agglutinated strips, or in cut, flaked, granulated or powdered forms. It may be light yellowish orange, yellowish grey to pale yellow, or colourless. It is tough when damp, brittle when dry. Powdered agar is white to yellowish white or pale yellow.

FUNCTIONAL USES   Thickener, stabilizer, emulsifier

CHARACTERISTICS

IDENTIFICATION

Solubility   Insoluble in cold water; soluble in boiling water

Gel formation with water
Passes test
See description under TESTS

Precipitate formation with ammonium sulfate solution
Passes test
See description under TESTS

Precipitate formation with lead acetate solution
Passes test
See description under TESTS

Microscopy   Passes test
See description under TESTS

PURITY

Water absorption   Passes test
See description under TESTS

Loss on drying	Not more than 22% after drying at 105° until the difference between two weighings is less than 1 mg (about 5 h). Unground agar should be cut into pieces from 2 to 5 mm² before drying.
Total ash	Not more than 6.5% on the dried basis
Acid-insoluble ash	Not more than 0.5% on the dried basis
Foreign insoluble matter	Not more than 1% See description under TESTS
Arsenic	Not more than 3 mg/kg (Method II)
Lead	Not more than 5 mg/kg Prepare a sample solution as directed for organic compounds in the Limit Test, using 5 µg of lead ion (Pb) in the control
Starch and dextrins	Not detectable See description under TESTS
Gelatin and other proteins	Not detectable See description under TESTS
Microbiological criteria	Total plate count: Not more than 5,000 colonies per gram. Initially prepare a 10^{-1} dilution by adding a 50 g sample to 450 ml of Butterfield's phosphate buffered dilution water and homogenizing in a high speed blender. Yeasts and moulds: Not more than 500 colonies per gram Coliforms: Negative by test Salmonella: Negative by test

TESTS

IDENTIFICATION TESTS

Gel formation with water

Prepare a 1.0% solution of the sample in boiling water in a flask and place the flask in water at 30° for 15 min. A firm, resistant gel is formed. Place the flask in water at 70° for 1 h, the gel is not molten. When heating the flask at higher temperature than 95°, gel is liquefied to form a clear solution.

Precipitate formation with ammonium sulfate solution

A warm (40°) 0.5% solution of the sample gives a precipitate with half its volume of a warm (40°) 40% ammonium sulfate solution. This test distinguishes agar from alginates, gum arabic, gum ghatti, karaya gum, pectin and tragacanth.

Precipitate formation with lead acetate solution

A warm 0.5% solution of the sample gives a precipitate with one fifth its volume of basic lead acetate TS. This test distinguishes agar from methyl cellulose.

Microscopy

Place a few fragments of unground agar or some powder on a slide and add some drops of water or chloral hydrate TS. When examined under a microscope, agar in water appears granular and somewhat filamentous. In chloral hydrate TS, the powdered agar appears more transparent than in water.

PURITY TESTS

Water absorption

Place 5 g of the sample in a 100-ml graduated cylinder, fill to the mark with water, mix, and allow to stand at 25° for 24 h. Pour the contents of the cylinder through moistened glass wool, allowing the water to drain into a second 100-ml graduated cylinder. Not more than 75 ml of water should be obtained.

Foreign insoluble matter   Boil 5 g of the sample with 500 ml of water and 12 ml of sulfuric acid under a reflux condenser for 2 h. Allow to cool and filter through a tared, fine, sintered glass crucible. Wash flask and filter with 50 ml of water, dry at 105° to constant weight and weigh. Calculate as percentage.

Starch and dextrins

To a warm (40°) 0.5% solution of the sample, add 2 drops of iodine TS. Where the drops fall, a red-violet colour appears. After mixing, the solution should be golden brown and not blue or reddish.

Gelatin and other proteins

To a warm (40°) 0.5% solution of the sample add 1 volume of warm (40°) picric acid TS. No turbidity should appear within 10 min.

METHOD OF ASSAY   Threshold gel concentration: Prepare serial dilutions of the sample with known solids content (0.15%, 0.20%, 0.25%, etc.) and place in tubes, 150 mm long by 16 mm internal diameter, stoppered at both ends. Cool for 1 h at 20-25°. Allow cylinders of gel to slide from the tubes to a level surface. The lowest concentration of gel that resists gravity without rupture for 5-30 sec is the threshold concentration of the sample.

ALGINIC ACID

Prepared at the 49th JECFA (1997)
superseding specifications prepared at the 44th JECFA (1995),
published in FNP 52 Addendum 3 (1995)

SYNONYMS   INS No. 400

DEFINITION   Alginic acid is a naturally occurring hydrophilic colloidal polysaccharide obtained from the various species of brown seaweed (*Phaeophyceae*). It is a linear copolymer consisting mainly of residues of ß-1,4-linked D-mannuronic acid and α-1,4-linked L-glucuronic acid. These monomers are often arranged in homopolymeric blocks separated by regions approximating an alternating sequence of the two acid monomers.

C.A.S. number   9005-32-7

Chemical formula $(C_6H_8O_6)_n$

Structural formula   Structural formula from Phillips, Wedlock and Williams: Gums and Stabilizers for the Food Industry 5 (1990) by permission of Oxford University Press.

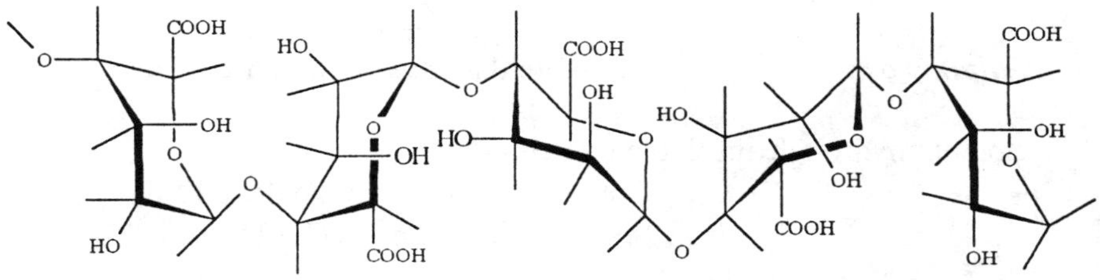

$$\underline{\quad\quad} G(^1C_4) \underline{\quad\quad} G(^1C_4) \underline{\quad\quad} M(^4C_1) \underline{\quad\quad} M(^4C_1) \underline{\quad\quad} G$$

$$\qquad\quad \alpha\text{-}1,4 \qquad\qquad \alpha\text{-}1,4 \qquad\qquad \text{ß-}1,4 \qquad\qquad \text{ß-}1,4$$

The number and sequence of the Mannuronate and Glucuronate residues shown above vary in the naturally occurring alginate. The associated water molecules are not shown.

Formula weight   Structural unit: 176.13 (theoretical)
                                                   200 (actual average)
                           Macromolecule :   10,000 - 600,000 (typical average)

Assay   Yields, on the dried basis not less than 20.0% and not more than 23.0% of carbon dioxide (CO_2), equivalent to not less than 91.0% and not more than 104.5% of alginic acid $(C_6H_8O_6)_n$.

DESCRIPTION   Occurs as white to yellowish brown filamentous, grainy, granular or powdered forms

FUNCTIONAL USES   Stabilizer, thickener, gelling agent, emulsifier

CHARACTERISTICS

IDENTIFICATION

Solubility   Insoluble in water and organic solvents; dissolves slowly in solutions of sodium carbonate, sodium hydroxide and trisodium phosphate

pH   2.0-3.5 (0.3 in 10 suspension)

Precipitate formation with calcium chloride
          Passes test
          See description under TESTS

Precipitate formation with with ammonium sulfate
          Passes test
          See description under TESTS

Test for alginate   Passes test
          See description under TESTS

PURITY

Loss on drying   Not more than 15% (105°, 4 h)

Sulfated ash   Not more than 8% on the dried basis

Sodium hydroxide insoluble matter
          Not more than 2% on the dried basis
          See description under TESTS

Arsenic   Not more than 3 mg/kg (Method II)

Lead   Not more than 5 mg/kg
          Prepare a sample as directed for organic compounds in the Limit Test, using 5 µg of lead ion (Pb) in the control

Microbiological criteria Total plate count: Not more than 5,000 colonies per gram.

          Initially prepare a 10^{-1} dilution by adding a 50 g sample to 450 ml of Butterfield's phosphate buffered dilution water and homogenizing in a high speed blender.

          Yeasts and moulds: Not more than 500 colonies per gram

          Coliforms: Negative by test

          Salmonella: Negative by test

TESTS

IDENTIFICATION TESTS

Precipitate formation with calcium chloride

To a 0.5% solution of the sample in sodium hydroxide TS add one-fifth of its volume of a 2.5% solution of calcium chloride. A voluminous, gelatinous precipitate is formed. This test distinguishes alginic acid from gum arabic, sodium carboxymethyl cellulose, carrageenan, gelatin, gum ghatti, karaya gum, carob bean gum, methyl cellulose and tragacanth gum.

Precipitate formation with ammonium sulphate

To a 0.5% solution of the sample in sodium hydroxide TS add one-half of its volume of a saturated solution of ammonium sulfate. No precipitate is formed. This test distinguishes alginic acid from agar, sodium carboxymethyl cellulose, carrageenan, de-esterified pectin, gelatin, carob bean gum, methyl cellulose and starch.

Test for alginate

Dissolve as completely as possible 0.01 g of the sample by shaking with 0.15 ml of 0.1 N sodium hydroxide and add 1 ml of acid ferric sulfate TS. Within 5 min, a cherry-red colour develops that finally becomes deep purple.

PURITY TESTS

Sodium hydroxide insoluble matter

Weigh accurately about 1 g of the sample and dissolve in 100 ml of sodium hydroxide TS, centrifuge and decant. Wash the residue five times with water by mixing, centrifuging and decanting. Transfer the residue by means of water to a tared fine glass filter, dry for 1 h at 105°, cool and weigh. Calculate as percentage of the dry weight.

METHOD OF ASSAY

Proceed as directed under Carbon Dioxide Determination by Decarboxylation in the *General Methods*. Each ml of 0.25 $\underline{N}$ sodium hydroxide consumed is equivalent to 5.5 mg of carbon dioxide (CO_2) or 25 mg of alginic acid (equivalent weight 200).

ALUMINIUM POWDER

Prepared at the 49th JECFA (1997)
superseding specifications prepared at the 39th JECFA (1992),
published in FNP 52 Addendum 1 (1992)

SYNONYMS	CI Pigment Metal
	CI (1975) No. 77000, INS No. 173
DEFINITION	Aluminium powder is produced by grinding aluminium in the presence of edible vegetable oils and/or food grade fatty acids.
Chemical name	Aluminium
C.A.S number	7429-90-5
Chemical formula	Al
Atomic weight	26.98
Assay	Not less than 99.0%
DESCRIPTION	A silvery grey powder
FUNCTIONAL USES	Colour, surface colourant

CHARACTERISTICS

IDENTIFICATION

Solubility	Insoluble in water
	Insoluble in organic solvents
	Soluble in dilute hydrochloric acid
Test for Aluminium	Passes test

PURITY

Loss on drying	Not more than 0.5% (105°)
Arsenic	Not more than 3 mg/kg
Lead	Not more than 20 mg/kg
Heavy metals	Not more than 40 mg/kg
	Test 0.5 g of the sample as directed in the Limit Test (Method II)
METHOD OF ASSAY	Wash a small sample in hexane, repeating to remove traces of any associated oil or fatty acid. Transfer about 0.2 g of the sample, accurately weighed, to a 500-ml flask fitted with a rubber stopper carrying a 150-ml separating funnel, an inlet tube connected to a cylinder of carbon dioxide and an outlet tube dipping into a water-trap. Add 60 ml of freshly boiled and cooled water and disperse the sample; replace the air by carbon dioxide and add, by the

separating funnel, 100 ml of a solution containing 56 g of ferric ammonium sulfate and 7.5 ml of sulfuric acid in freshly boiled and cooled water. While maintaining an atmosphere of carbon dioxide in the flask, heat to boiling and boil for 5 min. After the sample has dissolved, cool rapidly to 20°, and dilute to 250 ml with freshly boiled and cooled water. To 50 ml of this solution, add 15 ml of phosphoric acid and titrate with 0.1 N potassium permanganate. 1 ml of 0.1 N potassium permanganate = 0.8994 mg Al.

AMMONIUM ALGINATE

Prepared at the 49th JECFA (1997)
superseding specifications prepared at the 44th JECFA (1995),
published in FNP 52 Addendum 3 (1995)

SYNONYMS INS No. 403

DEFINITION Ammonium alginate is the ammonium salt of alginic acid.

C.A.S. number 9005-34-9

Chemical formula $(C_6H_{11}NO_6)_n$

Structural formula Structural formula from Phillips, Wedlock and Williams: Gums and Stabilizers for the Food Industry 5 (1990) by permission of Oxford University Press.

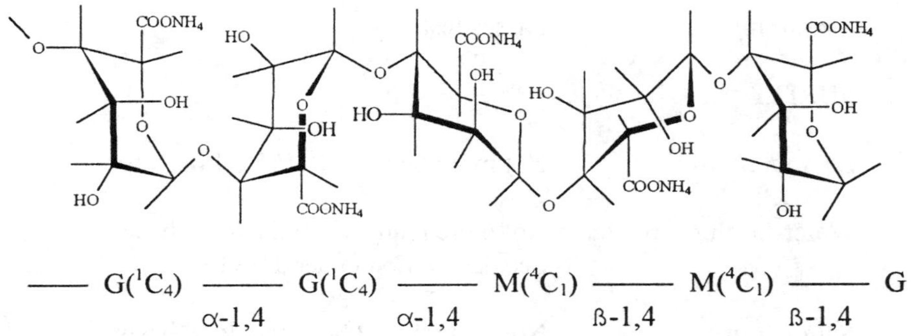

$$\text{---} \; G(^1C_4) \; \text{---} \; G(^1C_4) \; \text{---} \; M(^4C_1) \; \text{---} \; M(^4C_1) \; \text{---} \; G$$
$$\alpha\text{-}1,4 \qquad \alpha\text{-}1,4 \qquad \text{ß-}1,4 \qquad \text{ß-}1,4$$

The number and sequence of the Mannuronate and Glucuronate residues shown above vary in the naturally occuring alginate. The associated water molecules are not shown.

Formula weight Structural unit : 193.16 (theoretical)
217 (actual average)
Macromolecule : 10,000 - 600,000 (typical average)

Assay Yields, on the dried basis, not less than 18.0% and not more than 21.0% of carbon dioxide (CO_2), equivalent to not less than 88.7% and not more than 103.6% of ammonium alginate $C_6H_{11}NO_6)_n$.

DESCRIPTION Occurs as white to yellowish brown filamentous, grainy, granular or powdered forms

FUNCTIONAL USES Stabilizer, thickener, gelling agent, emulsifier

CHARACTERISTICS

IDENTIFICATION

Solubility   Dissolves slowly in water forming a viscous solution; insoluble in ethanol, and ether

Precipitate formation with calcium chloride
> Passes test
> See description under TESTS

Precipitate formation with ammonium sulfate
> Passes test
> See description under TESTS

Test for alginate   Passes test
> See description under TESTS

Ammonium   Passes test

PURITY

Loss on drying   Not more than 15% (105°, 4 h)

Water-insoluble matter   Not more than 2% on the dried basis
> See description under TESTS.

Sulfated ash   Not more than 7% on the dried basis

Arsenic   Not more than 3 mg/kg (Method II)

Lead   Not more than 5 mg/kg
> Prepare a sample solution as directed for organic compounds in the Limit Test, using 5 μg of lead ion (Pb) in the control

Microbiological criteria Total plate count: Not more than 5,000 colonies per gram.

> Initially prepare a 10^{-1} dilution by adding a 50 g sample to 450 ml of Butterfield's phosphate buffered dilution water and homogenizing in a high speed blender.

> Yeasts and moulds: Not more than 500 colonies per gram

> Coliforms: Negative by test

> Salmonella: Negative by test

TESTS

IDENTIFICATION TESTS

Precipitate formation with calcium chloride

To a 0.5% solution of the sample in sodium hydroxide TS add one-fifth of its volume of a 2.5% solution of calcium chloride. A voluminous, gelatinous precipitate is formed. This test distinguishes ammonium alginate from gum arabic, sodium carboxymethyl cellulose, carrageenan, gelatin, gum ghatti, karaya gum, carob bean gum, methyl cellulose and tragacanth gum.

Precipitate formation with ammonium sulphate

To a 0.5% solution of the sample in sodium hydroxide TS add one-half of its volume of a saturated solution of ammonium sulfate. No precipitate is formed. This test distinguishes ammonium alginate from agar, sodium carboxymethyl cellulose, carrageenan, de-esterified pectin, gelatin, carob bean gum, methyl cellulose and starch.

Test for alginate

Dissolve as completely as possible 0.01 g of the sample by shaking with 0.15 ml of 0.1 N sodium hydroxide and add 1 ml of acid ferric sulfate TS. Within 5 min, a cherry-red colour develops that finally becomes deep purple.

PURITY TESTS

Water-insoluble matter

Disperse 2 g of the sample, weighed to the nearest 0.1 mg, in 800 ml of water in a 2,000-ml flask. Neutralize to pH 7 with sodium hydroxide TS and then add 3 ml in excess. Add 40 ml of hydrogen peroxide solution containing 30% by weight H_2O_2, cover the flask and boil for 1 h with frequent stirring. Filter while hot through a tared Gooch crucible provided with a glass fibre filter (2.4 cm, No. 934 AH, Reeve Angel & Co., Clifton, N.Y., or equivalent filter). If slow filtration is caused by high viscosity of the sample solution, boil until the viscosity is reduced enough to permit filtration. Wash the crucible thoroughly with hot water, dry the crucible and its contents at 105° for 1 h, cool and weigh. Calculate as percentage of the dry weight.

METHOD OF ASSAY

Proceed as directed under Carbon Dioxide Determination by Decarboxylation in the *General Methods*. Each ml of 0.25 N sodium hydroxide consumed is equivalent to 5.5 mg of carbon dioxide (CO_2) or 27.12 mg of ammonium alginate (equivalent weight 217).

CALCIUM ALGINATE

Prepared at the 49th JECFA (1997)
superseding specifications prepared at the 44th JECFA (1995),
published in FNP 52 Addendum 3 (1995)

SYNONYMS   INS No. 404

DEFINITION   Calcium alginate is the Calcium salt of alginic acid.

C.A.S. number   9005-35-0

Chemical formula $(C_6H_7Ca_{1/2}O_6)_n$

Structural formula   Structural formula from Phillips, Wedlock and Williams: Gums and Stabilizers for the Food Industry 5 (1990) by permission of Oxford University Press.

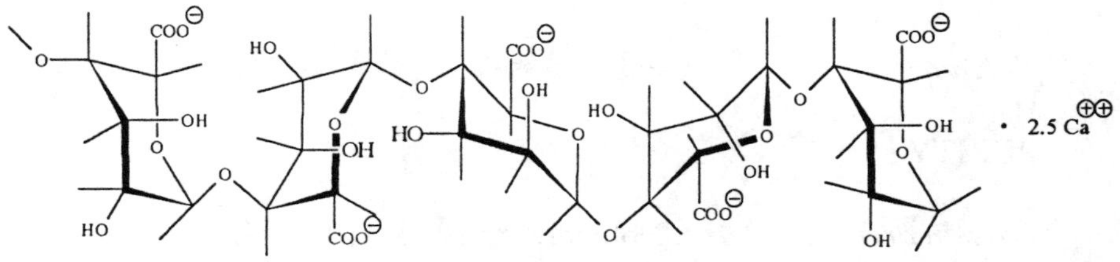

$$ \underline{\quad\quad} G(^1C_4) \underline{\quad\quad} G(^1C_4) \underline{\quad\quad} M(^4C_1) \underline{\quad\quad} M(^4C_1) \underline{\quad\quad} G $$

$$ \alpha\text{-}1,4 \quad\quad \alpha\text{-}1,4 \quad\quad \text{ß-}1,4 \quad\quad \text{ß-}1,4 $$

The number and sequence of the Mannuronate and Glucuronate residues shown above vary in the naturally occurring alginate. The associated water molecules are not hown.

Formula weight   Structural unit :   195.16 (theoretical)
                                                   219 (actual average)
                        Macromolecule: 10,000 - 600,000 (typical average)

Assay   Not less than 18.0% and not more than 21.0% of carbon dioxide (CO_2), equivalent to not less than 89.6% and not more than 104.5% of calcium alginate $(C_6H_7Ca_{1/2}O_6)_n$ on the anhydrous basis.

DESCRIPTION   Occurs as white to yellowish brown filamentous, grainy, granular and powdered forms

FUNCTIONAL USES   Stabilizer, thickener, gelling agent, emulsifier

CHARACTERISTICS

IDENTIFICATION

Solubility   Insoluble in water and ether; slightly soluble in ethanol; slowly soluble in solutions of sodium polyphosphate, sodium carbonate, and substances that combine with calcium ions.

Precipitate formation with calcium chloride
    Passes test
    See description under TESTS

Precipitate formation with with ammonium sulfate
    Passes test
    See description under TESTS

Test for alginate   Passes test
    See description under TESTS

Calcium   Passes test

PURITY

Loss on drying   Not more than 15% (105°, 4 h)

Arsenic   Not more than 3 mg/kg (Method II)

Lead   Not more than 5 mg/kg
   Prepare a sample solution as directed for organic compounds in the Limit Test, using 5 µg of lead ion (Pb) in the control

Microbiological criteria Total plate count: Not more than 5,000 colonies per gram.

   Initially prepare a 10^{-1} dilution by adding a 50 g sample to 450 ml of Butterfield's phosphate buffered dilution water and homogenizing in a high speed blender.

   Yeasts and moulds: Not more than 500 colonies per gram

   Coliforms: Negative by test

   Salmonella: Negative by test

TESTS

IDENTIFICATION TESTS

Precipitate formation with calcium chloride
   To a 0.5% solution of the sample in sodium hydroxide TS add one-fifth of its volume of a 2.5% solution of calcium chloride. A voluminous, gelatinous precipitate is formed. This test distinguishes calcium alginate from gum arabic, sodium carboxymethyl cellulose, carrageenan, gelatin, gum ghatti, karaya gum, carob bean gum, methyl cellulose and tragacanth gum.

Precipitate formation with ammonium sulphate

To a 0.5% solution of the sample in sodium hydroxide TS add one-half of its volume of a saturated solution of ammonium sulfate. No precipitate is formed. This test distinguishes calcium alginate from agar, sodium carboxymethyl cellulose, carrageenan, de-esterified pectin, gelatin, carob bean gum, methyl cellulose and starch.

Test for alginate

Dissolve as completely as possible 0.01 g of the sample by shaking with 0.15 ml of 0.1 N sodium hydroxide and add 1 ml of acid ferric sulfate TS. Within 5 min, a cherry-red colour develops that finally becomes deep purple.

METHOD OF ASSAY

Proceed as directed under Carbon Dioxide Determination by Decarboxylation in the *General Methods*. Each ml of 0.25 N sodium hydroxide consumed is equivalent to 5.5 mg of carbon dioxide (CO_2) or 27.38 mg of calcium alginate (equivalent weight 219).

CALCIUM PROPIONATE

Prepared at the 49th JECFA (1997)
superseding specifications prepared at the 44th JECFA (1995),
published in FNP 52 Addendum 3 (1995)

SYNONYMS   Calcium propanoate, INS No. 282

DEFINITION

Chemical name   Calcium propionate

C.A.S. number   4075-81-4

Chemical formula $C_6H_{10}CaO_4$

Structural formula $(CH_3CH_2COO^-)_2\ Ca^{++}$

Formula weight   186.22

Assay   Not less than 98.0% on the dried basis

DESCRIPTION   White crystals, powder or granules with not more than a faint odour of propionic acid

FUNCTIONAL USES   Preservative, antimould and antirope agent

CHARACTERISTICS

IDENTIFICATION

Solubility   Freely soluble in water, soluble in ethanol

Positive test for calcium Passes test

Positive test for propionate
                          Warm the sample with sulfuric acid. The propionic acid evolved may be recognized by its odour.

Positive test for alkali salt of organic acid
                          Ignite the sample at a relatively low temperature. The alkaline organic acid residue effervesces with acid.

PURITY

Loss on drying   Not more than 4% (105°, 2 h)

pH   7.5 - 10.5 (1 in 10 soln)

Water insoluble matter   Not more than 0.3%
                          See description under TESTS

Fluoride   Not more than 30 mg/kg

Weigh 5 g of the sample to the nearest mg and proceed as directed in the Fluoride Limit Test (Method I or III)

Iron

Not more than 50 mg/kg
Test 0.5 g of the sample as described in the Limit Test using 2.5 ml of Iron Standard Solution (25 µg) in the control

Lead

Not more than 5 mg/kg
Prepare a sample solution as directed for organic compounds in the Limit Test, using 5 µg of lead ion (Pb) in the control

TESTS

PURITY TESTS

Water-insoluble matter

Weigh 5 g of the sample to the nearest mg, transfer into a 100-ml beaker and add 50 ml of water. Stir until all the sample appears to be completely dissolved. Filter through a Gooch crucible, tared to an accuracy of ± 0.2 mg. Rinse the beaker with 20 ml of water. Dry the crucible with its contents in a 60°-oven to constant weight. Cool in a desiccator, weigh, and calculate as percentage.

METHOD OF ASSAY

Dissolve in a beaker 2.5 g of the sample, weighed to the nearest mg, in 5 ml of hot dilute hydrochloric acid TS. Cool, transfer to a 250-ml volumetric flask, dilute to volume with water, and mix. Transfer 50 ml of the solution to a 400-ml beaker, add 100 ml of water, 25 ml of sodium hydroxide TS, 40 mg of murexide indicator preparation and 3 ml of naphthol green TS. An alternative indicator is hydroxynaphthol blue, of which 0.25 g is used. In this case the naphthol green TS is omitted. Titrate with 0.05 M disodium ethylenediaminetetraacetate until the solution is deep blue in colour. Each ml of 0.05 M disodium ethylenediaminetetraacetate is equivalent to 9.311 mg of $C_6H_{10}CaO_4$.

CARBON DIOXIDE

Prepared at the 49th JECFA (1997)
superseding specifications prepared at the 29th JECFA (1985),
published in FNP 34 (1986)

SYNONYMS	INS No. 290

DEFINITION

C.A.S. number	124-38-9
Chemical formula	CO_2
Formula weight	44.01
Assay	Not less than 99% of CO_2, by volume

DESCRIPTION
Colourless, odorless gas, 1 litre of which weighs about 1.98 g at 0° and 760 mm of mercury. Under a pressure of about 59 atmospheres it may be condensed to a liquid, a portion of which forms a white solid (Dry Ice) upon rapid evaporation. Solid carbon dioxide evaporates without melting upon exposure to air. Commercial carbon dioxide is shipped and handled in pressurized cylinders or low pressure bulk liquid systems, or in solid blocks.

FUNCTIONAL USES
Propellant, freezing agent, carbonating agent, preservative, extraction solvent

CHARACTERISTICS
The following specifications apply to gaseous carbon dioxide as produced from its condensed liquid or solid phase by evolution to the gas phase at normal environmental conditions. Additional specifications may be applied to liquid or solid forms of carbon dioxide by vendors or by specific users of commercial carbon dioxide products.

IDENTIFICATION

Precipitate formation
When a stream of the sample is passed through a solution of barium hydroxide, a white precipitate is produced which dissolves with effervescence in dilute acetic acid.

Detector tube test
Passes test
See description under TEST

PURITY

Acidity
Passes test
See description under TESTS

Phosphine, hydrogen sulfide, and other organic reducing substances
Passes test
See description under TESTS

Carbon monoxide
Not more than 10 µl/l
See description under TESTS

Non-volatile hydrocarbons

Not more than 10 mg/kg
See description under TESTS

Volatile hydrocarbons   Not more than 50 µl/l
See description under TESTS

Water   Passes test
See description under TESTS

TESTS

IDENTIFICATION TESTS

Detector tube test

Pass 100±5 ml, released from the vapor phase of the contents of the container, through a carbon dioxide detector tube (see below) at the rate specified for the tube: The indicator change extends throughout the entire indicating range of the tube.

Detector tube is a fuse-sealed glass tube (Draeger or equivalent) that is designed to allow gas to be passed through it and that contains suitable adsorbing filters and support media for the indicators hydrazine and crystal violet. (The Draeger Reference Number is CH 30801, National Draeger Inc., P.O. Box 120, Pittsburgh, PA 15205-0120, USA; the measuring range is 0.01% to 0.30%).

PURITY TESTS

Acidity

Transfer 50 ml of water, previously boiled and cooled to room temperature, into a Nessler tube. Introduce 1,000 ml of the sample into the water through a tube (1 mm internal diameter) keeping the opening of the tube within 2 mm from the bottom of the vessel. Add 0.1 ml of methyl orange TS. The red colour produced is not darker than the colour of an identical control solution to which has been added 1.0 ml of 0.01 N hydrochloric acid instead of the carbon dioxide.

Phosphine, hydrogen sulfide, and other organic reducing substances

Transfer 25 ml of silver ammonium nitrate TS and 3 ml of ammonia TS into a Nessler tube. In the absence of light, introduce 1,000 ml of the sample in the same manner as in the test of Acidity. No brown colour is produced.

Carbon monoxide

Principle:

Carry out the test on the first portion of gas issuing from the cylinder. Use 5.0 l of the sample mixed with an equal volume of carbon monoxide-free nitrogen and 10 l of carbon monoxide-free nitrogen as the control. The difference between the volumes of 0.002 N sodium thiosulfate used in the two titrations is not greater than 0.5 ml.

Apparatus:

The apparatus consists of the following parts connected in series:
-U-tube containing anhydrous silica gel impregnated with chromium trioxide.
-Scrubber bottle (dreschel type) containing 100 ml of a 40% w/v solution of potassium hydroxide.

-U-tube containing phosphorus pentoxide dispersed on previously granulated, fused pumice.
-Tube containing recrystallized iodic anhydride (I_2O_5) in granules, previously dried at 200° and kept at a temperature of 120°. The iodic anhydride is packed in the tube in 1-cm columns separated by 1-cm columns of glass wool to give an effective length of 5 cm.
-Flask containing 2.0 ml of potassium iodide TS and 3 drops of starch solution TS.

Procedure:

Flush the apparatus with 5.0 l of carbon dioxide-free air and, if necessary, discharge the blue colour in the iodide solution by adding the smallest necessary quantity of freshly prepared 0.002 N sodium thiosulfate. Continue flushing until not more than 0.045 ml of 0.002 N sodium thiosulfate is required after passing 5.0 l of carbon dioxide-free air. Pass the gas from the cylinder through the apparatus.

Flush the last traces of liberated iodine into the reaction flask by passing through the apparatus 1.0 l of carbon monoxide-free air. Titrate the liberated iodine with 0.002 N sodium thiosulfate. Carry out a blank assay using 10 l of carbon monoxide-free nitrogen. The difference between the volumes of 0.002 N sodium thiosulfate solution used in the two titrations should not be more than 0.5 ml.

Non-volatile hydrocarbons

Pass a sample of liquid carbon dioxide from storage container or sample cylinder through a commercial carbon dioxide snow horn directly into an open, clean container. Weigh 500 g of this sample into a clean beaker. Allow the carbon dioxide solid to sublime completely, with a watch-glass placed over the beaker to prevent ambient contamination. Wash the beaker with a residue-free solvent, and transfer the solvent from the beaker to a clean, tared watch-glass or petri dish with two additional rinses of the beaker with the solvent. Allow the solvent to evaporate, using heating to 104° until the watch-glass or petri dish is at a constant weight. Determine the weight of the residue by difference. The weight of the residue does not exceed 5 mg.

Volatile hydrocarbons

Standard preparation: Flush a 500-ml glass, septum-equipped sampling bulb with helium, and inject into the bulb a 5.00-ml sample of methane. Allow the bulb to stand for 15 min to permit the gases to mix, and then inject 2.50 ml of the mixture into a second 500-ml sampling bulb, also flushed with helium, and allow this tube to stand for 15 min to permit the gases to mix. This mixture is a nominal 50 ppm v/v standard. Determine the exact concentration from the exact volumes of the the gas-sampling bulbs. To determine these volumes, weigh the empty tubes, fill them with water, and reweigh. From the weight of the water and its temperature, calculate the volumes of the tubes.

Chtomatographic system: The gas chromatograph is equipped with the flame ionization detector and a 1.8-m x 3-mm od metal column packed with 80- to

100-mesh Hayesep Q (or equivalent). The carrier gas is helium at a flow rate of 30 ml/min. The injector temperature and the detector temperatures both are maintained at 230°. The column temperature is programmed according to the following steps: It is held at 70° for 1 min, then increased to 200° at a rate 20°/min, and then held at 200° for 10 min. The parameters for the detector are sensitivity range: 10^{-12} A/mV; attenuation: 32. The concentration of volatile hydrocarbons is reported in methane equivalents. The various gas chromatographic responses, excluding the carbon dioxide response, are summed to yield the total volatile hydrocarbon concentration. The composition of hydrocarbons present will vary from sample to sample. Typical retention times are methane: 0.4 min; carbon dioxide: 0.8 min; hexane: 14.4 min.

Procedure: Inject in triplicate 1.00 ml of the standard preparation into the gas chromatograph, and average the peak area responses. The relative standard deviation should not exceed 5.0%. Similarly, inject in triplicate 1.00 ml of sample, sum the average peak areas of the individual peaks, except for the carbon dioxide peaks, and calculate the concentration v/v in the sample by formula:

$$\mu l/L = S(A_U/A_S),$$

in which S is the calculated ppm of methane in the standard preparation (approximately 50 $\mu l/l$), A_U is the sum of the averages of the individual peak area responses in the sample, and A_S is the average area of the standard preparation area responses.

Water

Water vapor detector tube. A fuse-sealed glass tube (Draeger or equivalent) that is designed to allow gas to be passed through it and that contains suitable absorbing filters and support media for the indicator, which consists of a selenium sol in suspension of sulphuric acid. (The Draeger Reference Number is CH 67 28531, National Draeger Inc., P.O. Box 120, Pittsburgh, PA 15205-0120, USA; the mesuring range is 5 to 200 mg/m^3).

Pass 24,000 ml of the gas sample through a suitable water-absorption tube not less than 100 mm in length, which previously has been flushed with about 500 ml of the sample and weighed. Regulate the flow so that about 60 min will be required for passage of the gas. The gain in weight of the absorption tube does not exceed 1.0 mg.

METHOD OF ASSAY

Transfer a 1 in 3 potassium hydroxide solution into a gas pipette of adequate volume. Measure accurately about 1,000 ml of the sample into a gas burette containing a 1 in 10 sodium chloride solution. Transfer the sample into the gas pipette and shake well. When the volume of gas remaining unabsorbed is constant (V ml), the content of carbon dioxide is calculated by:

$$\text{Content v}/\text{v}\% = \frac{\text{Vol of sample ml} - \text{V ml}}{\text{Vol of sample ml}} \times 100$$

TENTATIVE

CARTHAMUS RED

Prepared at the 49th JECFA (1997)
superseding specifications prepared at the 39th JECFA (1992),
published in FNP 52 Addendum 1 (1992)

Information required on the levels of carthamin in carthamus red and on Method of Assay

SYNONYMS   Safflower red, carthamic acid, CI Natural Red 26 (No. 75140)

DEFINITION   Carthamus Red is obtained from the dried petals of *Carthamus tinctorius* L. To obtain carthamus red, carthamus yellow is extracted from the petals with water and the residue treated with aqueous sodium hydroxide or other alkali. Carthamus red is precipitated from the extract by addition of acid, separated by filtration and dried. The principal colouring matter is carthamin.

Class   Flavonoid

Chemical formula $C_{43}H_{42}O_{22}$ (carthamin)

Formula weight   910.81 (carthamin)

Assay   Not less than 80% total colouring matters on a volatile matter-free basis

DESCRIPTION   Dark red to red-brown powder with a characteristic slight odour

FUNCTIONAL USES   Colour

CHARACTERISTICS

IDENTIFICATION

Solubility   Very slightly soluble in water
Very slightly soluble in ethanol
Practically insoluble in ether

Spectrophotometry   A solution of the sample in dimethyl formamide is red and shows an absorption maximum between 525-535 nm.

Thin layer chromatography
Carthamin appears as a red spot with an Rf value of about 0.40
See description under TESTS

Colour reaction I   Passes test
See description under TESTS

Colour reaction II   Passes test
See description under TESTS

PURITY

Lead

Not more than 10 mg/kg
Prepare a sample solution as directed for the organic compounds in the Limit Test, using 10 µg of lead ion (Pb) in the control.

Synthetic dyes

Passes test
See description under TESTS

TESTS

IDENTIFICATION TESTS

Thin layer chromatography

Activate some silica gel for 1 h at 110° and prepare a TLC plate. Prepare an 0.02% solution of the sample in dimethylformamide and apply 20 µl to the plate. Allow to dry and develop using a mixture of n-butanol, acetic acid and water (4:1:2 by volume) until the solvent front has ascended about 10 cm. Allow to dry. Carthamin appears as a red spot with an Rf value of about 0.40.

Colour reaction I

Dissolve 10 mg of the sample in 50 ml water. The colour of the solution is red. Add alkali to raise the pH to above 7. The colour changes to orange-yellow.

Colour reaction II

To 0.05 g of the sample add 2 ml of 5% phosphoric acid, heat for 1 h on a water bath. After cooling, filter and wash the residue with 3 ml of water. Combine the filtrate and the washings. Neutralize the combined solution with sodium hydroxide TS, add 5 ml of Fehling's TS and heat on a water bath for 10 min. A red precipitate is produced.

PURITY TESTS

Synthetic dyes

Basic dyes: To 1 g of the sample add 100 ml of 1% sodium hydroxide solution, and mix well. Extract 30 ml of this solution with 15 ml of ether. Then extract the ether layer twice with dilute acetic acid (5 ml); the dilute acetic acid layer does not contain any colour.

Acidic dyes: To 1 g of the sample add 1 ml of ammonia TS and 8 ml of water, and shake well. Discard an oily layer when separated. Proceed as directed (Ascending Chromatography) in the *General Methods* using 20 µl of the solution as the sample solution, and a mixture of pyridine and ammonia TS (2:1 by volume) as the developing solvent. Stop the development when the solvent front has advanced about 15 cm from the point of application. No spot is observed at the solvent front after drying under daylight. If any spot is observed, it should be decolourized when sprayed with a solution of stannous chloride in hydrochloric acid (2 in 5).

METHOD OF ASSAY

Place about 10 mg of the sample, previously dried and accurately weighed, in a 300-ml ground stoppered flask, add 150 ml of dimethylformamide, dissolve by shaking occasionally and allow stand for 2 hours. Filter this solution through a glass filter into a 200-ml volumetric flask. Wash the flask and filter with two 25-ml portions of dimethylformamide, combine the filtrate and the washings, add dimethylformamide to volume and mix. Determine the absorbance (A) at the maximum absorbance in the range of 525-535 nm using a 1-cm cell. Calculate the content using the absorptivity of carthamus red (information required).

CARTHAMUS YELLOW

Prepared at the 49th JECFA (1997)
superseding specifications prepared at the 31st JECFA (1987),
published in FNP 38 (1988)

SYNONYMS	Safflower yellow, CI Natural Yellow 5
DEFINITION	Carthamus Yellow is obtained by extracting the corolla (petals) of *Carthamus tinctorius* L. with water or slightly acidified water and drying the extract. The principal colouring matters are safflomin A (hydroxysafflor yellow A) and safflomine B (safflor yellow B). Besides the colour pigments carthamus yellow consists of sugars, salts and/or proteins naturally occurring in the source materials. Food grade materials such as dextrin may be added as carriers for manufacturing dry, powdered items of commerce.

Class: Flavonoid

C.A.S number:
I. 78281-02-4 (Safflomin A)
II. 120478-62-8 (Safflomin B)

Chemical formula:
I. $C_{27}H_{32}O_{16}$ (Safflomin A)
II. $C_{48}H_{54}O_{27}$ (Safflomin B)

Formula weight:
I. 612.5 (Safflomin A)
II. 1062 (Safflomin B)

Assay: Content of colouring matter not less than declared

DESCRIPTION Yellow to dark brown crystals, paste, powder or liquid with a faint characteristic odour.

FUNCTIONAL USES Colour

CHARACTERISTICS

IDENTIFICATION

Solubility Very soluble in water, practically insoluble in ether and ethanol

Spectrophotometry A solution of the sample in citric acid/disodium hydrogen phosphate buffer solution (pH 5.0) is yellow and shows an absorption maximum at 400-408 nm.

Colour reaction Make the solution of the sample in water alkaline by 10% sodium hydroxide solution; the colour changes from yellow to orange-yellow

Thin layer chromatography
Carthamus yellow appears as two main yellow spots with Rf-values in the range of 0.2-0.5
See description under TESTS

PURITY

Lead Not more than 10 mg/kg

Prepare a sample solution as directed for the organic compounds in the Limit Test, using 10 μg of lead ion (Pb) in the control

Synthetic dyes Passes test
See description under TESTS

TESTS

IDENTIFICATION TESTS

Thin layer chromatography

Activate cellulose for 20 min at 60-80° and prepare a TLC plate. Prepare a 10% solution of the sample in methanol and apply 20 μl to the plate. Allow to dry and develop using a mixture of n-butanol, acetic acid and water (4:1:2 by volume) until the solvent front has ascended about 10 cm. Allow to dry. The main components of carthamus yellow appear as two yellow spots with Rf values in the range 0.2-0.5.

PURITY TESTS

Synthetic dyes

Basic dyes: To 1 g of the sample add 100 ml of 1% sodium hydroxide solution, and mix well. Extract 30 ml of this solution with 15 ml of ether. Then extract the ether layer twice with dilute acetic acid (5 ml); the dilute acetic acid layer does not contain any colour.

Acidic dyes: To 1 g of the sample add 1 ml of ammonia TS and 8 ml of water, and shake well. Discard an oily layer when separated. Proceed as directed under *Paper Chromatography (Ascending Chromatography)* in the *General Methods* using 20 μl of the solution as the sample solution, and a mixture of pyridine and ammonia TS (2:1 by volume) as the developing solvent. Stop the development when the solvent front has advanced about 15 cm from the point of application. No spot is observed at the solvent front after drying under daylight. If any spot is observed, it should be decolourized when sprayed with a solution of stannous chloride in hydrochloric acid (2 in 5).

METHOD OF ASSAY

Transfer about 0.15 g of the sample, accurately weighed, in a 100-ml volumetric flask; dissolve in and dilute to volume with citric acid/disodium hydrogen phosphate buffer solution (pH 5.0). Transfer 5.0 ml of this solution to a 100-ml volumetric flask; dilute to volume with the buffer solution, and centrifuge if necessary. Determine the absorbance (A) at 400 nm in a 1-cm cell with the buffer solution as a blank and calculate the the percent of colouring matter (P) with the following formula:

$$P = \frac{A}{51.38} \times \frac{20}{W} \times 100$$

in which W is the weight of the sample in mg.

When the absorbance (A) exceeds 0.7, the amount of sample should be adjusted.

CITRIC ACID

Prepared at the 49th JECFA (1997)
superseding specifications prepared at the 46th JECFA (1996),
published in FNP 52 Addendum 4 (1996)

SYNONYMS	INS No. 330

DEFINITION

Chemical name   2-hydroxy-1,2,3-propanetricarboxylic acid

C.A.S. number   77-92-9 (anhydrous)
                              5949-29-1 (monohydrate)

Chemical formula $C_6H_8O_7$ (anhydrous)
                              $C_6H_8O_7 \cdot H_2O$ (monohydrate)

Structural formula

$$\begin{array}{cc}
\begin{array}{c}
CH_2-COOH \\
| \\
HO-C-COOH \\
| \\
CH_2-COOH \\
\text{Anhydrous}
\end{array}
&
\begin{array}{c}
CH_2-COOH \\
| \\
HO-C-COOH \quad \cdot \quad H_2O \\
| \\
CH_2-COOH \\
\text{Monohydrate}
\end{array}
\end{array}$$

Formula weight   192.13 (anhydrous)
                            210.14 (monohydrate)

Assay   Not less than 99.5% and not more than 100.5% on the anhydrous basis

DESCRIPTION   White or colourless, odourless, crystalline solid. The monohydrate form effloresces in dry air

FUNCTIONAL USES   Synergist for antioxidants, sequestrant, acidity regulator, flavouring agent

CHARACTERISTICS

IDENTIFICATION

Solubility   Very soluble in water; freely soluble in ethanol; slightly soluble in ether

Positive Test for citrate   Passes test

PURITY

Water   Anhydrous: Not more than 0.5% (Karl Fischer method)
               Monohydrate: Not less than 7.5% and not more than 8.8% (Karl Fischer method)

Sulphated ash   Not more than 0.05%

Lead	Not more than 0.5 mg/kg
	Prepare a sample solution as directed for organic compounds in the Limit Test and determine the lead content by atomic absorption spectrometry
Oxalate	Passes test
	See description under TESTS
Readily carbonizable substances	
	Passes test
	See description under TESTS

TESTS

PURITY TESTS

Oxalate	Neutralize 10 ml of a 10% solution of the sample with dilute ammonia TS. Add 5 drops of dilute acetic acid TS, cool and add 2 ml of calcium chloride TS. No turbidity should be produced.
Readily carbonizable substances	
	Heat 1.0 g of sample with 10 ml of 98% sulfuric acid in a water bath at $90\pm1°$ for 60 min. No colour darker than *Matching Fluid K* (25°) should be produced (not more than 0.5 absorbance units at 470 nm in a 10 mm cell).

METHOD OF ASSAY   Weigh, to the nearest mg, 2.5 g of the sample and place in a tared flask. Dissolve in 40 ml of water and titrate with 1N sodium hydroxide, using phenolphthalein TS as the indicator. Each ml of 1N sodium hydroxide is equivalent to 64.04 mg of $C_6H_8O_7$.

DIACETYLTARTARIC AND FATTY ACID ESTERS OF GLYCEROL

Prepared at the 49th JECFA (1997)
superseding specifications prepared at the 44th JECFA (1995),
published in FNP 52 Addendum 3 (1995)

SYNONYMS   Diacetyltartaric acid esters of mono- and diglycerides, DATEM, INS No. 472e

DEFINITION   The product consists of mixed glycerol esters of mono- and diacetyltartaric acid and fatty acids of food fats. It is made by the interaction of diacetyltartaric anhydride and mono- and diglycerides. The commercial product often consists of mixtures of the product described above with mono- and diglycerides.

The article of commerce may be further specified as to acid value, total tartaric acid content, free acetic acid content, saponification value, iodine value, free fatty acid content, solidification point of the free fatty acids and ash content.

Structural formula   The majors components are:

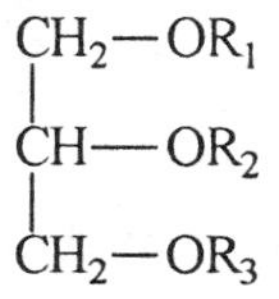

$$
\begin{array}{l}
CH_2-OR_1 \\
| \\
CH-OR_2 \\
| \\
CH_2-OR_3
\end{array}
$$

in which

1) one or two of the R groups is a fatty acid moiety
2) the other R groups are either
- diacetylated tartaric acid moiety
- monoacetylated tartaric acid moiety
- tartaric acid moiety
- acetic acid moiety
- hydrogen

DESCRIPTION   The esters range in appearance from sticky, viscous liquids through a fat-like consistency to yellow waxes which hydrolyse in moist air to liberate acetic acid.

FUNCTIONAL USES   Emulsifier

CHARACTERISTICS

   IDENTIFICATION

   Solubility   Dispersible in cold and hot water, soluble in methanol and ethanol

   Test for 1,2-diols   To a solution of 500 mg in 10 ml methanol, add dropwise, lead acetate TS. A white flocculent, insoluble precipitate is formed.

Test for fatty acids	Passes test
Test for acetic acid	Passes test
Test for tartaric acid	Passes test
Test for glycerol	Passes test

PURITY

Acids	Acids other than acetic, tartaric and fatty acids, shall not be detectable
Total acetic acid	Not less than 8% and not more than 32% after hydrolysis See description under TESTS
Total tartaric acid	Not less than 10% and not more than 40% after saponification See description under TESTS
Total glycerol	Not less than 11% and not more than 28 % after saponification See description under TESTS
Free glycerol	Not more than 2.0%
Heavy metals	Not more than 10 mg/kg Test 2 g of the sample as directed in the Limit Test (Method II)

TESTS

PURITY TESTS

Total acetic acid

Apparatus:

Assemble a modified Hortvet-Sellier distillation apparatus as shown in the figure, using a sufficiently large (approximately 38- x 203-mm) inner Sellier tube and large distillation trap.

Procedure:

Transfer 4 g of sample, accurately weighed into the inner tube of the assembly, and insert the tube in the outer flask containing about 300 ml of recently boiled hot water. To the sample add 10 ml of approximately 4N perchloric acid [35 ml (60 g) of 70% perchloric acid in 100 ml of water], and connect the inner tube to a water-cooled condenser through the distillation trap. Distil by heating the outer flask so that 100 ml of distillate is collected within 20 to 25 min. Collect the distillate in 100-ml portions, add phenolphthalein TS to each portion, and titrate with 0.5N sodium hydroxide. Continue the distillation until a 100-ml portion of the distillate requires no more than 0.5 ml of 0.5N sodium hydroxide for neutralization. (Caution: Do not distil to dryness.) Calculate the weight, in mg, of volatile acids in the sample taken by the formula V x e, in which V is the total volume, in ml, of 0.5N sodium hydroxide consumed in the series of titrations and e is the equivalence factor 30.03.

Total tartaric acid

Standard Curve:

Transfer 100 mg of reagent-grade tartaric acid, accurately weighed, into a 100-ml volumetric flask, dissolve it in about 90 ml of water, add water to volume, and mix well. Transfer 3.0-. 4.0-, 5.0-, and 6.0-ml portions into separate 19- x 150-mm matched cuvettes, and add sufficient water to make 10.0 ml. To each cuvette add 4.0 ml of a freshly prepared 1 in 20 solution of sodium metavanadate and 1.0 ml of acetic acid. (Note: Use these solutions within 10 min after colour development.) Prepare a blank in the same manner, using 10 ml of water in place of the tartaric acid solutions. Set the instrument at zero with the blank, and then determine the absorbance of the four solutions of tartaric acid at 520 nm with a suitable spectrophotometer or a photoelectric colorimeter equipped with a 520-nm filter. From the data thus obtained, prepare a curve by plotting the absorbances on the ordinate against the corresponding quantities, in mg, of the tartaric acid on the abscissa.

Test Preparation:

Transfer about 4 g of the sample, accurately weighed, into a 250-ml Erlenmeyer flask, and add 80 ml of approximately 0.5N potassium hydroxide and 0.5 ml of phenolphthalein TS. Connect an air condenser at least 65 cm in length to the flask, and heat the mixture on a hot plate for about 2.5 h. Add to the hot mixture approximately 10% phosphoric acid until it is definitely acid to congo red test paper. Reconnect the air condenser, and heat until the fatty acids are liquified and clear. Cool and then transfer the mixture into a 250-ml separator with the aid of small portions of water and chloroform. Extract the liberated fatty acids with three successive 25-ml portions of water, and add the washings to the separator containing the water layer. Transfer the contents of the first separator to a 250-ml beaker, heat on a steam bath to remove traces of chloroform, filter through acid-washed, fine-texture filter paper into a 500-ml volumetric flask, and finally dilute to volume with water (Solution I). Pipet 25.0 ml of this solution into a 100-ml volumetric flask, and dilute to volume with water (Solution II). Retain the rest of Solution I for the determination of total glycerol.

Procedure:

Transfer 10.0 ml of Solution II prepared under Test Preparation into a 19- x 150-mm cuvette, and continue as directed under Standard Curve, beginning with "To each cuvette add 4.0 ml of a...". From the standard curve determine the weight, in mg, of tartaric acid in the final dilution, multiply this by 20, and divide the result by the weight of the original sample for obtaining the percentage of tartaric acid.

Total glycerol

Procedure:

Transfer 5.0 ml of Solution I prepared in the test for total Tartaric Acid into a 250-ml glass-stoppered Erlenmeyer or iodine flask. Add to the flask 15 ml of glacial acetic acid and 25.0 ml of periodic acid solution, prepared by dissolving 2.7 g of periodic acid (H_5IO_6) in 50 ml of water, adding 950 ml of glacial acetic acid, and mixing thoroughly; protect this solution from light. Shake the mixture for 1 or 2 min, allow it to stand for 15 min, add 15 ml of potassium iodide solution (15 in 100) and 15 ml of water, swirl, let stand

1 min, and then titrate the liberated iodine with 0.1N sodium thiosulfate, using starch TS as the indicator. Perform a Residual Blank Titration using water in place of the sample. The corrected volume is the number of ml of 0.1N sodium thiosulfate required for the glycerol and the tartaric acid in the sample represented by the 5 ml of Solution I. From the percentage determined in the Assay for Tartaric Acid calculate the volume of 0.1N sodium thiosulfate required for the tartaric acid in the titration. The difference between the corrected volume and the calculated volume required for the tartaric acid is the number of ml of 0.1N sodium thiosulfate consumed due to the glycerol in the sample. One ml of 0.1N sodium thiosulfate is equivalent to 2.303 mg of glycerol and to 7.505 mg of tartaric acid.

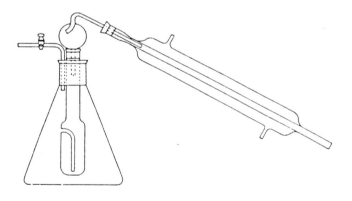

Figure   Modified Hortvet-Sellier Distillation Apparatus

ETHYL HYDROXYETHYL CELLULOSE

Prepared at the 49th JECFA (1997)
superseding specifications prepared at the 29th JECFA (1985),
published in FNP 34 (1986)

SYNONYM   INS No. 467

DEFINITION   Ethyl Hydroxyethyl Cellulose is cellulose in which both ethyl and hydroxyethyl groups are attached to the anhydroglucose units by ether linkages.   Ethyl hydroxyethyl cellulose is prepared from cellulose by treatment with alkali, ethylene oxide and ethyl chloride.   The article of commerce may be specified further by the viscosity of its aqueous solutions.

Chemical names   Ethyl hydroxyethyl cellulose, 2-hydroxyethyl ether of ethyl cellulose

C.A.S. number   9004-58-4

Chemical formula $[C_6H_7O_2(OH)_x(OC_2H_5)_y[O(CH_2CH_2O)_mH]_z]_n$

where n is the degree of polymerisation
$x + y + z$ $= 3$
y $= 0.7 - 1.5$ (degree of ethyl substitution, DS)
$m + z$ $= 0.5 - 2.5$ (molar hydroxyethyl substitution, MS)

Structural formula

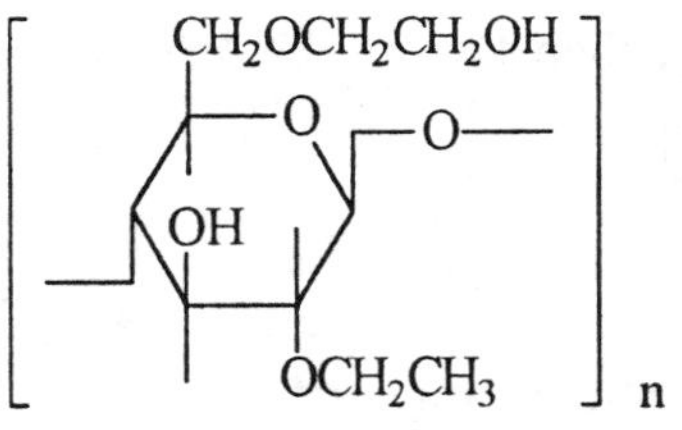

Possible structural formula for a repeating unit of an ethyl hydroxyethyl cellulose with a DS = 1.0 and a MS = 1.0

Formula weight   Unsubstituted structural unit: 162.14
Structural unit with DS = MS = 1.0: 234
Structural unit with DS = 1.0; MS = 2.0: 278
Structural unit with DS = 1.5; MS = 0.5: 226
Macromolecules: from about 40,000 (n about 175)
up to about 350,000 (n about 1,300)

Assay   Not less than 7% and not more than 19% of ethoxyl groups ($-OC_2H_5$), and not less than 10% and not more than 38% of oxyethylene groups ($-OCH_2CH_2-$), on the dried and salt-free basis.

DESCRIPTION   Hygroscopic white or slightly yellowish or greyish, odourless granules or fine powder.

FUNCTIONAL USES   Emulsifier, stabilizer, thickener

CHARACTERISTICS

IDENTIFICATION

Solubility   Swelling in water, producing a clear to opalescent, viscous, colloidal solution; insoluble in boiling water and ethanol.

Foam formation   Vigorously shake a 0.1% solution of the sample. A layer of foam appears. This test permits the distinction of cellulose ethers from sodium carboxymethyl cellulose, alginates, and natural gums.

Precipitate formation   To 5 ml of an 0.5% solution of the sample add 5 ml of a 5% solution of copper sulfate or of aluminium sulfate. No precipitate appears. This test permits the distinction of cellulose ethers from sodium carboxymethyl cellulose, gelatine, carob bean gum and tragacanth.

Precipitate formation by warming

A 1% water solution of a sample is slowly heated from room temperature, while stirring. At a distinct temperature above 35°, a cloudy precipitate occurs which disappears completely during cooling.

Substituent content   Determine the substituents by gas chromatography as given in Method of Assay

PURITY

Loss on drying   Not more than 10% (105° , to constant weight)

Chlorides   Not more than 2%
        See description under Tests

Lead   Not more than 5 mg/kg
        Prepare a sample solution as directed for organic compounds in the Limit Test, using 5 µg of lead (Pb) ion in the control.

Ethylene oxides, 1,4-dioxane and ethylene chlorohydrin
        Not more than 0.5 mg/kg, individually
        See description under TESTS

Mono and diethylene glycol
        Not more than 1%, individually or in combination
        See description under TESTS

TESTS

PURITY TESTS

Chlorides   Weigh 2 g of dried dried sample, and disperse in about 100 ml of boiling, distilled water by swirling the flask. When the solution is homogeneous, or after at least one hour, add a pinch of sodium bicarbonate and exactly 1.0 ml of the potassium chromate TS indicator. Titrate with 0.1 M silver nitrate to a weakly brown colour. Titrate to the same colour a blank, containing 100 ml distilled water, bicarbonate, and 1.0 ml of potassium chromate TS indicator.

Chloride content (%) = [35.5 x M x (A-B)]/10 x W
Sodium chloride content (%) = [58.5 x M x (A-B)]/10 x W

where:

W = weight of the sample (g)
M = molarity of silver nitrate (mol/l)
A = silver nitrate consumed by sample (ml)
B = silver nitrate consumed by blank (ml)

Ethylene oxide, dioxane, ethylene chlorohydrin

Principle: Ethylene oxide (EO), ethylene chlorohydrin (EKH) and dioxane are determined by head space gas chromatography with mass selective detection (GC-MSD).

Apparatus: Gas chromatograph (Hewlett Packard 5890 or equivalent) equipped with a mass selective detector (Hewlett Packard 5970 or equivalent).

Chromatographic conditions: EKH and dioxane: Column, 15 m, 0.25 mm i.d. DB 5 ms, 0.15 μm (or equivalent). Temperature programmed 40° (2 min), increased to 150° at 15°C/min. Split injection, 150°; Carrier, He, 20 ml/min; interface, 275°; ms dwell time 100 msec.; monitor 43, 44, 57 and 88 amu.

Chromatographic conditions: EO: Column, 50 m, 0.32 mm i.d., CP Sil 5 CB, 5 μm (or equivalent). Temperature programmed 100° (1 min) to 250° at 15°/min. Split injection, 150°; Carrier, He, 20 ml/min.; interface, 275°, ms dwell time 100 msec; monitor 29, 43, 44 and 72 amu.

Regents and Solutions Standards: Accurately weigh approximately 200 mg each of dioxane and EKH and 20 mg EO into a 100 ml volumetric flask containing 50 ml distilled water. Fill to 100 ml. Dilute this standard 1:10, 1:100, and 1:1000. An internal standard is made by accurately weighing approximately 40 mg of methyl ethyl ketone (MEK) and diluting to 100 ml with distilled water. A 1:1000 dilution of this solution gives a 0.4 μg/ml standard solution.

Equipment: Headspace vials, 20 ml, with teflon coated septa; gas tight syringe, 1,000 to 2,500 μl; block or oil bath heater, 80°.

Procedure:

Response factors: Accurately weigh 1.0 g of the sample into each of 4 vials, add 0.5 ml of internal standard to each and add 0, 0.2, 0.4, or 0.6 ml of the 1:1000 standards to one of each vial. Add sufficient buffer to bring the total volume in each vial to 1.5 ml. Cap and place vials into the heater at 80° for 20 min. Inject 1.0 ml of the headspace into the GC-MSD. Monitor ions amu 44,

EO; 43, MEK; 88, dioxane; 57, EKH. Plot the amount of each compound added to the vial against the ratio of the analyte peak area to the MEK peak area. The response factor, R_f, for each analyte is given by the inverse of the x coefficient of the linear regression of the data.

Analysis: Inject 1 ml headspace of unknowns containing MEK internal standard. Record peak areas of unknowns and the internal standard.

Calculation: The EO, EKH, and dioxane concentrations are calculated from the peak areas in the unknown by the following:

$$\text{Content (mg / kg)} = \frac{A_{UNK}}{A_{MEK}} \times C_{MEK} \times R_f$$

where

A_{UNK}	= area of unknown peak
A_{MEK}	= area of MEK peak
C_{MEK}	= concentration of MEK in the sample
R_f	= response factor of the unknown compared to MEK

Mono- and diethylene glycols

Principle: mono- and diethylene glycol are determined by gas chromatography after extraction with acetone.

Apparatus: Gas chromatograph (Hewlett Packard 5980 or equivalent) equipped with an FID detector. Chromatographic conditions: Column, 25 m, 0.52 mm id. CP wax 57 B, 0.5 μm (or equivalent). Temperature programmed 90° (2 min), increased to 250° at 20°/min., final hold, 10 min. Split injection, 250°. Carrier He, 27 ml/min. Injection volume, 1 μl.

Standard solution: Accurately weigh about 20 mg of each glycol into a 25 ml volumetric flask and fill to mark with acetone. This standard is diluted 1:5 and 1:20.

Procedure: Weigh 0.5 g EHEC sample into a 25 ml volumetric flask, add 20 ml acetone, stopper, and stir 2 h at room temperature. Fill flask to volume. Allow the EHEC to settle and inject 1 μl into the chromatograph. Similarly inject 1 μl of the standard solution.

Calculation: The amount of each ethylene glycol is calculated as follows:

$$\% \text{ Glycol} = \frac{A_{SAM}}{A_{STD} \times W} \times C_{STD} \times V_{SAM} \times 100$$

where

A_{SAM}	= peak area of the sample
A_{STD}	= peak area of standard
C_{STD}	= glycol concentration in the standard (mg/ml)
V_{SAM}	= volume in which the sample was dissolved
W	= weight of the sample in mg

The calculated amount of glycol is divided by 0.75 to account for the 75% recovery of the glycols.

METHOD OF ASSAY   Determination of the ethoxyl group

Principle: The sample is oxidized with chromium trioxide and the ethoxyl groups quantitatively transformed into acetic acid. Acetic acid is distilled and determined by titration.

Reagents:

-0.020N sodium hydroxide (carbon dioxide-free)
-0.020N sodium thiosulphate: standardized against 0.020N iodine solution.
-Sodium hydrogen carbonate (analytical grade)
-Aqueous 30% solution of chromium trioxide (analytical grade)

Equipment: The apparatus shown in the following picture is used.

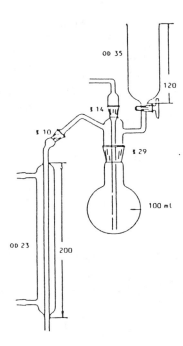

Procedure: Accurately weigh approximately 50 mg of the sample into a 100-ml round bottomed flask; add 10 ml of chromic acid solution and immerse the flask two thirds into an oil bath. The rest of the apparatus is fixed to the flask, and nitrogen is blown through at a rate of 1-2 bubbles per sec. The temperature of the bath is gradually raised over 30 min to 155° and held. Distillation starts at 135-140°. When 5 ml has been distilled, 5 ml of boiled distilled water is added from the graduated 50 ml dropping funnel. This procedure is continued until 50 ml of water has been added and consequently 55 ml of faintly yellow distillate has been collected. The distillate is quantitatively transferred to a flask and the distillate is titrated with 0.020N sodium hydroxide (carbon dioxide-free) to a phenolphthalein end-point. The solution is boiled 1 min and cooled to room temperature. The titration is continued until the pink colour remains stable for 10 sec.

About 0.5 g of sodium hydrogen carbonate is added to the titrated solution followed by 10 ml of 10% sulfuric acid. When carbon dioxide evolution has ceased, 1 g of potassium iodide is added; the flask is shaken and kept 5 min in the dark. Liberated iodine is titrated with 0.020N sodium thiosulfate using 1% starch solution as the indicator.

Chromium trioxide solution (10 ml) is distilled and titrated as described above to provide a blank test. It is necessary to run a new blank when a new chromium trioxide solution has been prepared or if changes have been made in the apparatus.

Calculations:

$$\% \text{ Ethoxyl} = \frac{45 \times 0.020 \times (A - (B \times E))}{10 \times I}$$

A =   ml of sodium hydroxide used
B =   ml of sodium thiosulfate used
C =   ml of sodium hydroxide used in blank test
D =   ml of sodium thiosulfate used in blank test
0.020 =   normality of sodium hydroxide and sodium thiosulfate
I =   grams of sample (calculated dry and free from ash)
E =   C/D

The theoretical value for E is 0.667; in practice it is usually higher (0.7-0.8).

Determination of the total ethoxyl and oxyethylene groups

Principle:

$ROC_2H_5 + HI = ROH + C_2H_5I$

$ROCH_2CH_2OH + HI = RI + ICH_2CH_2I + 2H_2O$

Ethylene iodide is partly converted to ethylene, partly to ethyl iodide. The former is absorbed in bromine solution, the latter in silver nitrate solution. Ethoxyl groups present in the sample will be transformed to ethyl iodide. Conversion of silver iodide to silver bromide with bromine is carried out, followed by thiosulphate titration of the iodine liberated.

Reagents:

-Hydriodic acid: A constant boiling mixture with water (126-127°) containing 57% HI is made in the following manner: Hypophosphorous acid (10-15 ml) is added to 250 ml of HI and the mixture boiled for 4-5 h under reflux in a carbon dioxide atmosphere. The acid is immediately put into 10-ml ampoules of brown glass, which are sealed and stored in a dark place.

-Silver nitrate solution: Silver nitrate (15 g) is dissolved in 50 ml of distilled water. The solution is poured into 400 ml of absolute ethanol, and a few drops of conc. nitric acid are added.

-Bromine solution: Bromine (1 ml) is added to 300 ml of glacial acetic acid which is saturated with dried potassium bromide (about 0.23 g per 100 ml of acetic acid).

-Potassium acetate: 100 g is dissolved in a mixture of 900 ml of acetic acid and 100 ml of acetic anhydride.

-Sodium thiosulfate solution 0.1N: Standardized against a 0.1N iodine solution which in turn has been standardized against 0.1N arsenic trioxide solution. Thiosulfate can also be standardized against potassium iodate purchased as a standard.

Equipment: The apparatus shown in the figure below is used. Tube A is filled halfway with 6% sodium hydrogen carbonate solution, and tube B is filled halfway with 10% cadmium sulfate solution. The silver nitrate solution (5 ml) is pipeted into tube C, and 10 ml of the bromine solution is transferred from the first to the second leg by careful tilting of the tube D. Tube E is filled halfway with 20% potassium iodide solution.

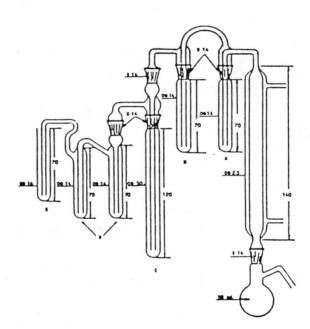

Procedure: Weigh 50-60 mg of the sample into the reaction flask, and add 6 ml of hydriodic acid and a few boiling stones. Fix the flask to the apparatus and immerse it in an oil bath at 140-145°. Circulate tap water through the condenser on top of the flask. Pass carbon dioxide through the apparatus at a rate of about 1 bubble per sec. Continue heating about 2 h (the end of the reaction manifests itself by agglomeration of the precipiate in tube C and clearing up of the solution). Five minutes before the end of the analysis, heat tube C to 50-60° in a water bath. Loosen tubes D and E first, and then tube C. Add to tube D, 5 ml of 20% potassium iodide solution. Mix the bromine and the potassium iodide solutions by carefully purging the tube with carbon dioxide. During this whole procedure, tube E must be left connected to tube D. Then transfer the contents of tube D to a 500-ml Erlenmeyer flask containing 10 ml of 20% potassium iodide solution and 50 ml of distilled water. Rinse tube D well with distilled water, and flood down the contents of tube E in the flask; dilute to 150 ml, and add 5 ml of 10% sulfuric acid. Titrate liberated iodine with 0.05N sodium thiosulfate. Prepare a blank by adding 10 ml of the bromine solution to 10 ml of 20% potassim iodide solution, 150 ml of water, and 5 ml of 10% sulfuric acid and titrate it as described above.

In a 500-ml Erlenmeyer flask, mix 15 ml of the potassium acetate solution with 1 ml bromine. Quantitatively transfer the precipitate and solution in tube C into the Erlenmeyer flask. Allow the flask to stand for 10 min, then add 10 ml of the sodium acetate solution. Eliminate the excess of bromine by carefully adding formic acid dropwise. When the colour of the solution has disappeared, add three more drops. (The colour of the precipitate is always slightly yellow; it is necessary, therefore, to let it settle and observe the colour of the solution only). After 3 min, add 3 g of potassium iodide and 15 ml of 10% sulfuric acid, and titrate the liberated iodine with 0.1N sodium thiosulfate using 1% starch solution as the indicator. Prepare and titrate a blank containing reagents only.

Calculations:

$$\text{Ethoxyl produced by } C_2H_4 \text{ (tubes D, E)} = \frac{22.5 \times N \times (B - A)}{10 \times I}$$

$$\text{Ethoxyl produced by } C_2H_5I \text{ (tube C)} = \frac{7.4 \times C \times N}{10 \times I}$$

where

A = ml of thiosulfate for titration of bromine solution
B = ml of thiosulfate for titration of the blank test on the bromine solution
C = ml of thiosulfate for titration of the silver nitrate solution plus the precipitate
N = normality of thiosulfate solution
I = grams of sample, calculated dry and free from ash

Both hydroxyethoxyl and ethoxyl are reported as ethoxyl.

GELLAN GUM

Prepared at the 49th JECFA (1997)
superseding specifications prepared at the 46th JECFA (1996),
published in FNP 52 Addendum 4 (1996)

SYNONYM	INS No. 418

DEFINITION
Gellan gum is a high molecular weight polysaccharide gum produced by a pure culture fermentation of a carbohydrate by *Pseudomonas elodea*, purified by recovery with isopropyl alcohol, dried, and milled. The high molecular weight polysaccharide is principally composed of a tetrasaccharide repeating unit of one rhamnose, one glucuronic acid, and two glucose units, and is substituted with acyl (glyceryl and acetyl) groups as the O-glycosidically-linked esters. The glucuronic acid is neutralized to a mixed potassium, sodium, calcium, and magnesium salt. It usually contains a small amount of nitrogen containing compounds resulting from the fermentation procedures.

C.A.S. number
71010-52-1

Formula weight
Approximately 500,000

Assay
Yields, on the dried basis, not less than 3.3% and not more than 6.8% of carbon dioxide (CO_2).

DESCRIPTION
Off-white powder

FUNCTIONAL USES
Thickening agent, gelling agent, stabilizer

CHARACTERISTICS

IDENTIFICATION

Solubility
Soluble in water, forming a viscous solution; insoluble in ethanol

Gel test with calcium ion
Passes test
See description under TESTS

Gel test with sodium ion
Passes test
See description under TESTS

PURITY

Loss on drying
Not more than 15% (105°, 2½ h)

Lead
Not more than 2 mg/kg
Prepare a sample solution as directed for organic compounds in the Limit Test and determine the lead content by atomic absorption

Nitrogen
Not more than 3%

Isopropyl alcohol
Not more than 750 mg/kg

See description under TESTS

Microbiological criteria Total plate count: Not more than 10,000 colonies per gram
E. coli   Negative by test
Salmonella: Negative by test
Yeasts and moulds: Not more than 400 colonies per gram
See description under TESTS

TESTS

IDENTIFICATION TESTS

Gel test with calcium ion

Add 1.0 g of the sample to 99 ml of water, and stir for about 2 h, using a motorized stirrer having a propeller-type stirring blade. Draw a small amount of this solution into a wide bore pipet and transfer into a 10% solution of calcium chloride. A tough worm-like gel will be formed immediately.

Gel test with sodium ion

To the 1% solution of the sample prepared for the previous test, add 0.50 g of sodium chloride, heat to 80° with stirring, and hold at 80° for 1 min. Allow the solution to cool to room temperature. A firm gel is formed.

PURITY TESTS

Isopropyl alcohol

Isopropyl alcohol (IPA) Standard Solution:
Transfer 500.0 mg of chromatographic quality isopropyl alcohol into a 50-ml volumetric flask, dilute to volume with water, and mix. Pipet 10 ml of this solution into a 100-ml volumetric flask, dilute to volume with water, and mix.

Tertiary butyl alcohol (TBA) Standard Solution:
Transfer 500.0 mg of chromatographic quality tert-butyl alcohol into a 50-ml volumetric flask, dilute to volume with water, and mix. Pipet 10 ml of this solution into a 100-ml volumetric flask, dilute to volume with water, and mix.

Mixed Standard Solution:
Pipet 4 ml each of the IPA standard solution and of the TBA standard solution into a 125-ml graduated Erlenmeyer flask, dilute to about 100 ml with water, and mix. This solution contains approximately 40 μg each of isopropyl alcohol and of tert-butyl alcohol per ml.

Sample preparation:
Disperse 1 ml of a suitable antifoam emulsion, such as Dow-Corning G-10 or equivalent, in 200 ml of water contained in a 1000-ml round-bottom distilling flask. Add about 5 g of the sample, accurately weighed, and shake the flask for 1 h, on a wrist-action mechanical shaker. Connect the flask to a fractionating column and distil about 100 ml; adjust the heat so that foam does not enter the column. Add 4.0 ml of TBA Standard Solution to the distillate to obtain the Sample Preparation.

Procedure:
Inject about 5 μl of the Mixed Standard Solution into a suitable gas chromatograph equipped with a flame-ionization detector and a 1.8-m x 2.3-mm stainless steel column packed with 80/100-mesh Porapak QS or

equivalent. The carrier is helium flowing at 80 ml per min. The injection port temperature is 200°, the column temperature 165°, and the detector temperature 200°. The retention time of isopropyl alcohol is about 2 min, and that of tert-butyl alcohol about 3 min.

Determine the areas of the IPA and TBA peaks, and calculate the response factor, f, by the formula A_{IPA}/A_{TBA}, in which A_{IPA} is the area of the isopropyl alcohol peak, and A_{TBA} is the area of the tert-butyl alcohol peak.

Similarly, inject about 5 µl of the Sample Preparation, and determine the peak areas, recording the area of the isopropyl alcohol peak as a_{IPA}, and that of the tert-butyl alcohol peak as a_{TBA}. Calculate the isopropyl alcohol content, in mg/kg, in the sample taken by the formula:

$$(a_{IPA} \times 4000)(f \times a_{TBA} \times W)$$

in which W is the weight of the sample taken, in g.

| Microbiological test | Total plate count: Using aseptic technique, disperse 1 g of sample into 99 ml of phosphate buffer and use a Stomacher, shaker or stirrer to fully dissolve. Limit dissolving time to about 10 min and then pipette 1 ml of the solution into separate, duplicate, appropriately marked petri dishes. Pour over the aliquot of sample in each petri dish 12-15 ml of Plate Count Agar previously tempered to 44-46°. Mix well by alternate rotation and back and forth motion of the plates, allow the agar to solidify. Invert the plates and incubate for 48±2 h at 35±1°. |

After incubation count the growing colonies visible on each plate and record the number of colonies. Take the average of both plates, and multiply by the sample dilution factor, 100. Where no colonies are visible, express the result as less than 100 cfu/g.

E. coli determination: Using aseptic technique, disperse 1 g of sample in 99 ml of Lactose broth using either a Stomacher, shaker or stirrer to fully dissolve the sample. Limit the dissolving time to about 15 min and then lightly seal the container and incubate the broth for 18-24 h at 35±1°. Using a sterile pipette, inoculate 1 ml of the incubate into a tube containing 10 ml GN broth. Incubate for 18-24 h and then streak any GN broths showing positive growth or gas production onto duplicate plates of Levine EMB agar. Incubate the plates for 24±2 h at 35±1° and then examine for colonies typical of *E. coli* i.e. showing strong purple growth with dark centre and a green metallic sheen sometimes spreading onto the agar. Record any typical *E. coli* colonies as presumptive positive, otherwise negative.

Streak any well isolated suspect colonies onto a plate of PCA and incubate for 18-24 h at 35±1°. Perform a Gram stain on any growth to confirm it is Gram negative. If so, disperse any colony growth into a small volume of 0.85% saline and perform chemical tests to confirm the identity of the bacterial growth. This can most conveniently be done by using API 20E or Micro ID strips or equivalent systems.

After completion of the tests, identify the organism from the Identification manual of the system used and record the final result.

Media
GN Broth (Gram Negative Broth)

Peptone	20.0 g
Dextrose	1.0 g
Mannitol	2.0 g
Sodium citrate	5.0 g
Sodium deoxycholate	0.5 g
Potassium phosphate (dibasic)	4.0 g
Potassium phosphate (monobasic)	1.5 g
Sodium chloride	5.0 g

Make up to 1 litre with distilled or de-ionised water, pH 7.0±0.2 at 25°.

Salmonella determination: Using aseptic technique, disperse 5 g of sample into 200 ml of sterile lactose broth using either a Stomacher, shaker or stirrer to maximise dissolution over a 15 min period. Loosely seal the container and incubate at 35±1° for 24±2 h.

Continue as per method on page 221 of *FNP 5/Rev. 2 (1991)*. Identification can be more conveniently done using API or Micro ID systems or equivalent.

Yeasts and moulds: Using aseptic technique, disperse 1 g of sample into 99 ml of phosphate buffer and use a Stomacher, shaker or stirrer to fully dissolve. Limit dissolving time to about 10 min and then pipette 1 ml of the solution into separate, duplicate, appropriately marked petri dishes. Pour over the aliquot of sample in each petri dish 15-20 ml of Potato dextrose Agar (either acidified or containing antibiotic) previously tempered to 44-46°. Mix well by alternate rotation and back and forth motion of the plates, and allow the agar to solidify. Invert the plates and incubate for 5 days at 20-25°.

After incubation, count the growing colonies visible on each plate using a colony counter and record the number of colonies. Separate the yeasts from the moulds according to their morphology and count them separately. Take the average of both plates and multiply by the sample dilution factor, 100. Where no colonies are visible, express the result as less than 100 cfu/g.

METHOD OF ASSAY   Processed as directed in the test for Carbon Dioxide Determination by Decarboxylation in the *General Methods*, using about 1.2 g of the sample weighed accurately.

GUM ARABIC

Prepared at the 49th JECFA (1997)
superseding specifications prepared at the 44th JECFA (1995),
published in FNP 52 Addendum 3 (1995)

SYNONYMS	Acacia gum, arabic gum; INS No. 414

DEFINITION   Gum Arabic is a dried exudate obtained from the stems and branches of *Acacia senegal* (L.) Willdenow or closely related species of Acacia (fam. Leguminosae). *A. seyal* is a closely related species. Gum arabic consists mainly of high-molecular weight polysaccharides and their calcium, magnesium, and potassium salts, which on hydrolysis yield arabinose, galactose, rhamnose, and glucuronic acid. Items of commerce may contain extraneous materials such as sand and pieces of bark which must be removed before use in food. Gum arabic from *A. seyal* is sometimes referred to as gum talha.

C.A.S. number   9000-01-5

DESCRIPTION   Gum Arabic from *A. senegal* is a pale white to orange-brown solid, which breaks with a glassy fracture. The best grades are in the form of whole, spheroidal tears of varying size with a matte surface texture. When ground, the pieces are paler and have a glassy appearance. Gum from other acacia species may not have the characteristic tear shape and are often darker in colour. Gum from *A. seyal* is more brittle than the hard tears of *A. senegal*. Gum arabic is also available commercially in the form of white to yellowish-white flakes, granules, powder, roller-dried, or spray-dried material.

FUNCTIONAL USES   Emulsifier, stabilizer, and thickener

CHARACTERISTICS

   IDENTIFICATION

   Solubility   One gram dissolves in 2 ml of water forming a solution which flows readily and is acid to litmus, insoluble in ethanol

   Hydrolysis products   Passes test
   See description under TESTS

   Optical rotation   Gum from *A. senegal*: water solutions are levorotatory
   Gum from *A. seyal*: water solutions are dextrorotatory
   See description under TESTS

   PURITY

   Loss on drying   Not more than 15% (105°, 5 h) for granular and not more than 10% (105°, 4 h) for spray-dried material
   Unground samples should be powdered to pass through a No. 40 sieve and mixed well before weighing

Total ash	Not more than 4%
Acid insoluble ash	Not more than 0.5%
Acid insoluble matter	Not more than 1%
Arsenic	Not more than 3 mg/kg (Method II)
Lead	Not more than 5 mg/kg Prepare a sample solution as directed for organic compounds in the Limit Test, using 5 µg of lead ion (Pb) in the control
Starch or dextrin	Passes test See description under TESTS
Tannin-bearing gums	Passes test See description under TESTS
Microbiological criteria	*Salmonella* Spp. Negative per test *E. coli* Negative in 1 g

TESTS

IDENTIFICATION TESTS

Hydrolysis products

Identify arabinose, galactose, rhamnose and glucuronic acid as follows:

Boil a mixture of 100 mg of the sample and 20 ml of 10% sulfuric acid for 3 h. Allow to cool and add excess barium carbonate, mixing with a magnetic stirrer until the solution is of pH 7, and filter. Evaporate the filtrate in a rotary evaporator at 30-50° in vacuum until a crystalline or syrupy residue is obtained. Dissolve in 10 ml of 40% methanol. This is the hydrolysate.

Place 1 to 10 µl spots of the hydrolysate on the starting line of two chromatoplates and spots containing 1 to 10 µg of arabinose, galactose, rhamnose and glucuronic acid, expected to be present in the hydrolysate. Use two solvent systems one for each plate: A. a mixture of formic acid, methyl ethyl ketone, tertiary butanol and water (15:30:40:15 by volume) and B. a mixture of isopropanol, pyridine, acetic acid and water (40:40:5:20 by volume) to develop the plates. After development, spray with a solution of 1.23 g anisidine and 1.66 g phthalic acid in 100 ml ethanol and heat the plates at 100° for 10 min. A greenish yellow colour is produced with hexoses, a red colour with pentoses and a brown colour with uronic acids. Compare sample spots with those for the solutions of arabinose, galactose, rhamnose and glucuronic acid. Additional spots corresponding to mannose, xylose, and galacturonic acid should be absent.

Optical rotation

Test a solution of 10 g of sample (dry basis) in 100 ml of water (if necessary, previously filtered through a No. 42 paper or 0.8 µm millipore filter), using a 200-mm tube.

PURITY TESTS

Starch or dextrin	Boil a 1 in 50 solution of the sample, cool and add a few drops of iodine TS. No bluish or reddish colour should be produced.
Tannin-bearing gums	To 10 ml of a 1 in 50 solution of the sample add about 0.1 ml of ferric chloride TS. No blackish colouration or blackish precipitate should be formed.

HYDROGENATED POLY-1-DECENE

Prepared at the 49th JECFA (1997)

SYNONYMS	Hydrogenated polydec-1-ene, Hydrogenated poly-α-olefin, PAO, INS No. 907
DEFINITION	Hydrogenated poly-1-decene is a mixture of isoparaffinic molecules of known structure, prepared by hydrogenation of mixtures of tri-, tetra- penta- and hexa-1-decenes.

C.A.S. number   68037-01-4

Chemical formula $C_{10n}H_{20n+2}$, where n = 3 - 6

Formula weight   550 (average)

Assay   Not less than 99.5 % of hydrogenated poly-1-decene, having the following oligomer distribution:

C_{30}: 16 - 35 %
C_{40}: 42 - 61 %
C_{50}: 12 - 23 %
C_{60}: 1 - 9 %

DESCRIPTION   Colourless, odourless, viscous liquid

FUNCTIONAL USES   Glazing agent, releasing agent

CHARACTERISTICS

IDENTIFICATION

Solubility   Insoluble in water; slightly soluble in ethanol; soluble in toluene

Burning   The product burns with bright flame and a paraffin like characteristic smell.

Viscosity   6 cSt (100°)
See description under TESTS

PURITY

Hydrogenated decene dimer
          Not more than 0.5 % (calculated as C_{20}-oligomer)
          See METHOD OF ASSAY

Readily carbonisable substances
          Passes test
          See description under TESTS

Nickel   Not more than 1 mg/kg

Heavy metals   Not more than 10 mg/kg

Test 2 g of sample as directed in the Limit Test (Method II)

TESTS

IDENTIFICATION TESTS

Viscosity   Use the method as described in ASTM D 445 (American Society for Testing Materials)

PURITY TESTS

Readily carbonizable substances

Place 5 g of the sample in a glass-stoppered test tube that has previously been cleaned with a chromic acid cleaning solution, rinsed with water and dried in an oven (105°, 1 h). Add 5 ml of sulfuric acid TS, and place in a boiling water bath. After the test tube has been in the bath for 30 sec, remove quickly, and while holding the stopper in place, give three vigorous vertical shakes over an amplitude of about 10 cm. Repeat every 30 sec. Do not keep the test tube out of the bath longer than 3 sec for each shaking period. At the end of 10 min from the time when first placed in the water bath, remove the test tube. The sample remains unchanged in colour, and the acid does not become darker than a very slight straw colour (*Matching Fluid E , see General Methods*). No black material occurs at the interface between the two layers.

METHOD OF ASSAY

Hydrogenated poly-1-decene, oligomer distribution and the content of hydrogenated decene dimer: Determine by gas-liquid chromatography using the following conditions:

Column:	Capillary column, 16 m x 0.53 mm
Column film:	Nonpolar (polydimethyldisiloxane) film, thickness 0.1 μm, e.g. OV-1, DB-1
Carrier gas:	Helium
Flow rate:	10 ml/min
Injector pressure:	1.5 psi at 35°, constant flow
Detector type:	FID
Column temperature:	35° -1 min - 5°/min - 50° - 12°/ min - 170° - 10°/min - 310° - 45 min
Injection temperature:	35°
Sample size:	2 μl

Calibration:
Calibrate the instrument using a solution with known composition containing about 1.0 % of n-tetradecane, 1.0 % of n-hexadecane and 1.0 % of squalane (2,6,10,15,19,23-hexamethyl tetracosane) in pentane. The differences between peak areas of the compounds should be less than 10.0 % and the resolution between tetradecane and n-hexadecane should be between 2 and 5. Calculate the resolution (R) from the distance between n-tetradecane and n-hexadecane peaks at the peak maxima (d) and the width of the peaks at the baseline (Y): $R = [2(d_1 - d_2)/(Y_1 - Y_2)]$.

Sample preparation:
Take a small amount of the sample into an automatic pipette. Place a drop of the

sample in 1.00 ml of pentane, and mix well. Record the chromatogram for about 45 min.

Retention times:
The retention times for C_{20}, C_{30}, C_{40}, C_{50} and C_{60} are usually about 10.5, 16, 20, 23 and 26 min.

Calculation:
Calculate the level of hydrogenated decene dimer and the oligomer distribution by the method of area percentages (area normalization).

Calculate the percentage of hydrogenated poly-1-decene in the sample taken by the formula:

100 A/T

where

A = the sum of peak areas for C_{30}, C_{40}, C_{50} and C_{60}
T = the sum of all peak areas eluting in 45 min

ISOAMYL ACETATE

Prepared at the 49th JECFA (1997)
superseding specifications prepared at the 46th JECFA (1996),
published in FNP 52 Addendum 4 (1996)

SYNONYMS	Amyl acetate, isoamyl ethanoate
DEFINITION	A mixture of acetic acid esters of pentanols
Chemical name	3-Methylbutyl ethanoate (principal component)
C.A.S. number	123-92-2
Chemical formula	$C_7H_{14}O_2$
Structural formula	

$$CH_3COOCH_2CH_2\overset{\overset{\displaystyle CH_3}{|}}{\underset{\underset{\displaystyle CH_3}{|}}{CH}}$$

Molecular weight	130.19
Assay	Not less than 95.0% $C_7H_{14}O_2$
DESCRIPTION	Colourless, clear liquid, having a characteristic fruit-like odour
FUNCTIONAL USES	Carrier solvent, flavouring agent (see "flavouring agents" monograph)

CHARACTERISTICS

IDENTIFICATION

Solubility	Slightly soluble in water, insoluble in glycerol, practically insoluble in propylene glycol, soluble in ethanol, diethyl ether, ethyl acetate, most fixed oils and mineral oils
Refractive index	n_D^{20}: 1.400-1.404
Specific gravity	d_{25}^{25}: 0.868-0.878

PURITY

Non volatile residue	Not more than 7 mg/100 ml
Distillation range	Not less than 99% v/v distils between 135 and 143°
Heavy metals	Not more than 10 mg/kg
	Test 2 g of the sample as directed in the Limit Test (Method II)

Acid value   Not more than 1

METHOD OF ASSAY   Weigh accurately about 0.8 g of the sample and proceed as directed under the method for Ester Determination in the *General Methods*, using 65.10 as the equivalence factor (e) in the calculation.

MALTITOL SYRUP

Prepared at the 49th JECFA (1997)
superseding specifications prepared at the 46th JECFA (1996),
published in FNP 52 Addendum 4 (1996)

SYNONYMS

Hydrogenated high maltose-content glucose syrup, hydrogenated glucose syrup, dried maltitol syrup, maltitol syrup powder
INS No. 965

DEFINITION

A mixture consisting of mainly maltitol with sorbitol and hydrogenated oligo- and polysaccharides. It is manufactured by the catalytic hydrogenation of high maltose-content glucose syrup. The article of commerce is typically supplied as a syrup. It may also be dried and supplied as a solid product

Assay

Not less than 99.0% of total hydrogenated saccharides on the anhydrous basis and not less than 50.0% of maltitol on the anhydrous basis

DESCRIPTION

Colourless and odourless, clear viscous liquids or white crystalline masses

FUNCTIONAL USES

Sweetener, humectant, texturizer, stabilizer, bulking agent

CHARACTERISTICS

IDENTIFICATION TESTS

Solubility

Very soluble in water, slightly soluble in ethanol

Thin layer chromatography

Passes test
See description under TESTS

PURITY TESTS

Water

Not more than 31% (Karl Fischer)

Sulfated ash

Not more than 0.1 %
Test 3 g of sample as directed under the test for Ash (Sulfated ash)
Method I

Chloride

Not more than 50 mg/kg
Test 10 g of the sample by the Limit Test using 1.5 ml of 0.01 N hydrochloric acid in the standard

Sulfate

Not more than 100 mg/kg
Test 10 g of the sample by the Limit Test using 2.0 ml of 0.0l N sulfuric acid in the standard

Nickel

Not more than 2 mg/kg
See description under TESTS

Lead

Not more than 1 mg/kg

Prepare a sample solution as directed for organic compounds in the Limit Test and determine the lead content by atomic absorption spectrometry

Reducing sugars Not more than 0.3%
Proceed as described in the method for Reducing Substances (as glucose), Method II. The weight of cuprous oxide shall not exceed 50 mg

TESTS

IDENTIFICATION TEST

Thin layer chromatography

Examine by thin layer chromatography using silica gel as the coating substance

Standard solution:
Dissolve 50 mg of reference standard maltitol (available from US Pharmacopeial Convention, Inc., 12601 Twinbrook Parkway, Rockville, MD 20852, USA) in 20 ml water

Test solution:
Dissolve 50 mg of sample in 20 ml of water

4-Aminobenzoic acid reagent:
Prepare a solution by dissolving 1 g of 4-aminobenzoic acid in a solvent mixture composed of 18 ml acetic acid, 20 ml water and 1 ml phosphoric acid. Prepare this reagent immediately before use.

Sodium periodate reagent:
A solution of 0.2% w/v sodium periodate in water

Procedure:
Apply 2 µl of each of the standard and test solution to the bottom of the TLC plate. Develop the chromatogram over a path of 17 cm using as the mobile phase a mixture of 70 volumes of propanol, 20 volumes of ethyl acetate and 10 volumes of water. Allow the plate to dry in air and spray with a mixture of 2 volumes of 4-aminobenzoic acid reagent with 3 volumes of acetone. Heat at 100° for 15 min. Spray with the sodium periodate reagent. Heat at 100° for 15 min. The principal spot in the chromatogram obtained from the test solution corresponds in position, colour and size to the principal spot obtained from the standard solution.

PURITY TESTS

Nickel

Test solution:
Dissolve 20.0 g of the sample in a mixture of equal volumes of dilute acetic acid TS and water and dilute to 100 ml with the same mixture of solvents. Add 2.0 ml of a 1% w/v solution of ammonium pyrrolidinedithiocarbamate and 10 ml of methyl isobutyl ketone. Mix and allow the layers to separate and use the methyl isobutyl ketone layer for analysis.

Standard solutions:

Prepare three standard solutions in the same manner as the test solution but adding 0.5 ml, 1.0 ml, and 1.5 ml, respectively, of a standard nickel solution containing 10 mg/l Ni, in addition to the 20.0 g of the sample.

Procedure:
Set the instrument to zero using methyl isobutyl ketone prepared as described for the preparation of the test solution but omitting the substance to be examined. Use a nickel hollow-cathode lamp as source of radiation and an air-acetylene flame. The analysis wavelength for all solutions is 232.0 nm.

METHOD OF ASSAY   Total hydrogenated saccharides (%):

$$\frac{100 - (\text{Water\%} + \text{Sulfated ash\%} + \text{Reducing sugars\%})}{100 - \text{Water\%}} \times 100$$

Maltitol is determined by High Performance Liquid Chromatography (HPLC) using the following conditions:

Apparatus:
-Detection: Differential refractometer maintained at constant temperature
-Integrator recorder
-Liquid chromatograph (HPLC)
-Column: AMINEX HPX 87 C (resin in calcium form), length 30 cm, internal diameter 9 mm
-Eluent: Double distilled degassed water (filtered through Millipore membrane filter 0.45 µm)

Chromatographic conditions:
Column temperature: $85 \pm 0.5°$
Eluent flow rate: 0.5 ml/min

Standard preparation:
Dissolve an accurately weighed quantity of standard reference maltitol (available from US Pharmacopeial Convention Inc., 12601 Twinbrook Parkway, Rockville, MD 20852, USA) in water to obtain a solution having known concentration of about 10.0 mg of maltitol per ml.

Sample preparation:
Transfer about 1 g of the sample accurately weighed to a 50-ml volumetric flask, dilute with water to volume and mix.

Procedure:
Separately inject equal volumes (about 20 µl) of the sample preparation and the standard preparation into the chromatograph. Record the chromatograms and measure the responses of each maltitol peak. Calculate the quantity, in mg, of maltitol in the syrup by the following formula:

$$50 \times C \times \frac{R_U}{R_S}$$

in which C is the concentration, in mg per ml, of maltitol in the standard preparation; R_U is the peak response of maltitol from the sample preparation and R_S is the peak response of the standard preparation.

TENTATIVE

**MALTOGENIC AMYLASE
FROM *BACILLUS STEAROTHERMOPHILUS*
EXPRESSED IN *BACILLUS SUBTILIS***

Prepared at the 49th JECFA (1997)

These specifications are designated tentative because Appendix B "General Considerations and Specifications for Enzymes from Genetically Manipulated Microorganisms" of Annex 1 of the Compendium of Food Additive Specifications, FNP 52, Rome 1992, is tentative.

SYNONYMS   Maltogenase

SOURCES   Prepared by submerged fermentation of *Bacillus subtilis*, strain DN 252 (a derivative of *Bacillus subtilis* 168, strain QB 1133, BGSC1A289) which, through recombinant DNA techniques contains the gene coding for maltogenic amylase in the plasmid pDN1413. The gene is imported from *Bacillus stearothermophilus* (NCIB 11837).

ACTIVE PRINCIPLES   Exo-acting α-amylase

**SYSTEMATIC NAMES
AND NUMBERS**   Glucan 1,4-α-maltohydrolase, E.C. 3.2.1.133

REACTION CATALYZED   Exohydrolysis of 1,4-α-glucosidic linkages in amylose, amylopectin and related glucose polymers. Maltose units are successively removed from the non-reducing end of the polymer chain until the molecule is completely degraded or, in the case of amylopectin, a branch point is reached.

DESCRIPTION   Commercial preparations can be liquid, granulated or powdered form. The powdered form contains sodium chloride as a stabilizer, the granulated form contains sodium chloride and wheat grits, and the liquid form contains sodium chloride and sucrose.

FUNCTIONAL USES   Enzyme preparation
Retardation of staling in baked goods, preparation of high maltose glucose syrup

**GENERAL
SPECIFICATIONS**   Must conform to the "General Specifications for Enzyme Preparations used in Food Processing in Annex 1 of the Compendium of Food Additive Specifications, FAO Food and Nutrition Paper 52, Rome 1992.

CHARACTERISTICS

  IDENTIFICATION

  Maltogenic amylase activity   The sample shows maltogenic amylase activity
See description under TESTS

TESTS

  Maltogenic amylase activity   The method is based on the ability of the enzyme to hydrolyze maltotriose to maltose and glucose. The reaction is stopped by raising the pH of the reaction medium to about 11. The formed glucose is converted to gluconolactone by glucose dehydrogenase in the presence of NAD^+ which is converted to $NADH^+H^+$. The change in the concentration of NAD^+ is measured photometrically at 340 nm. One enzyme unit (Maltogenic Amylase Unit, MAU) is defined as the amount of enzyme which under standard assay conditions cleaves 1 µmol of maltotriose per minute. Assay conditions being as follows: Substrate concentration 10 mg/ml; temperature 37°; pH 5.0; incubation time 30 min.

Preparation of 20 mg/ml-maltotriose substrate:
Dissolve 1000 mg maltotriose (e.g. Sigma M8378) in 0.1M citrate buffer, pH 5.0, making a total volume of 50 ml (to be prepared each day of analysis).

Preparation of glucose dehydrogenase (GluDH) reagent:
Add buffer solution (Merck No. 14051 or equivalent) to the enzyme mixture (Merck No. 14055, bottles "1" and "2", or equivalent). Allow the mixture to stand for 15 min. Transfer the solution to a 500 ml volumetric flask, containing 200 ml of 0.1 M citrate buffer pH 5.0. Fill the flask to the mark with the same buffer. This solution can be stored for two weeks at room temperature (not in a refrigerator).

Preparation of standard enzyme solutions:
Dilute a maltogenic amylase standard with known activity in 10 mM NaCl to give the following enzyme units per ml: 0.015, 0.030, 0.045, 0.060 and 0.075.

Measurement of enzyme activity:
Add 500 µl of substrate solution (20 mg/ml maltotriose, prepared in 0.1 M citrate buffer, pH 5.0, pre-warmed to 37°) to an equal volume of enzyme solution also pre-warmed to 37°. Mix the resulting solution thoroughly and transfer to a water bath maintained at 37°. After 30 minutes remove the test tube from the water bath, and add 1000 µl of the stop reagent (0.06N NaOH) and shake vigorously. Add 3 ml of GluDH reagent and mix again. Leave the test tube at room temperature for exactly 30 min and measure optical density (OD) at 340 nm. Prepare a blank in a similar manner except that the stop reagent is added before the substrate.

Calculation of enzyme activity:
Draw the enzyme standard curve in a coordinate system using enzyme activity (MAU/ml) as the abscissa and ΔOD (sample - blank) as the ordinate. Calculate the activity of the sample by reading ΔOD of sample dilutions on the standard curve and then multiplying by the corresponding dilution factors. The standard curve is a straight line passing through the origin and linear regression can therefore be applied.

Basic standardisation:
Glucose solutions:
a) Stock solution: Accurately weigh 1.60 g of glucose, analytical grade, in a 1000-ml volumetric flask and make up to volume with demineralized water.

b) standard solutions: Dilute 1.0, 2.0, 3.0, 4.0, 5.0 and 6.0 ml of stock solution to volume with deionized water in 100-ml volumetric flask to give standard solutions of 88.8, 178, 266, 355, 444 and 533 μmol/l.

Standard curve:
Prepare the glucose standard curve by mixing 2.0 ml glucose solution with 3.0 ml GluDH reagent and incubating at room temperature for 30 min. Read OD at 340 nm. Prepare a common blank using deminaralized water instead of glucose solution. Plot glucose concentration (μmol/l) versus ΔOD.

Calculation:
Calculate the enzyme activity by reading the equivalent glucose concentration on the standard curve and inserting it in the following formula:

$$MAU / g = \frac{A \times 4 \times F}{30 \times 1000}$$

where:

A = reading on the standard curve, μmol/l
F = dilution factor of the enzyme solution, ml/g
4 = the ratio between amount of enzyme dilution in sample and amount of glucose solution in standard
30 = incubation time, 30 min
1000 = conversion from litre to ml

MICROCRYSTALLINE CELLULOSE

Prepared at the 49th JECFA (1997)
superseding specifications prepared at the 46th JECFA (1996),
published in FNP 52 Addendum 4 (1996)

SYNONYMS   Cellulose gel, INS No. 460

DEFINITION   Microcrystalline cellulose is a purified, partially depolymerized cellulose prepared by treating alpha-cellulose, obtained as a pulp from fibrous plant material, with mineral acids. The degree of polymerization is typically less than 400. Not more than 10% of the material has a particle size of less than 5 µm.

Chemical names   Cellulose

C.A.S. number   9004-34-6

Chemical formula $(C_6H_{10}O_5)_n$

Assay   Not less than 97% of carbohydrate calculated as cellulose on the dried basis

DESCRIPTION   Fine, white or almost white, odourless, free flowing crystalline powder

FUNCTIONAL USES   Emulsifier, stabilizer, anticaking and dispersing agent

CHARACTERISTICS

IDENTIFICATION

Solubility   Insoluble in water, ethanol, ether and dilute mineral acids. Slightly soluble in sodium hydroxide solution

Infrared absorption   The infrared absorption spectrum of a potassium bromide dispersion of the sample corresponds to the infrared spectrum in the Appendix

PURITY

Loss on drying   Not more than 7.0% (105°, 3 h)

pH   5.0 - 7.5
                          Shake 5 g of the sample with 40 ml of water for 20 min and centrifuge. Use the supernatant for pH determination

Water soluble substances
                          Not more than 0.24%
                          See description under TESTS

Sulfated ash   Not more than 0.05%
                          Proceed as directed under the test for Ash (Sulfated Ash, Method I) using 2 g of the sample

Lead   Not more than 2 mg/kg

Prepare a sample solution as directed for organic compounds in the Limit Test and determine the lead content by atomic absorption spectrometry

Starch   Not detectable
                See description under TESTS

TESTS

PURITY TESTS

Water soluble substances

Shake 5 g of the sample with approximately 80 ml of water for 10 min, filter through Whatman No. 42 or equivalent filter paper into a tared beaker, evaporate to dryness on a steam bath and dry at 105° for 1 h. Cool, weigh and calculate as percentage.

Starch

Mix 30 g of the sample with 270 ml of water in a high-speed (18,000 rpm) blender for 5 min. Transfer 100 ml of the mixture to a 100-ml graduated cylinder, and allow to stand for 3 h. A white opaque, bubble-free dispersion which does form a supernatant liquid at the surface, is obtained.

To 20 ml of this dispersion add a few drops of iodine TS, and mix. No purplish to blue or blue colour should be produced.

METHOD OF ASSAY

Transfer about 125 mg of the sample, accurately weighed, to a 300-ml Erlenmeyer flask, using about 25 ml of water. Add 50.0 ml of 0.5N potassium dichromate, mix, then carefully add 100 ml of sufuric acid, and heat to boiling. Remove from heat, allow to stand at room temperature for 15 min, cool in a water bath, and transfer into a 250-ml volumetric flask. Dilute with water almost to volume, cool to 25°, then dilute to volume with water, and mix. Titrate a 50.0-ml aliquot with 0.1N ferrous ammonium sulfate, using 2 or 3 drops of ortho-phenanthroline TS as the indicator, and record the volume required as S, in ml. Perform a blank determination, and record the volume of 0.1N ferrous ammonium sulfate required as B, in ml. Calculate the percentage of cellulose in the sample by the formula:

$$(B - S) \times \frac{338}{W}\%$$

in which W is the weight of sample taken, in mg, corrected for Loss on Drying.

APPENDIX

Infrared spectrum: **Microcrystalline cellulose**

% Transmittance   Absorbance

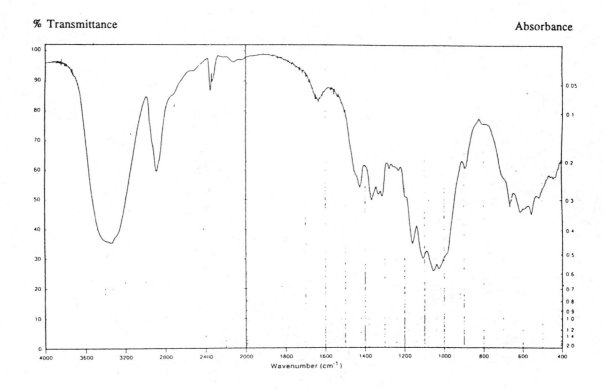

MICROCRYSTALLINE WAX

Prepared at the 49th JECFA (1997)
superseding specifications prepared at the 44th JECFA (1995),
published in FNP 52 Addendum 3 (1995)

SYNONYMS   Petroleum wax, INS No. 905(c)

DEFINITION   Microcrystalline wax is a refined mixture of solid, saturated hydrocarbons, mainly branched paraffin, obtained from petroleum

DESCRIPTION   Colourless or white, translucent and odourless wax

FUNCTIONAL USES   Component of chewing gum base, protective coating, antifoaming agent, surface finishing agent

CHARACTERISTICS

IDENTIFICATION

Solubility   Insoluble in water, very slightly soluble in ethanol, sparingly soluble in diethyl ether and hexane

Melting range   62-102°
                        See description under TESTS

Refractive Index $n_D^{100} = 1.434 - 1.448$

Infrared absorption   The infrared absorbance spectrum of the sample melted and prepared on a caesium or potassium bromide plate corresponds to the spectrum in the Appendix

PURITY

Viscosity, 100°   Not less than 11 cSt.
                        See description under TESTS

Carbon number at 5% distillation point
                        Not more than 5% of molecules with carbon number less than 25
                        See description under TESTS

Average molecular weight
                        Not less than 500
                        See description under TESTS

Residue on ignition   Not more than 0.1%
                        See description under TESTS

Colour   Passes test
                        See description under TESTS

Sulfur   Not more than 0.4%
                        See description under TESTS

Arsenic   Not more than 3 mg/kg (Method II)

Lead   Not more than 3 mg/kg
                              Test 3.3 g of the sample and proceed as described for organic compounds in
                              the Lead Limit Test, using 10 µg of lead ion in the control.

Polycyclic aromatic hydrocarbons

The sample shall meet the following ultraviolet absorbance limits when
subjected to the analytical procedure described under the TESTS.

nm	max. absorbance per cm path length
280 - 289	0.15
290 - 299	0.12
300 - 359	0.08
360 - 400	0.02

TESTS

IDENTIFICATION TEST

Melting range   Melt a quantity of the substance slowly, while stirring, until it reaches a
                              temperature of 90° or higher to completely melt the substance. Remove the
                              source of heat, and allow the molten substance to cool to a temperature of 8 to
                              10° above the expected melting point. Chill the bulb of an ASTM 14C
                              (American Society for Testing and Materials) or equal thermometer to 5°,
                              wipe it dry and while it is still cold dip into the molten substance so that
                              approximately the lower half of the bulb is submerged. Withdraw it
                              immediately, and hold it vertically away from the heat until the wax surface
                              dulls, then dip it for 5 min into a water bath having a temperature not higher
                              than 16°.

                              Fix the thermometer securely in a test tube so that the lower point is 15 mm
                              above the bottom of the test tube. Suspend the test tube in a water bath
                              adjusted to about 16°, and raise the temperature of the bath a the rate of 2°
                              per min to 30°, then change to a rate of 1° per min and note the temperature at
                              which the first drop of melted substance leaves the thermometer. Repeat the
                              determination twice on a freshly melted portion of the sample. If the variation
                              of three determinations is less than 1°, take the average of the three as the
                              melting point. If the variation of the three determinations is greater than 1°,
                              make two additional determinations and take the average of the five.

PURITY TESTS

Viscosity, 100°   Use the method as described in ASTM D 445

Carbon number at 5% distillation point

"Carbon number" is number of carbon atoms in a molecule. Determine the
carbon number distribution of the sample using the method as described in
ASTM D 5442.

NOTE: By optimizing the length of separation column and/or column temperature, waxes with carbon number higher than 45 can also be included.

The combined contents of components with carbon number less than 25 is not more than 5%.

Average molecular weight

Using the carbon number distribution obtained in the test for "Carbon number at 5% distillation point" calculate the average molecular weight by the following formula:

$$\text{Average molecular weight} = \frac{\sum_{i=17}^{i=i} C_i \, (14i + 2)}{100}$$

where

i = the carbon number
C_i is the content in % of components having a carbon number of i

Residue on ignition

Accurately weigh about 2 g of the sample in a tared porcelain or platinum dish and heat over a flame. The sample volatilizes without emitting an acrid odour. Ignite to not exceeding a very dull redness until free from carbon. Cool in a desiccator and weigh.

Colour

Melt about 10 g of the sample on a steam bath, and pour 5 ml of the liquid into a clear-glass, 16 x 150-mm bacteriological test tube: the warm, melted liquid is not darker than a solution made by mixing 3.8 ml of ferric chloride TS and 1.2 ml of cobaltous chloride TS in a similar tube, the comparison of the two being made in reflected light against a white background, the tubes being held directly against the background at such an angle that there is no fluorescence.

Sulfur

Use the method as described in ASTM D 2622

Polycyclic aromatic hydrocarbons

General Instructions

Because of the sensitivity of the test, the possibility of errors arising from contamination is great. It is of the greatest importance that all glassware be scrupulously cleaned to remove all organic matter such as oil, grease, detergent residues, etc. Examine all glassware, including stoppers and stopcocks, under ultraviolet light to detect any residual fluorescent contamination. As a precautionary measure it is a recommended practice to rinse all glassware with purified isooctane immediately before use. No grease is to be used on stopcocks or joints. Great care to avoid contamination of wax samples in handling and to assure absence of any extraneous material arising from inadequate packaging is essential. Because some of the polynuclear hydrocarbons sought in this test are very susceptible to photo-oxidation, the entire procedure is to be carried out under subdued light.

Apparatus

- Separatory funnels: 250-ml, 500-ml, 1,000-ml, and preferably 2000-ml capacity, equipped with tetrafluoroethylene polymer stopcocks.

- Reservoir: 500-ml capacity, equipped with a 24/40 standard taper male fitting at the bottom and a suitable balljoint at the top for connecting to the nitrogen supply. The male fitting should be equipped with glass hooks.

- Chromatographic tube: 180 mm in length, inside diameter to be 15.7 mm ± 0.1 mm, equipped with a coarse, fritted-glass disc, a tetrafluoroethylene polymer stopcock, and a female 24/40 standard tapered fitting at the opposite end. (Overall length of the column with the female joint is 235 mm). The female 24/40 standard tapered fitting at the opposite end.

- Disc: Tetrafluoroethylene polymer 2-inch diameter disc approximately 3/16-inch thick with a hole bored in the center to closely fit the stem of the chromatographic tube.

- Heating jacket: Conical, for 500-ml separatory funnel. (Used with variable transformer heat control).

- Suction flask: 250-ml or 500-ml filter flask.

- Condenser: 24/40 joints, fitted with a drying tube, length optional.

- Evaporation flask (optional): 250-ml or 500-ml capacity all-glass flask equipped with standard taper stopper having inlet and outlet tubes permitting passage of nitrogen across the surface of the liquid to be evaporated.

- Vacuum distillation assembly: All glass (for purification of dimethyl sulfoxide); 2 litre distillation flask with heating mantle; Vigreaux vacuum-jacketed condenser (or equivalent) about 45 cm in length and distilling head with separable cold finger condenser. Use of tetrafluoroethylene polymer sleeves on the glass joints will prevent freezing. Do not use grease on stopcocks or joints.

- Spectrophotometric cells: Fused quartz cells, optical path length in the range of 5.000 ± 0.005 cm; also for checking spectrophotometer performance only, optical path length in the range 1.000 ± 0.005 cm. With distilled water in the cells, determine any absorbance differences.

- Spectrophotometer: Spectral range 250-400 nm with spectral slit width of 2 nm or less, under instrument operating conditions for these absorbance measurements, the spectrophotometer shall also meet the following performance requirements:

Absorbance repeatability:	±0.01 at 0.4 absorbance
Absorbance accuracy:	±0.05 at 0.4 absorbance
Wavelength repeatability:	±0.2 nm
Wavelength accuracy:	±1.0 nm

- Nitrogen cylinder: Water-pumped or equivalent purity nitrogen in cylinder equipped with regulator and valve to control flow at 5 p.s.i.g.

Reagents and materials

- Organic solvents: All solvents used throughout the procedure shall meet the specifications and tests described in this specification. The isooctane, benzene, acetone, and methyl alcohol designated in the list following this paragraph shall pass the following test:

To the specified quantity of solvent in a 250-ml Erlenmeyer flask, add 1 ml of purified n-hexadecane and evaporate on the steam bath under a stream of nitrogen (a loose aluminium foil jacket around the flask will speed evaporation). Discontinue evaporation when not over 1 ml of residue remains. (To the residue from benzene add a 10 ml portion of purified isooctane, re-evaporate, and repeat once to insure complete removal of benzene).

Alternatively, the evaporation time can be reduced by using the optional evaporation flask. In this case the solvent and n-hexadecane are placed in the flask on the steam bath, the tube assembly is inserted, and a stream of nitrogen is fed through the inlet tube while the outlet tube is connected to a solvent trap and vacuum line in such a way as to prevent any flow-back of condensate into the flask.

Dissolve the 1 ml of hexadecane residue in isooctane and make to 25 ml volume. Determine the absorbance in the 5 cm path length cells compared to isooactane as reference. The absorbance of the solution of the solvent residue (except for methyl alcohol) shall not exceed 0.01 per cm path length between 280 and 400 nm. For methyl alcohol this absorbance value shall be 0.00.

- Isooctane (2,2,4-trimethylpentane): Use 180 ml for the test described in the preceding paragraph. Purify, if necessary, by passage through a column of activated silica gel, grade 12, Davison Chemical Company, Baltimore, Maryland, USA, or equivalent, about 90 cm in length and 5 cm to 8 cm in diameter.

- Benzene, reagent grade: Use 150 ml for the test. Purify, if necessary, by distillation or otherwise.

- Acetone, reagent grade: Use 200 ml for the test. Purify, if necessary, by distillation.

- Eluting mixtures:

1. 10% benzene in isooctane: Pipet 50 ml of benzene into a 500-ml glass-stoppered volumetric flask and adjust to volume with isooctane, with mixing.

2. 20% benzene in isooctane: Pipet 50 ml of benzene into a 250-ml glass-stoppered volumetric flask, and adjust to volume with isooctane, with mixing.

3. Acetone-benzene-water mixture: Add 20 ml of water to 380 ml of acetone and 200 ml of benzene, and mix.

- n-Hexadecane, 99% olefin-free: Dilute 1.0 ml of n-hexadecane to 25 ml with isooctane and determine the absorbance in a 5-cm cell compared to isooctane as reference point between 280-400 nm. The absorbance per centimeter path length shall not exceed 0.00 in this range. Purify, if necessary, by percolation through activated silica gel or by distillation.

- Methyl alcohol, reagent grade: Use 10.0 ml of methyl alcohol. Purify, if necessary, by distillation.

- Dimethyl sulfoxide: Pure grade, clear, water-white, m.p. 18° minimum. Dilute 120 ml of dimethyl sulfoxide with 240 ml of distilled water in a 500-ml separatory funnel, mix and allow to cool for 5-10 min. Add 40 ml of isooctane to the solution and extract by shaking the funnel vigourously for 2 min. Draw off the lower aqueous layer into a second 500-ml separatory funnel and repeat the extraction with 40 ml of isooctane. Draw off and discard the aqueous layer. Wash each of the 40-ml extracts three times with 50 ml portions of distilled water. Shaking time for each wash is 1 min. Discard the aqueous layers. Filter the first extract through anhydrous sodium sulfate pre-washed with isooctane (see Sodium sulfate under "Reagents and Materials" for preparation of filter), into a 250-ml Erlenmeyer flask, or optionally into the evaporating flask. Wash the first separatory funnel with the second 40-ml isooctane extract, and pass through the sodium sulfate into the flask. Then wash the second and first separatory funnels successively with a 10 ml portion of isooctane, and pass the solvent through the sodium sulfate into the flask. Add 1 ml of n-hexadecane and evaporate the isooctane on the steam bath under nitrogen. Discontinue evaporation when not over 1 ml of residue remains. To the residue, add a 10 ml portion of isooctane and re-evaporate to 1 ml of hexadecane. Again, add 10 ml of isooctane to the residue and evaporate to 1 ml of hexadecane to insure complete removal of all volatile materials. Dissolve the 1 ml of hexadecane in isooctane and make to 25 ml volume. Determine the absorbance in 5 cm path length cells compared to isooctane as reference. The absorbance of the solution should not exceed 0.02 per cm path length in the 280-400 nm range. (Note - Difficulty in meeting this absorbance specification may be due to organic impurities in the distilled water. Repetition of the test omitting the dimethyl sulfoxide will disclose their presence. If necessary to meet the specification, purify the water by redistillation, passage through an ion-exchange resin, or otherwise).

Purify, if necessary, by the following procedure: To 1.5 litre of dimethyl sulfoxide in a 2-litre glass-stoppered flask, add 6.0 ml of phosphoric acid and 50 g of Norit A (decolorizing carbon, alkaline) or equivalent. Stopper the flask, and with the use of a magnetic stirrer (tetrafluoroethylene polymer coated bar) stir the solvent for 15 min. Filter the dimethyl sulfoxide through four thicknesses of fluted paper (18.5 cm), Schleicher & Schuell No. 597, or equivalent. If the initial filtrate contains carbon fines, refilter through the same filter until a clear filtrate is obtained. Protect the sulfoxide from air and moisture during this operation by covering the solvent in the funnel and collection flask with a layer of isooctane. Transfer the filtrate to a 2-litre separatory funnel and draw off the dimethyl sulfoxide into the 2-litre distillation flask of the vacuum distillation assembly and distill at approximately 3-mm Hg pressure or less. Discard the first 200-ml fraction of the distillate and replace the distillate collection flask with a clean one.

Continue the distillation until approximately 1 litre of the sulfoxide has been collected.

At completion of the distillation, the reagent should be stored in glass-stoppered bottles since it is very hygroscopic and will react with some metal containers in the presence of air.

Phosphoric acid, 85% reagent grade

- Sodium borohydride, 98%

- Magnesium oxide (Sea Sorb 43, Food Machinery Company, Westvaco Division distributed by chemical supplier firms, or equivalent): Place 100 g of the magnesium oxide in a large beaker, add 700 ml of distilled water to make a thin slurry, and heat on a steam bath for 30 min with intermittent stirring. Stir well initially to insure that all the absorbent is completely wetted. Using a Buchner funnel and a filter paper of suitable diameter, filter with suction. Continue suction until water no longer drips from the funnel. Transfer the absorbent to a glass trough lined with aluminium foil (free from rolling oil). Break up the magnesia with a clean spatula and spread out the absorbent on the aluminium foil in a layer about 1-2 cm thick. Dry at 160±1° for 24 h. Pulverize the magnesia with mortar and pestle. Sieve the pulverized absorbent between 60-180 mesh. Use the magnesia retained on the 180-mesh sieve.

- Celite 545, Johns-Manvill Company, diatomaceous earth, or equivalent.

- Magnesium oxide-Celite 545 mixture (2+1) by weight: Place the magnesium oxide (60-180 mesh) and the Celite 545 in 2 to 1 proportions, respectively, by weight in a glass-stoppered flask large enough for adequate mixing. Shake vigorously for 10 min. Transfer the mixture to a glass trough lined with aluminium foil (free from rolling oil) and spread it out on a layer about 1 to 2 cm thick. Reheat the mixture at 160±10 for 2 h, and store in a tightly closed flask.

- Sodium sulfate, anhydrous, reagent grade, preferably in granular form: For each bottle of sodium sulfate reagent used, establish as follows the necessary sodium sulfate prewash to provide such filters required in the method: Place approximately 35 g of anhydrous sodium sulfate in a 30 ml coarse, fritted-glass funnel or in a 65 ml filter funnel with glass wool plug; wash with successive 15 ml portions of the indicated solvent until a 15 ml portion of the wash shows 0.00 absorbance per cm path length between 280 nm and 400 nm when tested as prescribed under "Organic solvents." Usually three portions of wash solvent are sufficient.

Procedure

Before proceeding with the analysis of a sample, determine the absorbance in a 5 cm path cell between 250 nm and 400 nm for the reagent blank by carrying out the procedure, without a wax sample, at room temperature, recording the spectra after the extraction stage and after the complete procedure as precribed. The absorbance per centimeter path length following the extraction stage should not exceed 0.040 in the wavelength range from

250 to 400 nm; the absorbance per cm path length following the complete procedure should not exceed 0.070 in the wavelength range from 250 to 299 nm, inclusive, nor 0.045 in the wavelength range from 300 nm to 400 nm.

If in either spectrum the characteristic benzene peaks in the 250-260 nm region are present, remove the benzene by the procedure under "Organic solvents" and record absorbance again.

Place 300 ml of dimethyl sulfoxide in a 1-litre separatory funnel and add 75 ml of phosphoric acid. Mix the contents of the funnel and allow to stand for 10 min. (The reaction between the sulfoxide and the acid is exothermic. Release pressure after mixing, then keep funnel stoppered). Add 150 ml of isooctane and shake to pre-equilibrate the solvents. Draw off the individual layers and store in glass-stoppered flasks.

Place a representative 1-kg sample of wax, or if this amount is not available, the entire sample, in a beaker of a capacity about three times the volume of the sample and heat with occasional stirring on a steam bath until the wax is completely melted and homogenous. Weigh four 25 ± 0.2 g portions of the melted wax in separate 100 ml beakers. Reserve three of the portions for later replicate analyses as necessary. Pour one weighed portion immediately after remelting (on the steam bath) into a 500 ml separatory funnel containing 100 ml of the pre-equilibrated sulfoxide-phosphoric acid mixture that has been heated in the heating jacket at a temperature just high enough to keep the wax melted. (Note: In pre-heating the sulfoxide-acid mixture, remove the stopper of the separatory funnel at intervals to release the pressure).

Promptly complete the transfer of the sample to the funnel in the jacket with portions of the pre-equilibrated isooctane, warming the beaker, if necessary, and using a total volume of just 50 ml of the solvent. If the wax comes out of solution during these operations, let the stoppered funnel remain in the jacket until the wax redissolves. (Remove stopper from the funnel at intervals to release pressure).

When the wax is in solution, remove the funnel from the jacket and shake it vigorously for 2 min. Set up three 250-ml separatory funnels with each containing 30 ml of pre-equilibrated isooctane. After separation of the liquid phases, allow to cool until the main portion of the wax-isooctane solution begins to show a precipitate. Gently swirl the funnel when precipitation first occurs on the inside surface of the funnel to accelerate this process. Carefully draw off the lower layer, filter it slowly through a thin layer of glass wool fitted loosely in a filter funnel into the first 250-ml separatory funnel, and wash in tandem with the 30-ml portions of isooctane contained in the 250-ml separatory funnels. Shaking time for each wash is 1 min. Repeat the extraction operation with two additional portions of the sulfoxide-acid mixture, replacing the funnel in the jacket after each extraction to keep the wax in solution and washing each extractive in tandem through the same three portions of isooctane.

Collect the successive extracts (300 ml total) in a separatory funnel (preferably 2-litre), containing 480 ml of distilled water, mix, and allow to cool for a few minutes after the last extract has been added. Add 80 ml of isooctane to the solution and extract by shaking the funnel vigorously for 2 min. Draw off the lower aqueous layer into a second separatory funnel (preferably 2-litre) and repeat the extraction with 80 ml of isooctane. Draw off and discard the aqueous layer. Wash each of the 80-ml extracts three times with 100-ml portions of distilled water. Shaking time for each wash is 1 min. Discard the aqueous layers. Filter the first extract through anhydrous sodium sulfate pre-washed with isooctane (see Sodium sulfate under "Reagents and Materials" for preparation of filter) into a 250-ml Erlenmeyer flask (or optionally into the evaporation flask). Wash the first separatory funnel with the second 80-ml isooctane extract and pass through the sodium sulfate. Then wash the second and first separatory funnels successively with a 20-ml portion of isooctane and pass the solvent through the sodium sulfate into the flask. Add 1 ml of n-hexadecane and evaporate the isooctane on the steam bath under nitrogen. Discontinue evaporation when not over 1 ml of residue remains. To the residue, add a 10-ml portions of isooctane, reevaporate to 1 ml of hexadecane, and repeat this operation once more.

Quantitatively transfer the residue with isooctane to a 25-ml volumetric flask, make to volume, and mix. Determine the absorbance of the solution in the 5-cm path length cells compared to isooctane as reference between 280-400 nm (take care to lose none of the solution in filling the sample cell). Correct the absorbance values for any absorbance derived from reagents as determined by carrying out the procedure without a wax sample. If the corrected absorbance does not exceed the limits prescribed in the Characteristics, the wax meets the ultraviolet absorbance specifications. If the corrected absorbance per centimeter path length exceeds the limits prescribed in the Characteristics, proceed as follows:

Quantitatively transfer the isooctane solution to a 125-ml flask equipped with 24/40 joint and evaporate the isooctane on the steam bath under a stream of nitrogen to a volume of 1 ml of hexadecane. Add 10 ml of methyl alcohol and approximately 0.3 g of sodium borohydride (Minimize exposure of the borohydride to the atmosphere. A measuring dipper may be used). Immediately fit a water-cooled condenser equipped with a 24/40 joint and with a drying tube into the flask, mix until the borohydride is dissolved, and allow to stand for 30 min at room temperature, with intermittent swirling. At the end of this period, disconnect the flask and evaporate the methyl alcohol on the steam bath under nitrogen until the sodium borohydride begins to come out of the solution. Then add 10 ml of isooctane and evaporate to a volume of about 2-3 ml. Again, add 10 ml of isooctane and concentrate to a volume of approximately 5 ml. Swirl the flask repeatedly to assure adequate washing of the sodium borohydride residues.

Fit the tetrafluoroethylene polymer disc on the upper part of the stem of the chromatographic tube, then place the tube with the disc on the suction flask and apply the vaccum (approximately 135-mm Hg pressure). Weigh out 14 g of the 2+1 magnesium oxide-Celite 545 mixture and pour the adsorbent mixture into the chromatographic tube in approximately 3 cm layers. After the addition of each layer, level off the top of the adsorbent with a flat glass rod or metal plunger by pressing down firmly until the adsorbent is well packed. Loosen the topmost few ml of each adsorbent layer with the end of a metal rod before the addition of the next layer. Continue packing in this manner until all the 14 g of the adsorbent is added to the tube. Level off the top of the adsorbent by pressing down firmly with a flat glass rod or metal plunger to make the depth of the adsorbent bed approximately 12.5 cm in depth. Turn off the vacuum and remove the suction flask. Fit the 500-ml reservoir onto the top of the chromatographic column and pre-wet the column by passing 100 ml of isooctane through the column. Adjust the nitrogen pressure so that the rate of descent of the isooctane coming off of the column is between 2-3 ml per min. Discontinue pressure just before the last of the isooctane reaches the level of the adsorbent. (Caution: Do not allow the liquid level to recede below the adsorbent level at any time). Remove the reservoir and decant the 5 ml isooctane concentrate solution onto the column and with slight pressure again allow the liquid level to recede to barely above the adsorbent level. Rapidly complete the transfer similarly with two 5 ml portions of isooctane, swirling the flask repeatedly each time to assure adequate washing of the residue. Just before the final 5 ml wash reaches the top of the adsorbent, add 100 ml of isooctane to the reservoir and continue the percolation at the 2-3 ml per minute rate. Just before the last of the isooctane reaches the adsorbent level, add 100 ml of 10% benzene in isooctane to the reservoir and continue the percolation at the aforementioned rate. Just before the solvent mixture reaches adsorbent level, add 25 ml of 20% benzene in isooctane to the reservoir and continue the percolation at 2-3 ml per minute until all this solvent mixture has been removed from the column. Discard all the elution solvents collected up to this point. Add 300 ml of the acetone-benzene-water mixture to the reservoir and percolate through the column to elute the polynuclear compounds. Collect the eluate in a clean 1-litre separatory funnel. Allow the column to drain until most of the solvent mixture is removed. Wash the eluate three times with 300 ml portions of distilled water, shaking well for each wash. (The addition of small amounts of sodium chloride facilitates separation). Discard the aqueous layer after each wash. After the final separation, filter the residual benzene through anhydrous sodium sulfate pre-washed with benzene (see Sodium sulfate under "Reagents and Materials" for preparation of filter) into a 250-ml Erlenmeyer flask (or optionally into the evaporation flask). Wash the separatory funnel with two additional 20 ml portions of benzene which are also filtered through the sodium sulfate. Add 1 ml of n-hexadecane and completely remove the benzene by evaporation under nitrogen, using the special procedure to eliminate benzene as previously described under "Organic Solvents". Quantitatively transfer the residue with isooctane to a 25-ml volumetric flask and adjust the volume. Determine the absorbance of the solution in the 5 cm path length cells compared to isooctane as reference between 250 - 400 nm. Correct for any absorbance derived from the reagents as determined by carrying out the procedure without a wax sample. If either spectrum shows the characteristic benzene peaks in the 250 - 260 nm region, evaporate the solution to remove benzene by the procedure under "Organic Solvents". Dissolve the residue, transfer quantitatively, and adjust to volume in isooctane in a 25-ml volumetric flask. Record the absorbance again. If the corrected absorbance does not exceed the limits prescribed in the Characteristics the wax meets the ultraviolet absorbance specifications.

Appendix

Infrared spectrum   Microcrystalline wax

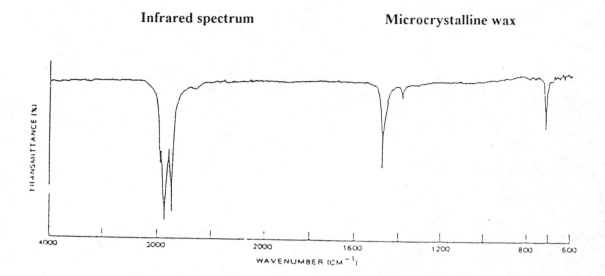

MIXED CAROTENOIDS

Prepared at the 49th JECFA (1997)
superseding specifications prepared at the 37th JECFA (1990),
published in FNP 52 (1992)

DEFINITION

Mixed carotenoids are obtained by solvent extraction of alfalfa, removal of chlorophylls through saponification and subsequent purification of the carotenoids by solvent extraction. The main colouring principle consists of carotenoids of which lutein accounts for the major part. Variable amounts of neoxanthin, violaxanthin and β-carotene are present.

Mixed carotenoids may contain fats, oils and waxes naturally occurring in the plant material. Vegetable oils may be added for standardizing purposes. Only the following solvents may be used for the extraction: methanol, ethanol, propan-2-ol, hexane, acetone, dichloromethane and methyl ethyl ketone. (Note: Articles of commerce may contain approved food additives in order to formulate water soluble products.)

Class

Carotenoid

C.A.S. number

Lutein: 127-40-2

Chemical name

Lutein: 3,3'-dihydroxy-d-carotene; ß, ε-carotene-3,3'-diol

Chemical formula

Lutein: $C_{40}H_{56}O_2$

Structural formula:

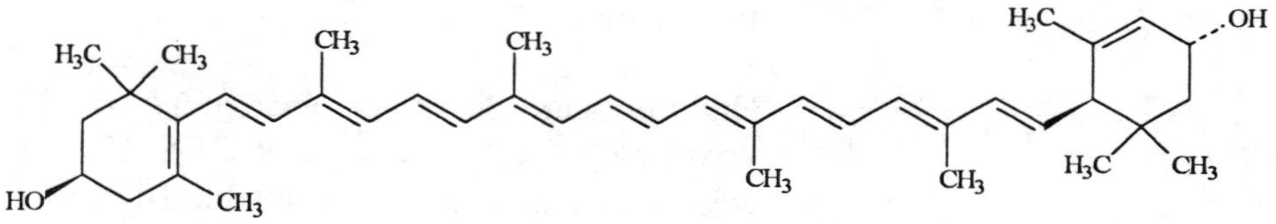

Formula weight

Lutein: 568.88

Assay

Content of total colouring matter (calculated as lutein) not less than declared

DESCRIPTION

Dark, yellowish brown liquids with a weak hay-like odour

FUNCTIONAL USES

Colour

CHARACTERISTICS

IDENTIFICATION

Solubility

Insoluble in water; soluble in hexane.

Spectrophotometry

A chloroform solution of the sample shows maximum absorption at about 445 nm

| Carr-Price test | A solution of the sample in chloroform turns blue on addition of an excess of Carr-Price TS. |

PURITY

Lead	Not more than 5 mg/kg Prepare a sample solution as directed for organic compounds in the Limit Test, using 5 µg of lead ion (Pb) in the control
Synthetic colours	See description under TESTS
Residual solvent	Acetone, methanol, ethanol, propan-2-ol, and hexane, not more than 50 mg/kg, singly or in combination. Dichloromethane and methyl ethyl ketone, not more than 10 mg/kg, individually.

TESTS

PURITY TESTS

| Synthetic colours | A. Principle |

Unknown samples are compared to authentic alfalfa carotenoids. Ground dried alfalfa is extracted with dichloromethane. The extract is saponified and the carotenoids separated by reverse phase liquid chromatography. This test is qualitative and is intended to differentiate alfalfa mixed carotenoids from artificial colours.

B. Apparatus

High pressure liquid chromatograph (HPLC) equipped with a variable wavelength detector, a Zorbax ODS 150 mm x 4.6 mm id reverse phase column or equivalent, and a suitable 10-µl injection value.

C. Reagents

Acetonitrite, dichloromethane, ethyl acetate, acetone (all HPLC grade), n-decanol, butylated hydroxytoluene (BHT), potassium hydroxide, methanol, sodium sulfate (all analytical reagent or better grade). Add 1 g/l of BHT to all solvents. Add 0.1% (v/v) n-decanol to all mobile phases.

D. Chromatography and detection

Mobile phase: ethyl acetate: acetonitrile (12:88) 1.6 ml/min; injection volume 10 µl; detector wavelength 450 nm, full scale range 0.16 AUFS.

E. Procedure

Grind dried alfalfa to pass 1-mm mesh screen and thoroughly mix. Accurately weigh 1-2 g sample in a glass stoppered boiling tube. Add 30 ml dichlormethane: acetone (2:1) and shake. Let stand overnight. Add 20 ml dichloromethane, 2 ml 40% (w/v) methanolic potassium hydroxide, shake, and let stand 60 min. Add 30 ml of 10% (w/v) aqueous sodium sulfate, shake, and let stand 60 min. Remove an aliquot of the lower layer and centrifuge 10 min at 2000 rpm. Remove a 3-ml aliquot of the lower yellow layer, mix with 3 ml acetonitrile, and use this solution for analysis. Unknown mixed caroteniod samples are prepared by dissolving a 0.1-0.2 g sample in 50 ml of dichloromethane:acetonitrile (1:1). Inject 10 µl of alfalfa mixed carotenoid standard followed by 10 µl of unknown mixed carotenoid sample and compare chromatograms.

The approximate retention times for neoxanthin, violaxanthin, lutein, zeaxanthin, α-carotene, and β-carotene are 3.5, 3.9, 6.0, 7.0, 18, and 19 min, respectively. Unknown samples should be free of synthetic pigments, canthaxanthin, and apocarotenoic acid ethyl ester, which elute just before lutein.

METHOD OF ASSAY   Proceed as directed   in *General Methods*, Methods for Food Colours, Colouring Matters, Total Content by Spectrophotometry, Procedure 2, using the following conditions:

W = amount (g) to obtain adequate absorbance
$V_1 = V_2 = V_3 = 100$ ml
$v_1 = v_2 = 10$ ml
$A^{1\%}_{1cm} = 2500$
lambda$_{max}$ = app. 445 nm

MODIFIED STARCHES

Prepared at the 49th JECFA (1997)
superseding specifications prepared at the 35th JECFA (1989),
published in FNP 49 (1990)

Modified starches comprise the following:

Dextrin roasted starch: INS No. 1400
Acid treated starch: INS No. 1401
Alkaline treated starch: INS No. 1402
Bleached starch: INS No. 1403
Oxidized starch: INS No. 1404
Enzyme-treated starch: INS No. 1405
Monostarch phosphate: INS No. 1410
Distarch phosphate: INS No. 1412
Phosphated distarch phosphate: INS No. 1413
Acetylated distarch phosphate: INS No. 1414
Starch acetate: INS No. 1420
Acetylated distarch adipate: INS No. 1422
Hydroxypropyl starch: INS No. 1440
Hydroxypropyl distarch phosphate: INS No. 1442
Starch sodium octenylsuccinate: INS No. 1450

DEFINITION

Food starches which have one or more of their original characteristics altered by treatment in accordance with good manufacturing practice by one of the procedures listed in Table 1. In the case of starches treated with heat in the presence of acid or with alkali, the alteration is a minor fragmentation. When the starch is bleached, the change is essentially in the colour only. Oxidation involves the deliberate production of carboxyl groups. Treatment with reagents such as orthophosphoric acid results in partial substitution in the 2,6- or 3- position of the anhydroglucose unit unless the 6-position is occupied for branching. In cases of cross-bonding, where a polyfunctional substituting agent, such as phosphorus oxychloride, connects two chains, the structure can be represented by: Starch-O-R-O-Starch, where R = cross-bonding group and Starch refers to the linear and/or branched structure. The article of commerce can be specified by the parameter specific for the particular type of modification as indicated in Column 3 of Table 1, and may also be further specified as to the loss on drying, sulfated ash, protein and fat.

C.A.S. number

Starch acetate:	9045-28-7
Acetylated distarch adipate:	68130-14-3
Hydroxypropyl starch:	9049-76-7
Hydroxypropyl distarch phosphate:	53124-00-8

DESCRIPTION

Most modified starches are white or off-white, odourless powders. According to the drying method these powders can consist of whole granules having the appearance of the original native starch, or aggregates consisting of a number of granules (pearl starch, starch-grits) or, if pregelatinized, of flakes, amorphous powder or coarse particles.

FUNCTIONAL USES

Thickener, stabilizer, binder, emulsifier

CHARACTERISTICS

IDENTIFICATION

Solubility

Insoluble in cold water (if not pregelatinized); forming typical colloidal solutions with viscous properties in hot water; insoluble in ethanol.

Microscopy

Passes test
See description under TESTS

Iodine stain

Passes test
See description under TESTS

Copper reduction

Passes test
See description under TESTS

Differentiation test

Passes test for type of starch
See description under TESTS for:

1. Hypochlorite oxydised starch
2. Specific reaction for acetyl groups
3. Positive test for ester groups

PURITY

Sulfur dioxide

Not more than 50 mg/kg for modified cereal starches
Not more than 10 mg/kg for other modified starches unless otherwise specified in Table 1
See description under TESTS

Lead

Not more than 2 mg/kg
Prepare a sample solution as directed for organic compounds in the Limit Test and determine the lead content by atomic absorption spectrometry

Additional purity specifications for individual modified starches

See column 3 of Table 1
See description under TESTS

TESTS

IDENTIFICATION TESTS

Microscopy

Modified starches which have not been pregelatinized retain their granular structure and can be identified as starches by microscopic observation. Shape, size and sometimes striations are characteristics of the botanical origin. In polarized light under crossed nicol prisms the typical polarization cross will be observed

Iodine stain

Add a few drops of 0.1 $\underline{N}$ potassium tri-iodide to an aqueous suspension of the sample. These starches stain with iodine in the same way as native starches. The colour can range from dark blue to red

Copper reduction	Place about 2.5 g of the sample previously washed with water, in a boiling flask, add 10 ml of dilute hydrochloric acid (3%) and 70 ml of water, mix, reflux for about three hours and cool. Add 0.5 ml of the resulting solution to 5 ml of hot alkaline cupric tartrate TS. A copious red precipitate is produced
Differentiation test	To differentiate between various treated starches perform the following tests:

1. Test for hypochlorite-oxidized starch (not for slightly oxidized potato starch)

Principle:

Because of the carboxyl group content, hypochlorite-oxidized starch has anionic properties. It can be dyed with positively charged dyes such as methylene blue.

Procedure:

50 mg of the sample are kept in suspension for 5-10 min in 25 ml of a 1% aqueous dye solution and stirred occasionally. After decantation of the excess solution, the starch is washed with distilled water. Microscopic inspection clearly shows colouring, if the sample is hypochlorite-oxidized starch. By this test hypochlorite-oxidized starch is distinguished from native and acid modified starch of the same botanical origin.

2. Specific reaction of acetyl groups

Principle:

Acetate is liberated upon saponification of acetylated starch. After concentration the acetate is converted to acetone by heating with calcium hydroxide. The acetone thus produced stains blue with o-nitrobenzaldehyde.

Procedure:

About 10 g of the sample is suspended in 25 ml water to which is added 20 ml of 0.4 N NaOH. After shaking for 1 h the starch is filtered off and the filtrate evaporated in an oven at 110°. The residue is dissolved in a few drops of water and transferred to the test tube. Calcium hydroxide is added and if the sample is an acetylated starch, the tube heated thereby gives off acetone vapours. These produce a blue colour on a paper strip soaked in a fresh saturated solution of o-nitrobenzaldehyde in 2 N NaOH. The blue colour is more distinct when the original yellow colour of the reagents is removed with 1 drop of a 1 in 10 solution of hydrochloric acid.

3. Positive test for ester groups

The infrared spectrum of a thin film gives a typical absorption band at about 1720 cm^{-1} which is an indication for ester groups. The limit of detection is about 0.5% acetyl, adipyl or succinyl groups in the product.

PURITY TESTS

Sulfur dioxide

Scope:

The method is applicable, with minor modifications, to liquid or solid samples even in the presence of other volatile sulfur compounds.

Principle:

The sulfur dioxide is released from the sample in a boiling acid medium and is removed by a stream of carbon dioxide. The separated gas is collected in dilute hydrogen peroxide where it is oxidized to sulfuric acid and titrated with standard alkali. Alternatively, the sulfuric acid may be determined gravimetrically.

Apparatus:

"Monier-Williams" apparatus for the determination of sulfurous acid, constructed with standard-taper glass connections, can be obtained from any reliable scientific glass apparatus store. It is customary, however, to construct the apparatus with regular laboratory glassware using stopper connections (see Figure 1).

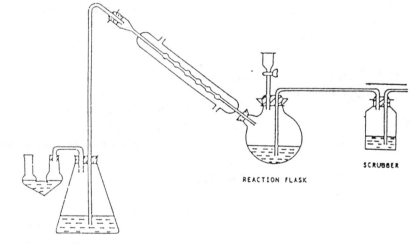

SCRUBBER

REACTION FLASK

Figure 1   RECEIVER

The assembly consists of a 1000-ml two-neck round-bottom boiling flask to which a gas-inlet tube, a 60-ml dropping funnel having a 2-mm bore stopcock, and a sloping Allihn reflux condenser are attached. A delivery tube connects the upper end of the condenser to the bottom of a 250-ml conical receiving flask, which is followed by a Peligot tube.

In operation, carbon dioxide is passed through the scrubber and bubbled through the heated reaction mixture, sweeping sulfur dioxide through the condenser and into the receivers where it is absorbed quantitatively.

Preparation of solutions:

Sodium carbonate solution: Dissolve approximately 15 g of Na_2CO_3 or 40 g of $Na_2CO_3 \cdot 10H_2O$ in distilled water, and dilute to 100 ml.

Hydrogen peroxide, 3%: Dilute 10 ml of C.P. (Chemical Purity) neutral 30% hydrogen peroxide (H_2O_2) with distilled water to 100 ml.

Procedure:

Pass carbon dioxide from a generator or cylinder through the sodium carbonate scrubber solution to remove chlorine, thence into the gas-inlet tube of the boiling flask. Place 15 ml of the 3% hydrogen peroxide in the receiving flask and 5 ml in the Peligot tube. Connect the apparatus and introduce into the boiling flask, by means of the dropping funnel, 300 ml of distilled water and 20 ml of concentrated hydrochloric acid. Boil the contents approximately 10 min in a current of carbon dioxide. Weigh, to the nearest g, 100 g of the sample and disperse in approximately 300 ml of recently-boiled distilled water. Transfer the slurry to the boiling flask by means of dropping funnel, regulating the sample addition rate and the gas flow rate through the apparatus to prevent drawback of hydrogen peroxide, inclusion of air, or burning of sample. Boil the mixture gently for 1 h in a slow current of carbon dioxide. Stop the flow of water in the condenser just before the end of the distillation. When the delivery tube just above the receiving flask becomes hot, remove the tube from the condenser immediately. Wash the delivery tube and the Peligot tube contents into the receiving flask, and titrate with 0.1 N sodium hydroxide, using bromphenol blue indicator (see Note).

Perform a blank determination on the reagents, and correct results accordingly.

$$\% \text{ sulfur dioxide} = \frac{(S - B) \times 0.0032 \times 100}{W}$$

in which

S =   ml of 0.1 N sodium hydroxide used for the sample
B =   ml of 0.1 N sodium hydroxide used for the blank
W =   the weight (in grams) of the sample.

Note. A gravimetric determination may be made after titration. Acidify with HCl, precipitate with $BaCl_2$, settle, filter, wash, ignite, and weigh as $BaSO_4$.

Table 1. Additional purity specifications for individual chemically modified starches
(All percentages calculated on dry substance)

Modification	Process limitations	End-product specifications
Dextrin roasted starch	Dry heat treatment with hydrochloric acid or ortho-phosphoric acid	Final pH 2.5-7.0
Acid treated starch	Treatment with hydrochloric acid or ortho-phosphoric acid or sulfuric acid	Final pH 4.8-7.0
Alkaline treated starch	Treatment with sodium hydroxide or potassium hydroxide	Final pH 5.0-7.5
Bleached starch	Treatment with peracetic acid and/or hydrogen peroxide, or	Added carbonyl group not more than 0.1%
	sodium hypochlorite or sodium chlorite, or	No residual reagent
	sulfur dioxide or alternative permitted forms of sulfites, or	Residual sulfur dioxide not more than 50 mg/kg
	potassium permanganate or ammonium persulfate	Residual manganese not more than 50 mg/kg
Enzyme-treated starch	Treatment in an aqueous solution at a temperature below the gelatinization point with one or more food-grade amyolytic enzymes	Residual sulfur dioxide not more than 50 mg/kg
Oxidized starch	Treatment with sodium hypochlorite	Carboxyl groups not more than 1.1%

Residual sulfur dioxide not more than 50 mg/kg |
Monostarch phosphate	Esterification with ortho-phosphoric acid, or sodium or potassium ortho-phosphate, or sodium tripolyphosphate	Phosphate calculated as phosphorus not more than 0.5% for potato or wheat, and not more than 0.4% for other starches
Distarch phosphate	Esterification with sodium trimetaphosphate or phosphorus oxychloride	Phosphate calculated as phosphorus not more than 0.5% for potato and wheat, and not more than 0.4% for other starches
Phosphated distarch phosphate	Combination of treatments for Monostarch phosphate and Distarch phosphate	Phosphate calculated as phosphorus not more than 0.5% for potato and wheat, and not more than 0.4% for other starches
Acetylated distarch phosphate	Esterification by sodium trimetaphosphate or phosphorus oxychloride combined with esterification by acetic anhydride or vinyl acetate	Acetyl groups not more than 2.5%; phosphate calculated as phosphorus not more than 0.14% for potato and wheat, and 0.04% for other starches; and vinyl acetate not more than 0.1 mg/kg

Starch acetate	Esterification with acetic anhydride or vinyl acetate	Acetyl groups not more than 2.5%
Acetylated distarch adipate	Esterification with acetic anhydride and adipic anhydride	Acetyl groups not more than 2.5% and adipate groups not more than 0.135%
Hydroxypropyl starch	Esterification with propylene oxide	Hydroxypropyl groups not more than 7.0%; propylene chlorohydrin not more than 1 mg/kg
Hydroxypropyl distarch phosphate	Esterification by sodium trimetaphosphate or phosphorus oxychloride combined with etherification by propylene oxide	Hydroxypropyl groups not more than 7.0%; propylene chlorohydrin not more than 1 mg/kg; and residual phosphate calculated as phosphorus not more than 0.14% for potato and wheat, and not more than 0.04% for other starches
Starch sodium octenylsuccinate	Esterification by octenylsuccinic anhydride	Octenylsuccinyl groups not more than 3%; and residual octenylsuccinic acid not more than 0.3%

Methods for additional purity specifications:

pH   As specified in Column 3 of Table 1
                            Mix 20 g of the sample with 80 ml of water, and agitate continuously at a
                            moderate rate for 5 min (In the case of pregelatinized starches, 3 g should be
                            suspended in 97 ml of water). Determine the pH of the resulting suspension
                            by the method outlined in *General Methods*.

Carboxyl groups   As specified in Column 3 of Table 1.

                            Principle:

                            The carboxyl containing starch is leached with mineral acid to convert
                            carboxyl salts to the acid form. Cations and excess acid are removed by
                            washing with water. The washed sample is gelatinized in water and titrated
                            with standard alkali.

                            Note: Native phosphate groups present in potato starch increase the titre
                            found in this method (See note 6)

                            Reagents:

                            Hydrochloric Acid Solution, 0.10 N : Standardization unnecessary
                            Sodium Hydroxide Solution, 0.10 N : Standardized
                            Phenolphthalein Indicator, 1%

                            Procedure:

                            If necessary, grind sample completely through a laboratory cutting mill to
                            20 mesh or finer, taking precautions to prevent any significant change in
                            moisture, and mix thoroughly.

                            Weigh accurately a sample containing not more than 0.25 milli-equivalent of
                            carboxyl (Note 1), and transfer quantitatively to a 150-ml beaker. Add 25 ml
                            of 0.1 N hydrochloric acid and stir occasionally over a period of 30 min.
                            Vacuum filter the slurry through a medium porosity fritted-glass crucible or
                            small funnel, using a fine stream of water from a wash bottle to aid
                            quantitative transfer of the sample. Wash the sample with distilled water
                            (300 ml usually sufficient) until the filtrate is free from chloride determined
                            by silver nitrate test (Note 2).

                            Transfer the demineralized sample quantitatively to a 600 ml beaker with the
                            aid of distilled water, and slurry the sample in 300 ml of distilled water. Heat
                            sample dispersion in a steam bath or boiling water bath (Note 3), stirring
                            continuously until the starch gelatinizes, and continue heating for 15 min to
                            ensure complete gelatinization (Note 4).

                            Remove sample from bath and titrate while hot with standard 0.10 N sodium
                            hydroxide solution to a phenolphthalein end-point. The end-point may be
                            detected electrometrically at pH 8.3. A blank determination is run on the
                            original sample to correct for native acid substances (Note 5). Weigh the

same quantity of starch as taken for carboxyl titration, and slurry in 10 ml of distilled water. Stir at about 5-min intervals for 30 min.

Vacuum filter the slurry quantitativey through a medium porosity fritted-glass crucible or small funnel, and wash sample with 200 ml of distilled water. Transfer, gelatinize, and titrate the sample with standard 0.10 N sodium hydroxide in the same manner as the demineralized sample.

Calculation:

$$\text{Carboxyl groups (\%)} = \frac{(\text{ml 0.10N NaOH} - \text{Blank}) \times 0.0045 \times 100}{\text{Sample weight (g)}}$$

Notes and Precautions:

1. Sample size should not exceed 5.0 g for a mildly oxidized nor less than 0.15 g for a highly oxidized commercial starch.

2. Add 1 ml of 1% aqueous silver nitrate solution to 5 ml of filtrate. Turbidity or precipitation occurs within 1 min if chloride is present.

3. Heating on a hot plate or over a Bunsen burner is not recommended. Over-heating or scorching in amounts too small to be visible will cause sample decomposition and apparent high carboxyl results.

4. Thorough gelatinization facilitates rapid titration and accurate end-point detection.

5. A blank titration is run on a water washed sample to correct for acidic components which are not introduced by oxidation or derivatization. Free fatty acids complexed with amylose in common corn starch are the principal contributors to the blank titer.

6. A correction for phosphate content in potato starch (deduction) should be made after determining the phosphorus content of the sample being examined.

The deduction is calculated:

$$\frac{2 \times 45.02 \times P}{30.97} = 2.907 \times P$$

where:

P = phosphorus content (%)

Manganese content   As specified in Column 3 of Table 1.

Instrumentation:

Determine the manganese content with the use of an atomic absorption spectrophotometer at 279.5 nm.

Preparation of solutions:

-Standard solution: Prepare a solution containing 0.5 mg/l of manganese.

-Sample solution: Transfer 10.000 g of the sample into a 200-ml Kohlrausch volumetric flask, previously rinsed with 0.5 N hydrochloric acid, add 140 ml of 0.5 N hydrochloric acid, and shake vigorously for 15 min, preferably with a mechanical shaker. Dilute to volume with 0.5 N hydrochloric acid, and shake. Centrifuge approximately 100 ml of the mixture in a heavy-walled centrifuge tube at 2000 rpm for 5 min, and use the clear supernatant liquid in the following "procedure".

Procedure:

Aspirate distilled water through the air-acetylene burner for 5 min and obtain a base-line reading at 279.5 nm, following the manufacturer's instructions for operating the atomic absorption spectrophotometer. In the same manner aspirate a portion of the "Standard solution" and note the reading. Finally, aspirate the "Sample solution" and compare the reading with the reading for the "Standard solution", and multiply this value by 20 to obtain mg per kg of Mn in the original sample taken for analysis.

Phosphorus content   As specified in the Column 3 of Table 1.

Reagents:

-Ammonium Molybdate Solution (5%): Dissolve 50 g of ammonium molybdate tetrahydrate, $(NH_4)_6Mo_7O_{24} \cdot 4H_2O$, in 900 ml of warm water, cool to room temperature, dilute to 1000 ml with water, and mix.

-Ammonium Vanadate Solution (0.25%): Dissolve 2.5 of ammonium metavanadate, NH_4VO_3, in 600 ml of boiling water, cool to 60 - 70°, and add 20 ml of nitric acid. Cool to room temperature, dilute to 1000 ml with water, and mix.

-Zinc Acetate Solution (10%): Dissolve 120 g of zinc acetate dihydrate, $Zn(C_2H_3O_2)_2 \cdot 2H_2O$, in 880 ml of water, and filter through Whatman No. 2V or equivalent filter paper before use.

-Nitric Acid Solution (29%): Add 300 ml of nitric acid (sp. gr 1.42) to 600 ml of water, and mix.

-Standard Phosphorus Solution: (100 μg P in 1 ml): Dissolve 438.7 mg of monobasic potassium phosphate, KH_2PO_4, in water in a 1000-ml volumetric flask, dilute to volume with water, and mix.

Standard Curve:

Pipet 5.0, 10.0, and 15.0 ml of the Standard Phosphorus Solution into separate 100 ml volumetric flasks. To each of these flasks, and to a fourth blank flask, add in the order stated 10 ml of Nitric Acid Solution, 10 ml of Ammonium Vanadate Solution, and 10 ml of Ammonium Molybdate

Solution, mixing thoroughly after each addition. Dilute to volume with water, mix, and allow to stand for 10 min. Determine the absorbance of each standard solution in a 1 cm cell at 460 nm, with a suitable spectrophotometer, using the blank to set the instrument at zero. Prepare a standard curve by plotting the absorbance of each solution versus its concentration, in mg P per 100 ml.

Sample Pretreatment:

Place 20 to 25 g of the starch sample in a 250 ml beaker, add 200 ml of a 7 to 3 methanol-water mixture, disperse the sample, and agitate mechanically for 15 min. Recover the starch by vacuum filtration in a 150 ml medium-porosity fritted-glass or Buchner funnel, and wash the wet cake with 200 ml of the methanol-water mixture. Reslurry the wet cake in the solvent, and wash it a second time in the same manner. Dry the filter cake in an air oven at a temperature below 50°, then grind the sample to 20-mesh or finer, and blend thoroughly. Determine the amount of dry substance by drying a 5 g portion in a vacuum oven, not exceeding 100 mm of Hg, at 120° for 5 h. (NOTE: The treatment outlined above is satisfactory for starch products that are insoluble in cold water.

For pregelatinized starch and other water-soluble starches, prepare a 1% to 2% aqueous paste, place it in a cellophane tube, and dialyze against running distilled water for 30 to 40 h. Precipitate the starch by pouring the solution into 4 volumes of acetone per volume of paste, while stirring. Recover the starch by vacuum filtration in a medium-porosity fritted-glass or Buchner funnel, and wash the filter cake with absolute ethanol. Dry the filter cake, and determine the amount of dry substance as directed for water-insoluble starches).

Sample preparation:

Transfer about 10 g of the Treated Sample, calculated on the dry-substance and accurately weighed, into a Vycor dish, and add 10 ml of Zinc Acetate Solution in a fine stream, distributing the solution uniformly in the sample. Carefully evaporate to dryness on a hot plate, then increase the heat, and carbonize the sample on the hot plate or over a gas flame. Ignite in a muffle furnace at 550° until the ash is free from carbon (about 1 to 2 h), and cool. Wet the ash with 15 ml of water and wash slowly down the sides of the dish with 5 ml of Nitric Acid Solution. Heat to boiling, cool, and quantitatively transfer the mixture into a 200-ml volumetric flask, rinsing the dish with three 20-ml portions of water and adding the rinsings to the flask. Dilute to volume with water, and mix. Transfer an accurately measured aliquot (V, in ml) of this solution, containing not more than 1.5 mg of phosphorus, into a 100-ml volumetric flask and add 10 ml of Nitric Acid Solution, 10 ml of Ammonium Vanadate Solution, and 10 ml of Ammonium Molybdate Solution, mixing thoroughly after each addition. Dilute to volume with water, mix, and allow to stand for 10 min.

Procedure:

Determine the absorbance of the Sample Preparation in a 1 cm cell at 460 nm, with a suitable spectrophotometer, using the blank to set the instrument at zero. From the Standard Curve, determine the mg of phosphorus in the aliquot taken, recording this value as a. Calculate the amount in mg/kg of Phosphorus (P) in the original sample by the formula:

$$\frac{a \times 200 \times 1000}{V \times W}$$

in which W is the weight of the sample taken, in g.

Acetyl groups content

As specified in Column 3 of Table 1.

Accurately weigh about 5 g of the sample and transfer into a 250 ml conical flask. Suspend in 50 ml of water, add a few drops of phenolphthalein TS, and titrate with 0.1 N sodium hydroxide to a permanent pink end-point. Add 25.0 ml of 0.45 N sodium hydroxide, stopper the flask, and shake vigorously for 30 min, preferably with a mechanical shaker. (NOTE: the temperature should not exceed 30° or some starches may gelatinise). Remove the stopper, wash the stopper and sides of the flask with a few ml of water, and titrate the excess alkali with 0.2 N hydrochloric acid to the disappearance of the pink colour. Record the volume, in ml of 0.2 N hydrochloric acid required as S.

Perform a blank titration on 25.0 ml of 0.45 N sodium hydroxide, and record the volume, in ml, of 0.2 N hydrochloric acid required as B.

$$\text{Acetyl groups (\%)} = \frac{(B - S) \times N \times 0.043 \times 100}{W}$$

where:

N = the exact normality of the hydrochloric acid solution
W = the weight of the sample in grams.

Vinyl acetate content

Headspace Gas Chromatographic method

Chromatographic system

Use a gas chromatograph with 2 m x 2 mm (i.d.) glass column containing Porapak Q, 80-100 mesh (or equivalent) fitted with a flame ionisation detector, under the following conditions:

- air flow: 200 ml/min
- hydrogen flow: 30 ml/min
- nitrogen flow: 20 ml/min
- injection port temperature: 200°
- column temperature: 150°
- detector temperature: 200°

Standard preparation:

Accurately weigh 150 mg vinyl acetate (reagent grade) into a 100 ml volumetric flask. Dissolve and make up to volume with distilled water. Place

1 ml of this solution in a 10-ml volumetric flask and make up to volume with distilled water. Add 1 ml of this dilute solution to 30 g unmodified starch of the same botanical origin as the test substance in a 100 ml flask with a septum-liner. Seal the flask immediately with the septum-liner. This provides a standard starch preparation with a vinyl acetate content of 5 mg/kg

Procedure:

Weigh 30 g of the test substance into a 100-ml flask with a septum-liner. Seal the flask. Place the flask containing the test substance and the flask containing the standard preparation in a constant temperature water bath at 70° for 30 min. Withdraw 2.0 ml from the headspace volume of the flask containing the standard preparation using a gas-tight syringe, inject directly into the injection port of the gas chromatograph and record the peak height of the chromatogram. Similarly inject 2.0 ml of the headspace volume from the flask containing the test substance into the chromatograph. Calculate the content of vinyl acetate in the test substance from a comparison of the peak hights of the two chromatograms.

| Adipate group content | As specified in Column 3 of Table 1. |

Reagents and Solutions:

-N,N-Bis-trimethylsilyltrifluoroacetamide (BSTFA):
Macherey-Nagel, D 5160 Dueren, Germany or equivalent.

-Glutaric acid solution: Dissolve 1.00 g of glutaric acid (Merck or equivalent) in water and dilute to 1000 ml.

-Adipic acid solution: Dissolve 1.00 g of adipic acid (UCB, Brussels, Belgium or equivalent) in 900 ml of warm water, cool to room temperature, dilute to 1000 ml and mix.

Apparatus:

Chromatograph: Hewlett-Packard Model 7620A gas chromatograph or equivalent equipped with flame ionization detector and Model 3370A integrator.

Column parameters: 2-m stainless steel, 1.83 mm id, packed with 5% OV-17 on 80-100 mesh Chromosorb GAW-DMCS (Alltech Europe, Inc., B 9731 Eke, Belgium); precondition column 24 h at 350° with nitrogen carrier gas at 40 ml/min. Operating gas flow rates (ml/min): nitrogen carrier 30, hydrogen 40, air 400. Temperature: injection 280°, detector 250°, column 140°. Retention times (min): glutaric acid 2.83, adipic acid 4.50.

Calibration:

Weigh 1.0 g waxy corn starch into each of four 250-ml Erlenmeyer flasks. To each flask add 50 ml water and 1.0 ml of an aqueous solution containing 1.0 mg glutaric acid/ml. Add, to one flask, 0.25 ml of an aqueous solution containing 1.0 mg adipic acid per ml; to the other three, add 0.50 ml, 0.75 ml, and 1.0 ml, respectively. Each flask then contains 1.0 mg glutaric acid and, respectively, 0.25, 0.50, 0.75 and 1.0 mg adipic acid. Agitate flasks manually to disperse the starch fully and add 50 ml 4N sodium hydroxide. Continue agitation another 5 min., place each flask in water bath at ambient temperature, and carefully add 20 ml 12 N hydrochloric acid to each. When each flask is cool quantitatively transfer contents to 250 ml separatory funnel. Extract with 100 ml reagent grade ethyl acetate. Drain bottom aqueous layer into beaker and collect upper organic layer in 500-ml Erlenmeyer flask containing 20 g anhydrous sodium sulphate. Transfer aqueous portion back to separatory funnel and repeat ethyl acetate extraction twice more. Shake flasks periodically during 10 min and then filter contents through Whatman No. 1 paper into 1-litre round-bottom flasks. Rinse flasks and insoluble residues in filters twice with 50 ml of ethyl acetate. Under vacuum, (50 mm Hg) at temperature not exceeding 40°, evaporate total organic extraction and washings of each flask until completely dry.

The evaporation of ethyl acetate should be effected as quickly as possible because some hydrolysis takes place on standing. The products of hydrolysis cause a deterioration in the resolution of adipic acid in the chromatographic separation.

Successively add 2 ml pyridine and 1 ml N,N-bis-trimethylsilyltrifluoro-acetamide to the dry contents. Close round-bottom flasks with stopper and rinse internal surfaces thoroughly by swirling. Let flasks stand 1 h; then transfer ca 2 ml from each to small glass vials and immediately seal. Inject 4 µl into gas chromatograph.

Calculations:

Establish retention times for each acid and determine peak height for glutaric acid and for each level of adipic acid represented. A plot of peak height ratio of adipic acid to glutaric acid against amount of adipic acid is linear. This calibration curve may be used, but it is simpler to use a response factor (RF):

$$RF = \frac{H_I \times W_S}{H_S}$$

where:

H_S and H_I = peak heights of the standard adipic acid and glutaric acid, respectively; and W_S = weight of the standard adipic acid.

RF should be verified weekly.

Total adipate content   Accurately weigh about 1.0 g of the sample into a 250 ml Erlenmeyer flask, and add 50 ml water and 1.0 ml of an aqueous solution containing 1.0 mg glutaric acid/ml. Proceed as in Calibration, beginning "Agitate flasks manually...".

Free adipic acid content   Accurately weigh about 5.0 g of the sample into a 250 ml Erlenmeyer flask, add 100 ml water and 1.0 ml of the glutaric acid solution. Agitate for 1 h, filter through a 0.45 µm Millipore filter, add 1 ml concentrated hydrochloric acid to the filtrate and transfer it quantitatively to a 250 ml separating funnel. Proceed as in Calibration, beginning "Extract with 100 ml..."

Calculation:

For both preparations ("Total adipate content" and "Free adipic acid content") record peak heights for adipic acid and glutaric acid (internal standard). Calculate the amounts of total adipate and free adipic acid, respectively, contained in the sample as follows:

$$A = \frac{H_X \times RF}{H_{IX} \times S \times 10}$$

where:

A =	content of total adipate or free adipic acid respectively (%)
H_X =	peak height of adipic acid in the actual sample preparation
H_{IX} =	peak height of glutaric acid in the actual sample preparation
RF =	response factor for adipic acid
S =	weight of sample in the actual preparation (g)

Adipate groups (%) = Content of total adipate (%) - content of free adipic acid (%)

Hydroxypropyl group content

As specified in Column 3 of Table 1

Ninhydrin reagent: A 3% solution of 1,2,3,-triketohydrindene crystals in 5% aqueous sodium bisulfite solution.

Procedure:

Accurately weigh 50 - 100 mg of the sample into a 100-ml volumetric flask and add 25 ml of 1 N sulfuric acid. Prepare a sample of unmodified starch of the same source (i.e. corn or potato) in the same manner. Place the flasks in a boiling water bath and heat until the samples are in solution. Cool and dilute the contents to 100 ml with water. If necessary, dilute the sample further to assure the presence of no more than 4 mg of hydroxypropyl group per 100 ml, and then dilute the blank starch in the same proportion. Pipet 1 ml of the solutions into 25-ml graduated test tubes with glass stoppers and, with the tubes immersed in cold water, add dropwise 8 ml of concentrated sulfuric acid to each. Mix well and place the tubes in a boiling water bath for exactly 3 min. Immediately transfer the tubes to an ice bath until the solution is chilled. Add 0.6 ml of ninhydrin reagent, carefully allowing the reagent to run down the walls of the test tubes. Immediately shake well, and place the tubes in a 25° water bath for 100 min. Adjust the volume in each tube to 25 ml with concentrated sulfuric acid and mix by inverting the tubes several times. (Do not shake). Immediately transfer portions of the solutions to 1-cm cells designed for a Beckman Model B spectrophotometer, and after exactly 5 min, measure the absorption (A) at 590 nm, using the starch blank as the reference.

Prepare a calibration curve with 1-ml aliquots of standard aqueous solutions, containing 10, 20, 30, 40 and 50 µg of propylene glycol per ml.

Calculations:

$$\text{Hydroxypropyl groups (\%)} = \frac{C \times 0.7763 \times 10 \times F}{W}$$

where:

C = amount of propylene glycol in the sample solution read from the calibration curve (µg/ml)
F = dilution factor (if a further dilution has been necessary)
W = weight of sample (mg)

Propylene chlorohydrin   As specified in Column 3 of Table 1.

Apparatus

Gas Chromatograph
Use a Hewlett-Packard Model 5750 or equivalent. A dual-column instrument equipped with a flame-ionization detector is recommended. An integrator should be part of the recording system.

-Gas Chromatography column: Use a stainless steel column, 3 m x 3.2 mm (od), packed with 10% Carbowax 20 M on 80/100-mesh Gas Chrom 2, or equivalent. After packing and prior to use, condition the column overnight at 200°, using a helium flow of 25 ml per min.

-Concentrator: Use a Kuderna-Danish concentrator having a 500-ml flask, available from Kontes Glass Co., Vineland, N.J., USA, (Catalog No. K-57000), or equivalent.

-Pressure Bottles: Use 200 ml pressure bottles, with a Neoprene washer, glass stopper, and attached wire clamp, available from Fisher Scientific Co., Pittsburg, PA, USA (Vitro 400, Catalog No. 3-100), or equivalent.

Reagents:

-Diethyl ether: Use anhydrous, analytical reagent-grade diethyl ether, (NOTE: Some lots of diethyl ether contain foreign residues that interfere with the analysis and/or the interpretation of the chromatograms. If the ether quality is unknown or suspect, concentrate 50 ml to a volume of about 1 ml in the Concentrator, and then chromatograph a 2.0-µl portion using the conditions outlined under the Procedure. If the chromatogram is excessively noisy and contains signal peaks that overlap or interfere in the measurement of the peaks produced by the propylene chlorohydrin isomers, the ether should be redistilled.)

-Florisil: Use 60/100 mesh material, available from Floridin Co., 3 Penn Center, Pittsburg, PA 15235, USA, or an equivalent product available from Supelco, Bellefonte, PA 16823, USA.

-Propylene chlorohydrins: Use Eastman No. P1325 1-Chloro-2-propanol Practical, containing 25% 2-chloro-1-propanol, available from Eastman Kodak Co., Rochester, N.Y. 14650, USA.

-Standard preparation: Draw 25 µl of mixed propylene chlorohydrin isomers containing 75% of 1-chloro-2-propanol and 25% of 2-chloro- 1-propanol) into a 50-µl syringe. Accurately weigh the syringe and discharge the contents into a 500-ml volumetric flask partially filled with water. Reweigh the syringe, and record the weight of the chlorohydrins taken. Dilute to the volume with water, and mix. This solution contains about 27.5 mg of mixed chlorohydrins, or about 55 µg per ml. Prepare this solution fresh on the day of use.

Sample Preparation:

Transfer a blended representative 50.0 g sample into a Pressure Bottle, and add 125 ml of 2 N sulfuric acid. Clamp the top in place, and swirl the contents until the sample is completely dispersed. Place the bottle in a boiling water bath, heat for 10 min, then swirl the bottle to mix the contents, and heat in the bath for an additional 15 min. Cool in air to room temperature, then neutralize the hydrolyzed sample to pH 7 with 25% sodium hydroxide solution, and filter through Whatman No. 1 paper, or equivalent, in a Buchner funnel, using suction. Wash the bottle and filter paper with 25 ml of water, and combine the washings with the filtrate. Add 30 g of anhydrous sodium sulfate, and stir with a magnetic stirring bar for 5 to 10 min, or until the sodium sulfate is completely dissolved. Transfer the solution into a 500-ml separator equipped with a teflon plug, rinse the flask with 25 ml of water, and combine the washings with the sample solution. Extract with five 50 ml portions of diethyl ether, allowing at least 5 min in each extraction for adequate hase separation. Transfer the combined ether extracts in a Concentrator, place the graduated receiver of the concentrator in a water bath maintained at 50 - 55°, and concentrate the extract to a volume of 4 ml. (NOTE: Ether extracts of samples may contain foreign residues that interfere with the analysis and/or the interpretation of the chromatograms. These residues are believed to be degradation products arising during the hydrolysis treatment. Analytical problems created by their presence can be avoided through application of a clean-up treatment performed as follows: Concentrate the ether extract to about 8 ml, instead of 4 ml specified above. Add 10 g of Florisil, previously heated to 130° for 16 h just before use, to a chromatographic tube of suitable size, then tap gently, and add 1 g of anhydrous sodium sulfate to the top of the column. Wet the column with 25 ml of diethyl ether, and quantitatively transfer the concentrated extract to the column with the aid of small portions of the ether. Elute with three 25-ml portions of the ether, collect all of the eluate, transfer it to a concentrator, and concentrate to a volume of 4 ml). Cool the extract to room temperature, transfer it quantitatively to a 5.0-ml volumetric flask with the aid of small portions of diethyl ether, dilute to volume with the ether, and mix.

Control Preparations:

Transfer 50.0 g portions of unmodified (underivatized) waxy corn starch into five separate pressure bottles, and add 125 ml of 2 N sulfuric acid to each bottle. Add 0.0, 0.5, 1.0, 2.0, and 5.0 ml of the Standard Preparation to the bottles, respectively, giving propylene chlorohydrin concentrations, on the starch basis, of 0, 0.5, 1.0, 2.0, and 5.0 mg/kg, respectively. Calculate the exact concentration in each bottle from the weight of propylene chlorohydrins used in making the Standard Preparation. Clamp the tops in place, swirl until the contents of each bottle are completely dissolved, and proceed with the hydrolysis, neutralization, filtration, extraction, extract concentration, and final dilution as directed under Sample Preparation.

Procedure:

The operating conditions may be varied, depending upon the particular instrument used, but a suitable chromatogram is obtained with the Hewlett-Packard Model 5750 using a column oven temperature of 110°, isothermal; injection port temperature of 210°; detector temperature of 240°; and hydrogen (30 ml per min), helium (25 ml per min), or air (350 ml per min) as the carrier gas. A 1.0 mV full-scale recorder is recommended; range, attenuation, and chart speed should be selected to optimize signal characteristics. Inject 2.0 µl aliquots of each of the concentrated extracts, prepared as directed under Control Preparation, allowing sufficient time between injections for signal peaks corresponding to the two chlorohydrin isomers to be recorded (and integrated) and for the column to be purged. Record and sum the signal areas (integrator outputs) from the two chlorohydrin isomers for each of the controls. Using identical operating conditions, inject a 2.0-µl aliquot of the concentrated extract prepared as directed under Sample Preparation, and record and sum the signal areas (integrator outputs) from the sample.

Calculation:

Prepare a calibration plot on linear coordinate graph paper by plotting the summed signal areas for each of the controls against the calculated propylene chlorohydrin concentrations, in mg/kg, derived from the actual weight of chlorohydrin isomers used. Using the summed signal areas corresponding to the 1-chloro-2-propanol and 2-chloro-1-propanol from the sample, determine the concentration of mixed propylene chlorohydrins, in mg/kg, in the sample by reference to the calibration plot derived from the control samples. After gaining experience with the procedure and demonstrating that the calibration plot derived from the control samples is linear and reproducible, the number of controls can be reduced to one containing about 5 mg/kg of mixed propylene chlorohydrin isomers. The propylene chlorohydrin level in the sample can then be calculated as follows:

$$\text{Propylene chlorohydrins (mg / kg)} = \frac{C \times a}{A}$$

in which C is the concentration, in mg/kg, of propylene chlorohydrins (sum of isomers) in the control; a is the sum of signal areas produced by the propylene chlorohydrin isomers in the sample; and A is the sum of the signal areas produced by the propylene chlorohydrin isomers in the control.

Degree of substitution of starch sodium octenyl succinate

Principle:

The Degree of Substitution is determined by alkali consumed after acidification and thorough washing of the starch half ester.

Procedure:

Weigh out 5.0 g of sample in a 150-ml beaker. Wet out with a few ml of reagent grade isopropyl alcohol. Add, by pipette 25 ml of 2.5 N hydrochloric acid in isopropanol, allowing the acid to wash down any sample on the sides of the beaker. Stir for 30 min on a magnetic stir plate. Add 100 ml of 90% isopropanol from a graduated cylinder. Stir for 10 min. Filter the sample through a Buchner funnel and wash the filter cake with 90% isopropanol until the filtrate is negative for chloride ions. Use 0.1 N $AgNO_3$ to check for chloride ions. Transfer the filter cake to a 600-ml beaker and rinse the Buchner funnel to wash any starch into the beaker. Bring to a 300-ml volume with distilled water. Place for 10 min in a boiling water bath with stirring. Titrate while hot with 0.1 N NaOH to the phenolphthalein end-point.

Calculation:

Calculate as follows:

$$\text{Degree of substitution (DS)} = \frac{0.162 \times A}{1 - 0.210 \times A}$$

where:

A = milliequivalents of sodium hydroxide required per g of starch octenyl succinate.

Residual octenyl succinic acid in starch sodium octenyl succinate

Extraction and Preparation of Sample Solution:

Extract about 500 mg of starch with 15 ml of methanol overnight under constant shaking (weigh starch accurately). Filter the extraction mixture. Wash the starch on the filter with 7 ml of methanol. Repeat three times. Combine all filtrates (about 80% of the residuals are extracted by this procedure). Add 1 ml of 0.16 N methanolic KOH to the extracts. Dry the extracts with a flash evaporator at 30°. Dissolve the residue in 2 ml methanol. Take 0.5 ml of residue solution to the reaction vial. Add 0.5 ml derivative reagent (2.8 g of 2-p-dibromoacetophenone and 0.28 g 18-Crown-6 in 50 ml CH_3CN) to the reaction vial. Add 2 ml CH_3CN to the reaction vial. Cap the reaction vial and heat it at 80° for 30 min. Cool the reaction solution to room temperature (use within 24 h).

Liquid Chromatography Analysis:

Column:	Micro-Bondapack C_{18} (Waters)
Mobile Phase:	Gradient elution of 70% methanol in water to 80% methanol in water in 5 min. Curve 6 (Waters 660 solvent programmer)
Flow Rate:	1.5 ml/min
Detector:	UV at 254 nm, attenuation 0.16 AUFS
Injection volume:	5 µl

Preparation of Calibration Curve:

Prepare a 0.5 $\underline{M}$ solution of sodium octenyl succinate (Solution A). With a syringe take 0.25 ml of Solution A and place into a 25-ml volumetric flask. Dilute to mark with methanol (Solution B). Prepare three calibration standards by taking 0.5, 1 and 2 ml of Solution B and placing into three 50-ml round bottom flasks. Add to each 1 ml of 0.16 $\underline{N}$ methanolic KOH. Dry each solution with a flash evaporator at 30°. Dissolve the residue in 2.0 ml of methanol (Solution C_1, C_2 and C_3). Place 0.5 ml of the residue solution in the reaction vial. Add 0.5 ml derivative reagent (2.8 g of 2-p-dibromo-acetophenone and 0.28 g of 18-Crown-6 in 50 ml of CH_3CN) to the reaction vial. Add 2 ml of CN_3CN to the reaction vial. Cap the vial and heat to 80° for 30 min. Cool the reaction solution to room temperature (the derivative should be prepared as needed and used immediately). Inject 5 µl into the Liquid Chromatograph. The amount of residuals in each of the 5-µl injections are the following:

for Solution C_1	0.2375 µg
for Solution C_2	0.4750 µg
for Solution C_3	0.9500 µg

Plot peak height from Liquid Chromatograph Chart versus µg of residuals per 5 ml of solution.

Calculations:

Prepare a calibration curve according to the procedure. Using the peak height of the unknown sample from the Liquid Cromato-graph Chart, determine the level of residuals (calculated as octenyl succinic acid) in the injected volume from the calibration curve.

$$\% \text{ Residual in Starch} = \frac{300 \times \text{Value from Graph}}{\text{Weight of Starch (mg)}}$$

<u>Note</u>: The formula is corrected to 100% recovery by dividing by 0.80, so that 240/0.80 = 300.

TENTATIVE   **PETROLEUM JELLY**

Prepared at the 49th JECFA (1997)
superseding specifications prepared at the 44th JECFA (1995),
published in FNP 52 Addendum 3 (1995)

Information is required on methods of analysis and levels in commercial products of viscosity at 100°, carbon number distribution at 5% distillation point, average molecular weight, and oil content. Unless such data are provided before 31 March 1998, the specifications will be withdrawn.

SYNONYMS   Vaseline, Petrolatum
                            INS No. 905b

DEFINITION   Petroleum Jelly is a purified mixture of semi-solid, saturated hydrocarbons, mainly of paraffinic nature, obtained from petroleum. It may contain antioxidants approved for food use.

C.A.S. number   8009-03-8

DESCRIPTION   White to yellowish or light amber semisolid substance. It is transparent in thin layers and has not more than a slight fluorescence.

FUNCTIONAL USES   Lubricant, release agent, protective coating, anti-foaming agent.

CHARACTERISTICS

IDENTIFICATION

Solubility   Insoluble in water, very soluble in carbon disulfide, soluble in ether and hexane

Drop melting point   Between 38° and 60°
                            See description under TESTS

PURITY

Viscosity, 100°   Information required
                            See description under TESTS

Carbon number at 5% distillation point
                            Information required
                            See description under TESTS

Average molecular weight
                            Information required
                            See description under TESTS

Oil content   Information required
                            See description under TESTS

Residue on ignition   Not more than 0.05%
                            See description under TESTS

Colour	Passes test See description under TESTS
Acidity or alkalinity	Passes test See description under TESTS
Sulfur	Not more than 0.2% See description under TESTS
Arsenic	Not more than 3 mg/kg (Method II)
Lead	Not more than 3 mg/kg Prepare a sample solution as directed for organic compounds in the Limit Test and determine the lead content by atomic absorption spectrometry
Organic acids	Passes tests See description under TESTS

Fixed oils, fats and rosins

Passes test
See description under TESTS

Polycyclic aromatic hydrocarbons

The sample shall meet the following ultraviolet absorbance when subjected to the analytical procedure as described under the TESTS.

nm	max. absorbance per cm path length
280 - 289	0.25
290 - 299	0.20
300 - 359	0.14
360 - 400	0.04

TESTS

IDENTIFICATION TESTS

Drop melting point	Use the method as described in ASTM D 127 (American Society for Testing and Materials)

PURITY TESTS

Viscosity, 100°	Information required

Carbon number at 5% distillation point

Information required

Average molecular weight

Information required

Oil content	Information required

Residue on ignition	Accurately weigh about 4 g of the sample in a tared porcelain or platinum dish and heat over a flame. The sample volatiles without emitting any acrid odour. Ignite not to exceed very dull redness, until free from carbon. Cool in a desiccator and weigh.

Colour

Melt about 10 g of the sample on a steam bath, and pour about 5 ml of the liquid into a 150 x 16-mm clear-glass bacteriological test tube, keeping the sample melted. The petrolatum is not darker than a solution made by mixing 3.8 ml of ferric chloride TS and 1.2 ml of cobaltous chloride TS in a similar tube, the comparison of the two being made in reflected light against a white background, holding the sample tube directly against the background at such an angle that there is no fluorescence.

Acidity or alkalinity

Introduce 35 g of the sample into a 250-ml separator, add 100 ml of boiling water, and shake vigorously for 5 min. After the petrolatum and water have separated, draw of the water into a casserole, wash the sample in the separator with two 50-ml portions of boiling water, and add the washings to the casserole. To the accumulated 200 ml of water add 1 drop of phenolphthalein TS and boil. The solution does not acquire a pink colour. If the addition of phenolphthalein produces no pink colour, add 0.1 ml of methyl orange TS. No red pink colour is produced.

Sulfur

Use the method as described in ASTM D 2622

Organic acids

Weigh 20 g of the sample, add 50 ml of neutralized ethanol, and 50 ml of water, agitate throughly, and heat to boiling. Add 1 ml phenolphthalein TS, and titrate rapidly with 0.1$\underline{M}$ sodium hydroxide, with vigorous agitation to a sharp pink end-point, noting the colour change in the alcohol - water layer. Not more than 0.4 ml is required.

Fixed oils, fats and rosins

Digest 10 g of the sample at 100° with 10 g of sodium hydroxide and 50 ml of water for 30 min. Separate the water layer, and add to it an excess of diluted sulfuric acid TS. No oily or solid matter separates.

Polycyclic aromatic hydrocarbons

General Instructions

Because of the sensitivity of the test, the possibility of errors arising from contamination is great. It is of the greatest importance that all glassware be scrupulously cleaned to remove all organic matter such as oil, grease, detergent residues, etc. Examine all glassware, including stoppers and stopcocks, under ultraviolet light to detect any residual fluorescent contamination. As a precautionary measure it is a recommended practice to rinse all glassware with purified isooctane immediately before use. No grease is to be used on stopcocks or joints. Great care to avoid contamination of wax samples in handling and to assure absence of any extraneous material arising from inadequate packaging is essential. Because some of the polynuclear hydrocarbons sought in this test are very susceptible to photo-oxidation, the entire procedure is to be carried out under subdued light.

Apparatus
- Separatory funnels: 250-ml, 500-ml, 1,000-ml, and preferably 2000-ml capacity, equipped with tetrafluoroethylene polymer stopcocks.

- Reservoir: 500-ml capacity, equipped with a 24/40 standard taper male fitting at the bottom and a suitable balljoint at the top for connecting to the nitrogen supply. The male fitting should be equipped with glass hooks.

- Chromatographic tube: 180 mm in length, inside diameter to be 15.7 mm ± 0.1 mm, equipped with a coarse, fritted-glass disc, a tetrafluoroethylene polymer stopcock, and a female 24/40 standard tapered fitting at the opposite end. (Overall length of the column with the female joint is 235 mm). The female 24/40 standard tapered fitting at the opposite end.

- Disc: Tetrafluoroethylene polymer 2-inch diameter disc approximately 3/16-inch thick with a hole bored in the center to closely fit the stem of the chromatographic tube.

- Heating jacket: Conical, for 500-ml separatory funnel. (Used with variable transformer heat control).

- Suction flask: 250-ml or 500-ml filter flask.

- Condenser: 24/40 joints, fitted with a drying tube, length optional.

- Evaporation flask (optional): 250-ml or 500-ml capacity all-glass flask equipped with standard taper stopper having inlet and outlet tubes permitting passage of nitrogen across the surface of the liquid to be evaporated.

- Vacuum distillation assembly: All glass (for purification of dimethyl sulfoxide); 2 litre distillation flask with heating mantle; Vigreaux vacuum-jacketed condenser (or equivalent) about 45 cm in length and distilling head with separable cold finger condenser. Use of tetrafluoroethylene polymer sleeves on the glass joints will prevent freezing. Do not use grease on stopcocks or joints.

- Spectrophotometric cells: Fused quartz cells, optical path length in the range of 5.000 ± 0.005 cm; also for checking spectrophotometer performance only, optical path length in the range 1.000 ± 0.005 cm. With distilled water in the cells, determine any absorbance differences.

- Spectrophotometer: Spectral range 250-400 nm with spectral slit width of 2 nm or less, under instrument operating conditions for these absorbance measurements, the spectrophotometer shall also meet the following performance requirements:

Absorbance repeatability:	±0.01 at 0.4 absorbance
Absorbance accuracy:	±0.05 at 0.4 absorbance
Wavelength repeatability:	±0.2 nm
Wavelength accuracy:	±1.0 nm

- Nitrogen cylinder: Water-pumped or equivalent purity nitrogen in cylinder equipped with regulator and valve to control flow at 5 p.s.i.g.

Reagents and materials

- Organic solvents: All solvents used throughout the procedure shall meet the specifications and tests described in this specification. The isooctane, benzene, acetone, and methyl alcohol designated in the list following this paragraph shall pass the following test:

To the specified quantity of solvent in a 250-ml Erlenmeyer flask, add 1 ml of purified n-hexadecane and evaporate on the steam bath under a stream of nitrogen (a loose aluminium foil jacket around the flask will speed evaporation). Discontinue evaporation when not over 1 ml of residue remains. (To the residue from benzene add a 10 ml portion of purified isooctane, re-evaporate, and repeat once to insure complete removal of benzene).

Alternatively, the evaporation time can be reduced by using the optional evaporation flask. In this case the solvent and n-hexadecane are placed in the flask on the steam bath, the tube assembly is inserted, and a stream of nitrogen is fed through the inlet tube while the outlet tube is connected to a solvent trap and vacuum line in such a way as to prevent any flow-back of condensate into the flask.

Dissolve the 1 ml of hexadecane residue in isooctane and make to 25 ml volume. Determine the absorbance in the 5 cm path length cells compared to isooactane as reference. The absorbance of the solution of the solvent residue (except for methyl alcohol) shall not exceed 0.01 per cm path length between 280 and 400 nm. For methyl alcohol this absorbance value shall be 0.00.

- Isooctane (2,2,4-trimethylpentane): Use 180 ml for the test described in the preceding paragraph. Purify, if necessary, by passage through a column of activated silica gel, Grade 12, Davidson Chemical Company, Baltimore, Maryland, USA, or equivalent, about 90 cm in length and 5 cm to 8 cm in diameter.

- Benzene, reagent grade: Use 150 ml for the test. Purify, if necessary, by distillation or otherwise.

- Acetone, reagent grade: Use 200 ml for the test. Purify, if necessary, by distillation.

- Eluting mixtures:

1. 10% benzene in isooctane: Pipet 50 ml of benzene into a 500-ml glass-stoppered volumetric flask and adjust to volume with isooctane, with mixing.

2. 20% benzene in isooctane: Pipet 50 ml of benzene into a 250-ml glass-stoppered volumetric flask, and adjust to volume with isooctane, with mixing.

3. Acetone-benzene-water mixture: Add 20 ml of water to 380 ml of acetone and 200 ml of benzene, and mix.

- n-Hexadecane, 99% olefin-free: Dilute 1.0 ml of n-hexadecane to 25 ml with isooctane and determine the absorbance in a 5-cm cell compared to isooctane as reference point between 280-400 nm. The absorbance per centimeter path length shall not exceed 0.00 in this range. Purify, if necessary, by percolation through activated silica gel or by distillation.

- Methyl alcohol, reagent grade: Use 10.0 ml of methyl alcohol. Purify, if necessary, by distillation.

- Dimethyl sulfoxide: Pure grade, clear, water-white, m.p. 180 minimum. Dilute 120 ml of dimethyl sulfoxide with 240 ml of distilled water in a 500-ml separatory funnel, mix and allow to cool for 5-10 min. Add 40 ml of isooctane to the solution and extract by shaking the funnel vigourously for 2 min. Draw off the lower aqueous layer into a second 500-ml separatory funnel and repeat the extraction with 40 ml of isooctane. Draw off and discard the aqueous layer. Wash each of the 40 ml extracts three times with 50 ml portions of distilled water. Shaking time for each wash is 1 min. Discard the aqueous layers. Filter the first extract through anhydrous sodium sulfate prewashed with isooctane (see Sodium sulfate under "Reagents and Materials" for preparation of filter), into a 250-ml Erlenmeyer flask, or optionally into the evaporating flask. Wash the first separatory funnel with the second 40 ml isooctane extract, and pass through the sodium sulfate into the flask. Then wash the second and first separatory funnels successively with a 10 ml portion of isooctane, and pass the solvent through the sodium sulfate into the flask. Add 1 ml of n-hexadecane and evaporate the isooctane on the steam bath under nitrogen. Discontinue evaporation when not over 1-ml of residue remains. To the residue, add a 10-ml portion of isooctane and re-evaporate to 1 ml of hexadecane. Again, add 10 ml of isooctane to the residue and evaporate to 1 ml of hexadecane to insure complete removal of all volatile materials. Dissolve the 1 ml of hexadecane in isooctane and make to 25 ml volume. Determine the absorbance in 5 cm path length cells compared to isooctane as reference. The absorbance of the solution should not exceed 0.02 per cm path length in the 280-400 nm range. (Note Difficulty in meeting this absorbance specification may be due to organic impurities in the distilled water. Repetition of the test omitting the dimethyl sulfoxide will disclose their presence. If necessary to meet the specification, purify the water by redistillation, passage through an ion-exchange resin, or otherwise).

Purify, if necessary, by the following procedure: To 1.5 litres of dimethyl sulfoxide in a 2-litre glass-stoppered flask, add 6.0 ml of phosphoric acid and 50 g of Norit A (decolorizing carbon, alkaline) or equivalent. Stopper the flask, and with the use of a magnetic stirrer (tetrafluoro-ethylene polymer coated bar) stir the solvent for 15 min. Filter the dimethyl sulfoxide through four thicknesses of fluted paper (18.5 cm), Schleicher & Schuell No. 597, or equivalent. If the initial filtrate contains carbon fines, refilter through the same filter until a clear filtrate is obtained. Protect the sulfoxide from air and moisture during this operation by covering the solvent in the funnel and collection flask with a layer of isooctane. Transfer the filtrate to a 2-litre separatory funnel and draw off the dimethyl sulfoxide into the 2-litre distillation flask of the vacuum distillation assembly and distill at approximately 3-mm Hg pressure or less. Discard the first 200-ml fraction of the distillate and replace the distillate collection flask with a clean one.

Continue the distillation until approximately 1 litre of the sulfoxide has been collected.

At completion of the distillation, the reagent should be stored in glass-stoppered bottles since it is very hygroscopic and will react with some metal containers in the presence of air.

- Phosphoric acid, 85% reagent grade

- Sodium borohydride, 98%

- Magnesium oxide (Sea Sorb 43, Food Machinery Company, Westvaco Division, distributed by chemical supplier firms, or equivalent): Place 100 g of the magnesium oxide in a large beaker, add 700 ml of distilled water to make a thin slurry, and heat on a steam bath for 30 min with intermittent stirring. Stir well initially to insure that all the absorbent is completely wetted. Using a Buchner funnel and a filter paper of suitable diameter, filter with suction. Continue suction until water no longer drips from the funnel. Transfer the absorbent to a glass trough lined with aluminium foil (free from rolling oil). Break up the magnesia with a clean spatula and spread out the absorbent on the aluminium foil in a layer about 1-2 cm thick. Dry at $160\pm1°$ for 24 h. Pulverize the magnesia with mortar and pestle. Sieve the pulverized absorbent between 60-180 mesh. Use the magnesia retained on the 180-mesh sieve.

- Celite 545, Johns-Manville Company, diatomaceous earth, or equivalent.

- Magnesium oxide-Celite 545 mixture (2+1) by weight: Place the magnesium oxide (60-180 mesh) and the Celite 545 in 2 to 1 proportions, respectively, by weight in a glass-stoppered flask large enough for adequate mixing. Shake vigorously for 10 min. Transfer the mixture to a glass trough lined with aluminium foil (free from rolling oil) and spread it out on a layer about 1 to 2 cm thick. Reheat the mixture at $160 \pm 1°$ for 2 h, and store in a tightly closed flask.

- Sodium sulfate, anhydrous, reagent grade, preferably in granular form: For each bottle of sodium sulfate reagent used, establish as follows the necessary sodium sulfate prewash to provide such filters required in the method: Place approximately 35 g of anhydrous sodium sulfate in a 30 ml coarse, fritted-glass funnel or in a 65 ml filter funnel with glass wool plug; wash with successive 15 ml portions of the indicated solvent until a 15 ml portion of the wash shows 0.00 absorbance per cm path length between 280 nm and 400 nm when tested as prescribed under "Organic solvents." Usually three portions of wash solvent are sufficient.

Procedure

Before proceeding with the analysis of a sample, determine the absorbance in a 5 cm path cell between 250 nm and 400 nm for the reagent blank by carrying out the procedure, without a wax sample, at room temperature, recording the spectra after the extraction stage and after the complete procedure as precribed. The absorbance per centimeter path length following the extraction stage should not exceed 0.040 in the wavelength range from

250 to 400 nm; the absorbance per cm path length following the complete procedure should not exceed 0.070 in the wavelength range from 250 to 299 nm, inclusive, nor 0.045 in the wavelength range from 300 nm to 400 nm. If in either spectrum the characteristic benzene peaks in the 250-260 nm region are present, remove the benzene by the procedure under "Organic solvents" and record absorbance again.

Place 300 ml of dimethyl sulfoxide in a 1-litre separatory funnel and add 75 ml of phosphoric acid. Mix the contents of the funnel and allow to stand for 10 min. (The reaction between the sulfoxide and the acid is exothermic. Release pressure after mixing, then keep funnel stoppered). Add 150 ml of isooctane and shake to pre-equilibrate the solvents. Draw off the individual layers and store in glass-stoppered flasks.

Place a representative 1-kg sample of wax, or if this amount is not available, the entire sample, in a beaker of a capacity about three times the volume of the sample and heat with occasional stirring on a steam bath until the wax is completely melted and homogenous. Weigh four 25 ± 0.2 g portions of the melted wax in separate 100 ml beakers. Reserve three of the portions for later replicate analyses as necessary. Pour one weighed portion immediately after remelting (on the steam bath) into a 500 ml separatory funnel containing 100 ml of the pre-equilibrated sulfoxide-phosphoric acid mixture that has been heated in the heating jacket at a temperature just high enough to keep the wax melted. (Note: In pre-heating the sulfoxide-acid mixture, remove the stopper of the separatory funnel at intervals to release the pressure).

Promptly complete the transfer of the sample to the funnel in the jacket with portions of the pre-equilibrated isooctane, warming the beaker, if necessary, and using a total volume of just 50 ml of the solvent. If the wax comes out of solution during these operations, let the stoppered funnel remain in the jacket until the wax redissolves. (Remove stopper from the funnel at intervals to release pressure).

When the wax is in solution, remove the funnel from the jacket and shake it vigorously for 2 min. Set up three 250-ml separatory funnels with each containing 30 ml of pre-equilibrated isooctane. After separation of the liquid phases, allow to cool until the main portion of the wax-isooctane solution begins to show a precipitate. Gently swirl the funnel when precipitation first occurs on the inside surface of the funnel to accelerate this process. Carefully draw off the lower layer, filter it slowly through a thin layer of glass wool fitted loosely in a filter funnel into the first 250-ml separatory funnel, and wash in tandem with the 30-ml portions of isooctane contained in the 250-ml separatory funnels. Shaking time for each wash is 1 min. Repeat the extraction operation with two additional portions of the sulfoxide-acid mixture, replacing the funnel in the jacket after each extraction to keep the wax in solution and washing each extractive in tandem through the same three portions of isooctane.

Collect the successive extracts (300 ml total) in a separatory funnel (preferably 2-litre), containing 480 ml of distilled water, mix, and allow to cool for a few minutes after the last extract has been added. Add 80 ml of isooctane to the solution and extract by shaking the funnel vigorously for 2 min. Draw off the lower aqueous layer into a second separatory funnel (preferably 2-litre) and repeat the extraction with 80 ml of isooctane. Draw off and discard the aqueous layer. Wash each of the 80 ml extracts three times with 100-ml portions of distilled water. Shaking time for each wash is 1 min. Discard the aqueous layers. Filter the first extract through anhydrous sodium sulfate pre-washed with isooctane (see Sodium sulfate under "Reagents and Materials" for preparation of filter) into a 250-ml Erlenmeyer flask (or optionally into the evaporation flask). Wash the first separatory funnel with the second 80 ml isooctane extract and pass through the sodium sulfate. Then wash the second and first separatory funnels successively with a 20-ml portion of isooctane and pass the solvent through the sodium sulfate into the flask. Add 1 ml of n-hexadecane and evaporate the isooctane on the steam bath under nitrogen. Discontinue evaporation when not over 1 ml of residue remains. To the residue, add a 10-ml portions of isooctane, reevaporate to 1 ml of hexadecane, and repeat this operation once more.

Quantitatively transfer the residue with isooctane to a 25-ml volumetric flask, make to volume, and mix. Determine the absorbance of the solution in the 5-cm path length cells compared to isooctane as reference between 280-400 nm (take care to lose none of the solution in filling the sample cell). Correct the absorbance values for any absorbance derived from reagents as determined by carrying out the procedure without a wax sample. If the corrected absorbance does not exceed the limits prescribed in the Characteristics, the wax meets the ultraviolet absorbance specifications. If the corrected absorbance per centimeter path length exceeds the limits prescribed in the Characteristics, proceed as follows:

Quantitatively transfer the isooctane solution to a 125-ml flask equipped with 24/40 joint and evaporate the isooctane on the steam bath under a stream of nitrogen to a volume of 1 ml of hexadecane. Add 10 ml of methyl alcohol and approximately 0.3 g of sodium borohydride (Minimize exposure of the borohydride to the atmosphere. A measuring dipper may be used). Immediately fit a water-cooled condenser equipped with a 24/40 joint and with a drying tube into the flask, mix until the borohydride is dissolved, and allow to stand for 30 min at room temperature, with intermittent swirling. At the end of this period, disconnect the flask and evaporate the methyl alcohol on the steam bath under nitrogen until the sodium borohydride begins to come out of the solution. Then add 10 ml of isooctane and evaporate to a volume of about 2-3 ml. Again, add 10 ml of isooctane and concentrate to a volume of approximately 5 ml. Swirl the flask repeatedly to assure adequate washing of the sodium borohydride residues.

Fit the tetrafluoroethylene polymer disc on the upper part of the stem of the chromatographic tube, then place the tube with the disc on the suction flask and apply the vaccum (approximately 135-mm Hg pressure). Weigh out 14 g of the 2+1 magnesium oxide-Celite 545 mixture and pour the adsorbent mixture into the chromatographic tube in approximately 3 cm layers. After the addition of each layer, level off the top of the adsorbent with a flat glass rod or metal plunger by pressing down firmly until the adsorbent is well packed. Loosen the topmost few ml of each adsorbent layer with the end of a metal rod before the addition of the next layer. Continue packing in this manner until all the 14 g of the adsorbent is added to the tube. Level off the top of the adsorbent by pressing down firmly with a flat glass rod or metal plunger to make the depth of the adsorbent bed approximately 12.5 cm in depth. Turn off the vacuum and remove the suction flask. Fit the 500-ml reservoir onto the top of the chromatographic column and pre-wet the column by passing 100 ml of isooctane through the column. Adjust the nitrogen pressure so that the rate of descent of the isooctane coming off of the column is between 2-3 ml per min. Discontinue pressure just before the last of the isooctane reaches the level of the adsorbent. (Caution: Do not allow the liquid level to recede below the adsorbent level at any time). Remove the reservoir and decant the 5 ml isooctane concentrate solution onto the column and with slight pressure again allow the liquid level to recede to barely above the adsorbent level. Rapidly complete the transfer similarly with two 5 ml portions of isooctane, swirling the flask repeatedly each time to assure adequate washing of the residue. Just before the final 5 ml wash reaches the top of the adsorbent, add 100 ml of isooctane to the reservoir and continue the percolation at the 2-3 ml per minute rate. Just before the last of the isooctane reaches the adsorbent level, add 100 ml of 10% benzene in isooctane to the reservoir and continue the percolation at the aforementioned rate. Just before the solvent mixture reaches adsorbent level, add 25 ml of 20% benzene in isooctane to the reservoir and continue the percolation at 2-3 ml per minute until all this solvent mixture has been removed from the column. Discard all the elution solvents collected up to this point. Add 300 ml of the acetone-benzene-water mixture to the reservoir and percolate through the column to elute the polynuclear compounds. Collect the eluate in a clean 1-litre separatory funnel. Allow the column to drain until most of the solvent mixture is removed. Wash the eluate three times with 300-ml portions of distilled water, shaking well for each wash. (The addition of small amounts of sodium chloride facilitates separation). Discard the aqueous layer after each wash. After the final separation, filter the residual benzene through anhydrous sodium sulfate pre-washed with benzene (see Sodium sulfate under "Reagents and Materials" for preparation of filter) into a 250-ml Erlenmeyer flask (or optionally into the evaporation flask). Wash the separatory funnel with two additional 20-ml portions of benzene which are also filtered through the sodium sulfate. Add 1 ml of n-hexadecane and completely remove the benzene by evaporation under nitrogen, using the special procedure to eliminate benzene as previously described under "Organic Solvents". Quantitatively transfer the residue with isooctane to a 25 ml volumetric flask and adjust the volume. Determine the absorbance of the solution in the 5 cm path length cells compared to isooctane as reference between 250 - 400 nm. Correct for any absorbance derived from the reagents as determined by carrying out the procedure without a wax sample. If either spectrum shows the characteristic benzene peaks in the 250 - 260 nm region, evaporate the solution to remove benzene by the procedure under "Organic Solvents". Dissolve the residue, transfer quantitatively, and adjust to volume in isooctane in a 25 ml volumetric flask. Record the absorbance again. If the corrected absorbance does not exceed the limits prescribed in the Characteristics the substance meets the ultraviolet absorbance specifications.

POTASSIUM ALGINATE

Prepared at the 49th JECFA (1997)
superseding specifications prepared at the 44th JECFA (1995),
published in FNP 52 Addendum 3 (1995)

SYNONYMS   INS No. 402

DEFINITION   Potassium alginate is the potassium salt of alginic acid

   C.A.S. number   9005-36-1

   Chemical formula $(C_6H_7KO_6)_n$

   Structural formula   **Structural formula from Phillips, Wedlock, Williams: Gums and Stabilizers for the Food Industry 5 (1990) by permission of Oxford University Press.**

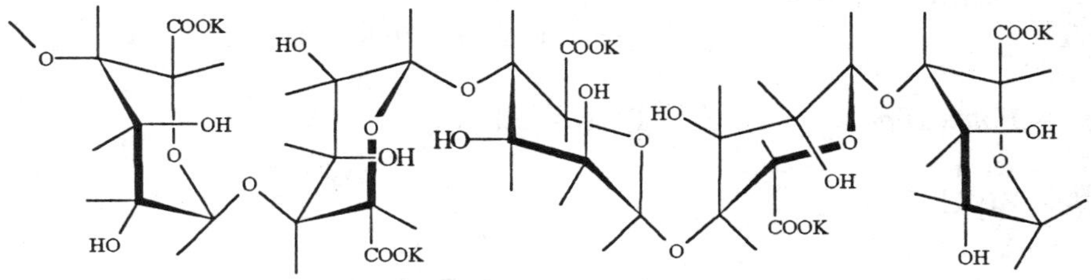

$$\underline{\quad\quad} G(^1C_4) \underline{\quad\quad} G(^1C_4) \underline{\quad\quad} M(^4C_1) \underline{\quad\quad} M(^4C_1) \underline{\quad\quad} G$$
$$\quad\quad\quad \alpha\text{-}1,4 \quad\quad\quad \alpha\text{-}1,4 \quad\quad\quad \beta\text{-}1,4 \quad\quad\quad \beta\text{-}1,4$$

The number and sequence of the Mannuronate and Glucuronate residues shown above vary in the naturally occurring alginate. The associated water molecules are not shown.

   Formula weight   Structural unit: 214.22 (theoretical)
                                                238 (actual average)
                  Macromolecule: 10,000 - 600,000 (typical average)

   Assay   Yields, on the dried basis, not less than 16.5% and not more than 19.5% of carbon dioxide (CO_2), equivalent to not less than 89.2% and not more than 105.5% of potassium alginate $(C_6H_7KO_6)_n$.

DESCRIPTION   Occurs as white to yellowish brown filamentous, grainy, granular or powdered forms

FUNCTIONAL USES   Stabilizer, thickener, gelling agent, emulsifier

CHARACTERISTICS

IDENTIFICATION

Solubility   Dissolves slowly in water forming a viscous solution; insoluble in ethanol and ether

Precipitate formation with calcium chloride
                     Passes test
                     See description under TESTS

Precipitate formation with ammonium sulfate
                     Passes test
                     See description under TESTS

Test for alginate   Passes test
                     See description under TESTS

Potassium   Passes test

PURITY

Loss on drying   Not more than 15% (105°, 4 h)

Water-insoluble matter   Not more than 2% on the dried basis
                     See description under TESTS

Arsenic   Not more than 3 mg/kg (Method II)

Lead   Not more than 5 mg/kg
                     Prepare a sample solution as directed for organic compounds in the Limit Test, using 2 g of the sample and 10 µg of lead ion (Pb) in the control

Microbiological criteria Total plate count: Not more than 5,000 colonies per gram.

                     Initially prepare a 10^{-1} dilution by adding a 50 g sample to 450 ml of Butterfield's phosphate buffered dilution water and homogenizing in a high speed blender.

                     Yeasts and moulds: Not more than 500 colonies per gram

                     Coliforms: Negative by test

                     Salmonella: Negative by test

TESTS

IDENTIFICATION TESTS

Precipitate formation with calcium chloride
                     To a 0.5% solution of the sample in sodium hydroxide TS add one-fifth of its volume of a 2.5% solution of calcium chloride. A voluminous, gelatinous

precipitate is formed. This test distinguishes potassium alginate from gum arabic, sodium carboxymethyl cellulose, carrageenan, gelatin, gum ghatti, karaya gum, carob bean gum, methyl cellulose and tragacanth gum.

Precipitate formation with ammonium sulphate

To a 0.5% solution of the sample in sodium hydroxide TS add one-half of its volume of a saturated solution of ammonium sulfate. No precipitate is formed. This test distinguishes potassium alginate from agar, sodium carboxymethyl cellulose, carrageenan, de-esterified pectin, gelatin, carob bean gum, methyl cellulose and starch.

Test for alginate

Moisten 1-5 mg of the sample with water and add 1 ml of acid ferric sulfate TS. Within 5 min, a cherry-red colour develops that finally becomes deep purple.

Water-insoluble matter

Disperse 2 g of the sample, weighed to the nearest 0.1 mg, in 800 ml of water in a 2,000-ml flask. Neutralize to pH 7 with sodium hydroxide TS and then add 3 ml in excess. Add 40 ml of hydrogen peroxide solution containing 30% by weight H_2O_2, cover the flask and boil for 1 h with frequent stirring. Filter while hot through a tared Gooch crucible provided with a glass fibre filter (2.4 cm, No. 934 AH, Reeve Angel & Co., Clifton, N.Y., or equivalent filter). If slow filtration is caused by high viscosity of the sample solution, boil until the viscosity is reduced enough to permit filtration. Wash the crucible thoroughly with hot water, dry the crucible and its contents at 105° for 1 h, cool and weigh. Calculate as percentage of the dry weight.

METHOD OF ASSAY

Proceed as directed under Carbon Dioxide Determination by Decarboxylation in the *General Methods*. Each ml of 0.25 N sodium hydroxide consumed is equivalent to 5.5 mg of carbon dioxide (CO_2) or 29.75 mg of potassium alginate (equivalent weight 238).

POTASSIUM PROPIONATE

*Prepared at the 49th JECFA (1997)
superseding specifications prepared at the 44th JECFA (1995),
published in FNP 52 Addendum 3 (1995)*

SYNONYMS   Potassium propanoate, INS No. 283

DEFINITION

    Chemical name   Potassium propionate

    C.A.S. number   327-62-8

    Chemical formula $C_3H_5KO_2$

    Structural formula $CH_3CH_2COO^-K^+$

    Formula weight   112.17

    Assay   Not less than 99.0 % on the dried basis

DESCRIPTION   White or colourless crystals

FUNCTIONAL USES   Preservative, antimould and antirope agent

CHARACTERISTICS

    IDENTIFICATION

    Solubility   Freely soluble in water, soluble in ethanol

    Positive test for potassium
        Passes test

Positive test for propionate
    Warm the sample with sulfuric acid. The propionic acid evolved may be recognized by its odour.

Positive test for alkali salt of organic acid
    Ignite the sample at a relatively low temperature. The alkaline residue effervesces with acid.

PURITY

    Loss on drying   Not more than 4% (105°, 2 h)

Water-insoluble matter   Not more than 0.1 %
    See description under TESTS

pH   7.5 - 10.5 (1 in 10 soln)

Iron   Not more than 30 mg/kg
                                    Test 0.5 g of the sample as described in the Limit Test using 1.5 ml of Iron
                                    Standard Solution (15 µg), in the control.

Lead   Not more than 5 mg/kg
                                    Prepare a sample solution as directed for organic compounds in the Limit
                                    Test, using 5 µg of lead ion (Pb) in the control.

TESTS

PURITY TESTS

Water-insoluble matter   Weigh 5 g of the sample to the nearest mg, transfer into a 100-ml beaker
                                    and add 50 ml of water. Stir until all the sample appears to be completely
                                    dissolved. Filter through a Gooch crucible, tared to an accuracy of $\pm$
                                    0.2 mg. Rinse the beaker with 20 ml of water. Dry the crucible with its
                                    contents in a 60° oven to constant weight. Cool in a desiccator, weigh, and
                                    calculate as percentage.

METHOD OF ASSAY   Weigh, to the nearest mg, 3 g of the sample previously dried at 105° for 2 h
                                    into a distillation flask and add 200 ml of 50% phosphoric acid. Boil for 2 h
                                    and collect the distillate. During distillation keep the volume in the flask at
                                    about 200 ml by adding water using dropping funnel. Titrate the distillate
                                    with 1N sodium hydroxide using phenolphthalein TS as indicator. Each ml of
                                    1N sodium hydroxide corresponds to 112.17 mg of $C_3H_5KO_2$.

TENTATIVE   **PROPIONIC ACID**

Prepared at the 49th JECFA (1997)
superseding specifications prepared at the 44th JECFA (1995),
published in FNP 52 Addendum 3 (1995)

Information required on method of analysis and levels for readily oxidizable substances

SYNONYMS   Propanoic acid, ethylformic acid, methylacetic acid, INS No. 280

DEFINITION

Chemical name	Propionic acid
C.A.S. number	79-09-4
Chemical formula	$C_3H_6O_2$
Structural formula	CH_3CH_2COOH
Formula weight	74.08
Assay	Not less than 99.5% on dried basis

DESCRIPTION   An oily liquid with a slightly pungent odour

FUNCTIONAL USES   Preservative, antimould, antirope agent, flavouring agent (see "flavouring agents" monograph)

CHARACTERISTICS

   IDENTIFICATION

   Solubility   Miscible with water and ethanol

   Specific gravity d_{20}^{20} : 0.993 – 0.997

   PURITY

   Distillation range 138.5 - 142.5°

   Non-volatile residue Not more than 0.01% when dried at 140° to constant weight

   Readily oxidizable substances
                         Information required

   Heavy metals   Not more than 10 mg/kg
                         Test 2 g of the sample as directed in the Limit Test (Method II).

   Aldehydes   Not more than 0.2% (as propionaldehyde)
                         See description under TESTS.

TESTS

PURITY TESTS

Aldehydes   Transfer 10.0 ml of the sample into a 250-ml glass-stoppered conical flask containing 50 ml of water and 10.0 ml of a 1 in 8 solution of sodium bisulfite. Stopper the flask, and shake vigorously. Allow the mixture to stand for 30 min, then titrate with 0.1N iodine to the same brownish yellow end-point obtained with a blank treated with the same quantities of the same reagents. The difference between the volume of 0.1N iodine required for the blank and that required for the sample is not more than 7 ml.

METHOD OF ASSAY

Mix 3 g of the sample, weighed to the nearest 0.1 mg, with 50 ml of water in a 250-ml flask. Add phenolphthalein TS, and titrate with 1N sodium hydroxide to the first appearance of a faint pink end-point which persists for at least 30 sec. Each ml of 1N sodium hydroxide is equivalent to 74.08 mg of $C_3H_6O_2$.

PROPYLENE GLYCOL

Prepared at the 49th JECFA (1997)
superseding specifications prepared at the 46th JECFA (1996),
published in FNP 52 Addendum 4 (1996)

SYNONYMS   Propanediol, Methyl glycol, INS No. 1520

DEFINITION

Chemical names   Propane-1,2-diol, 1,2-dihydroxypropane

C.A.S. number   57-55-6

Chemical formula $C_3H_8O_2$

Structural formula

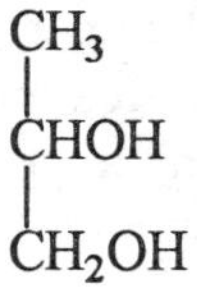

$$CH_3$$
$$|$$
$$CHOH$$
$$|$$
$$CH_2OH$$

Molecular weight   76.10

Assay   Not less than 99.5% on the anhydrous basis

DESCRIPTION   Clear, colourless, hygroscopic, viscous liquid

FUNCTIONAL USES   Solvent, glazing agent, humectant

CHARACTERISTICS

IDENTIFICATION

Solubility   Soluble in water, ethanol and acetone

Infrared absorption   The infrared spectrum of a potassium bromide dispersion of the sample corresponds with the infrared spectrum in the Appendix

PURITY

Distillation range   99% v/v distils between 185-189°

Specific gravity d_{20}^{20}: 1.035 - 1.040

Water   Not more than 1.0% (Karl Fischer)

Sulfated ash   Not more than 0.07%
                           Proceed as directed under the test for Ash (Sulfated ash, Method II), using 5 g of the sample

Heavy metals   Not more than 10 mg/kg

A solution of 2 g of the sample in 25 ml of water meets the requirements of the Limit Test (Method I)

Free acid

Passes test
Add 3-6 drops of phenol red TS to 50 ml water, then add 0.1N sodium hydroxide until solution remains red for 30 sec. To this solution add about 50 g of the sample accurately weighed. Titrate with 0.01N sodium hydroxide until the original red colour returns and remains for 15 sec. Not more than 1.67 ml of 0.01N sodium hydroxide are consumed by a sample of 50.0 g.

METHOD OF ASSAY

Inject a 10-µl portion of the sample into a suitable gas chromatograph equipped with a thermal conductivity detector and a stainless steel column, 1-m x 1/4-in, packed with 4% Carbowax 20 M on 40/60-mesh Chromosorb T, or equivalent materials. The carrier gas is helium flowing at 75 ml/min. The injection port temperature is 240°, the column temperature 120 to 200°, programmed at a rate of 5° per min, and the block temperature 250°. Under the conditions described, the approximate retention time for propylene glycol is 5.7 min, and 8.2, 9.0, and 10.2 min for the three isomers of dipropylene glycol, respectively. Measure the area under all peaks by any convenient means, calculate the normalized area percentage of propylene glycol, and report as weight percentage.

APPENDIX

Infrared spectrum: **Propylene glycol**

Infrared spectrum from Merck FT-IR Atlas through courtesy of Dr. K.G.R. Pachler, Mr. F. Matlok and Dr. H-U. Gremlich, c/o Merck, Darmstadt, and VCH Verlagsgesellschaft GmbH, Weinheim, Germany.

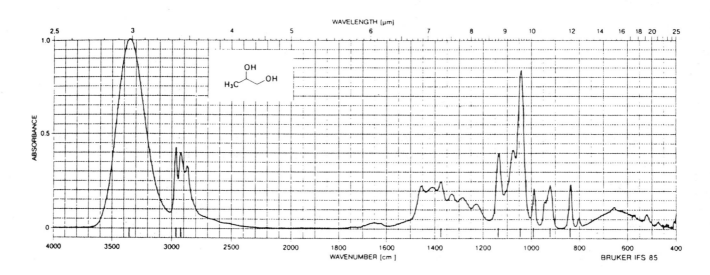

PROPYLENE GLYCOL ALGINATE

Prepared at the 49th JECFA (1997)
superseding specifications prepared at the 44th JECFA (1995),
published in FNP 52 Addendum 3 (1995)

SYNONYMS	1,2-propane-diol ester of alginic acid; hydroxypropyl alginate; propane 1,2-diol alginate; INS No. 405.

DEFINITION　Propylene glycol alginate is an ester of alginic acid in which some of the carboxyl groups are esterified with propylene glycol, some neutralized with an appropriate alkali and some remain free.

C.A.S. number　9005-37-2

Chemical formula　$(C_9H_{14}O_7)_n$ (esterified)

Formula weight　Structural unit :　234.21 (theoretical)
Macromolecule :　10,000 - 600,000 (typical average)

Assay　Yields, on the dried basis, not less than 16% and not more than 20% of carbon dioxide (CO_2).

DESCRIPTION　Occurs as white to yellowish brown filamentous, grainy, granular or powdered forms

FUNCTIONAL USES　Stabilizer, thickener, emulsifier

CHARACTERISTICS

IDENTIFICATION

Solubility　Soluble in water giving a viscous, colloidal solution; soluble in up to 60% aqueous ethanol depending upon degree of esterification.

Precipitate formation with sulphuric acid
　To 10 ml of a 1% solution of the sample add 1 ml of sodium hydroxide TS. Heat in a boiling water bath for about 5 min, cool and add 1 ml of dilute sulphuric acid TS. A gelatinous precipitate is formed.

Precipitate formation with lead acetate
　To 5 ml of a 1% solution of the sample add 1 ml of lead acetate TS. A gelatinous precipitate is formed

PURITY

Loss on drying　Not more than 20% (105°, 4 h)

Water-insoluble matter　Not more than 2% on the dried basis
　See description under TESTS

Total propylene glycol　Not less than 15% and not more than 45%.

See description under TESTS.

Free propylene glycol Not more than 15%
See description under TESTS

Arsenic Not more than 3 mg/kg (Method II)

Lead Not more than 5 mg/kg
Prepare a sample solution as directed for organic compounds in the Limit Test, using 5μg of lead ion (Pb) in the control

Microbiological criteria Total plate count: Not more than 5,000 colonies per gram.

Initially prepare a 10^{-1} dilution by adding a 50 g sample to 450 ml of Butterfield's phosphate buffered dilution water and homogenizing in a high speed blender.

Yeasts and moulds: Not more than 500 colonies per gram

Coliforms: Negative by test

Salmonella: Negative by test

TESTS

PURITY TESTS

Water-insoluble matter Disperse 2 g of the sample, weighed to the nearest 0.1 mg, in 800 ml of water in a 2,000-ml flask. Neutralize to pH 7 with sodium hydroxide TS and then add 3 ml in excess. Add 40 ml of hydrogen peroxide solution containing 30% by weight H_2O_2, cover the flask and boil for 1 h with frequent stirring. Filter while hot through a tared Gooch crucible provided with a glass fibre filter (2.4 cm, No 934 AH, Reeve Angel & Co, Clifton, N.Y., USA, or equivalent). If slow filtration is caused by high viscosity of the sample solution, boil until the viscosity is reduced enough to permit filtration. Wash the crucible thoroughly with hot water, dry the crucible and its contents at 105° for 1 h, cool and weigh. Calculate as percentage of the dry weight.

Total popylene glycol Sample solution:

Weigh, to the nearest 0.1 mg, 1 g of the sample previously dried and dissolve in 100 ml distilled water in a 400-ml beaker. After dissolution add 50 ml of 0.1 N sodium hydroxide and stir for 30 min. At the end of this period neutralize with 0.1 N hydrochloric acid and precipitate the gum with 25 ml of a 5% calcium chloride solution. Filter the mixture using fast filter paper collecting the filtrate in a 250-ml volumetric flask. Wash the precipitate with several small portions of distilled water combining the washings with the filtrate and dilute to the mark with distilled water.

Periodic acid, 0.029 M:

Add 5.500 g of periodic acid and 200 ml of distilled water to a 1-litre volumetric flask. Dilute to the mark with glacial acetic acid.

Procedure:

Pipette a 25-ml aliquot of the sample solution and 25 ml of the 0.029 M periodic acid into a 250-ml conical flask, swirl and let stand for 30 min. At the end of this period add approximately 2 g of potassium iodide and titrate with 0.1 N sodium thiosulfate using 1% starch solution as an indicator.

Perform a blank determination using 50 ml of distilled water and 25 ml of 0.029 M periodic acid. Calculate the percentage of propylene glycol by the formula:

$$\text{Propylene glycol \%} = \frac{3.8\,(A - B)}{W}$$

where

A = ml 0.1 N sodium thiosulfate used for blank
B = ml 0.1 N sodium thiosulfate used for sample
W = weight of the sample (in grams)

Free propylene glycol	Determine the percentage of free propylene glycol in the sample by extracting 2 g of sample for 2 hours under reflux, using 80 ml of propan-2-ol. Allow the solution to cool to room temperature, then determine the quantity of free propylene glycol using titration with 0.029 M periodic acid as described under the procedure for Total propylene glycol.
METHOD OF ASSAY	Proceed as directed under Carbon Dioxide Determination by Decarboxylation in the *General Methods*. Each ml of 0.25 N Sodium hydroxide consumed is equivalent to 5.5 mg of carbon dioxide (CO_2).

PROPYLENE GLYCOL ESTERS OF FATTY ACIDS

Prepared at the 49th JECFA (1997)
superseding specifications prepared at the 46th JECFA (1996),
published in FNP 52 Addendum 4 (1996)

SYNONYMS Propane-1,2-diol esters of fatty acids, INS No. 477

DEFINITION Propylene glycol esters of fatty acids are mixtures of propylene glycol mono- and diesters of saturated and unsaturated fatty acids derived from edible oils and fats. The products are produced either by direct esterification of propylene glycol with fatty acids or by transesterification of propylene glycol with oils or fats. When prepared by transesterification, the product may contain residual mono- and diglycerides and glycerol. The process may be followed by molecular distillation to separate the monoesters.

Structural formula

$$CH_3$$
$$|$$
$$CHOR_2$$
$$|$$
$$CH_2OR_1$$

where R_1 and R_2 represent one fatty acid moiety and hydrogen in the case of mono-esters and two fatty acid moieties in the case of di-esters

Assay Not less than 85% total fatty acid esters

DESCRIPTION White or cream coloured solids of waxy appearance, plastic products or viscous liquids

FUNCTIONAL USES Emulsifier

CHARACTERISTICS

IDENTIFICATION

Solubility Insoluble in water, soluble in ethanol and ethyl acetate

Positive test for fatty acids
Passes test

Positive test for propylene glycol
Passes test
Glycerol may also be detectable by TLC

PURITY

Heavy metals Not more than 10 mg/kg
Test 2 g of the sample as directed in the Limit Test (Method II)

Acid value Not more than 4

| *Acids* | Acids other than fatty acids shall not be detectable |

Dimer and trimer of propylene glycol
Not more than 0.5%

| Soap | Not more than 7% (as potassium stearate)
 See description under TESTS |

| Free propylene glycol | Not more than 1.5% (soap free)
 See description under TESTS |

| Total propylene glycol | Not less than 11% (soap free)
 See description under TESTS |

| *Sulfated ash* | Not more than 0.5% (soap free)
 Proceed as directed under the test for Ash (Sulfated Ash, Method I, if the sample is solid, or Method II, if liquid), using 5 g of the sample |

TESTS

PURITY TESTS

Soap

Prepare a solvent mixture consisting of equal parts, by volume, of toluene and methanol, add bromophenol blue TS, and neutralize with 0.5N hydrochloric acid, or use neutralized acetone as the solvent. Weigh accurately about 5 g of the sample, dissolve it in 100 ml of the neutralized solvent mixture, and titrate with 0.5N hydrochloric acid to a definite yellow endpoint. Calculate the percentage of soap in the sample by the formula:

$$\frac{V \times N \times e}{W}$$

in which V and N are the volume and normality, respectively, of the hydrochloric acid, W is the weight of the sample, in g, and e is the equivalence factor, $e = 31.0$.

Free propylene glycol

Reagents and Solutions:

Periodic Acid solution: Dissolve 5.4 g of periodic acid, H_5IO_6 in 100 ml of water, add 1900 ml of glacial acetic acid, and mix. Store in a light-resistant, glass-stoppered bottle or in a clear, glass-stoppered bottle protected from light.

Chloroform: Use chloroform meeting the following test: To each of three 500-ml flasks add 50.0 ml of Periodic Acid Solution, then add 50 ml of chloroform and 10 ml of water to two of the flasks and 50 ml of water to the third. To each flask add 20 ml of potassium iodide TS, mix gently, and allow to stand at least 1 min, but no longer than 5 min, before titrating. Add 100 ml of water, and titrate with 0.1N sodium thiosulfate, using a magnetic stirrer to keep the solution thoroughly mixed, to the disappearance of the brown iodine color, then add 2 ml of starch TS and continue the titration to the disappearance of the blue color. The difference between the volume of 0.1N sodium thiosulfate required in the titrations with and without the chloroform is not greater than 0.5 ml.

Procedure:

Melt the sample, if not liquid, at a temperature not higher than 100° above its melting point, and mix thoroughly. Transfer an accurately weighed portion of the sample, equivalent to about 30 mg of propylene glycol into a 100 ml beaker, and dissolve in 25 ml of chloroform. Transfer the solution with the aid of an additional 25 ml of chloroform, into a separator, wash the beaker with 25 ml of water, and add the washing to the separator. Stopper the separator tightly, shake vigorously for 30 to 60 sec, and allow the layers to separate. (Add 1 to 2 ml of glacial acetic acid to break emulsions formed due to the presence of soap.) Collect the aqueous layer in a 500-ml glass-stoppered Erlenmeyer flask, and extract the chloroform solution again using two 25-ml portions of water. To the combined aqueous extracts add 50.0 ml of Periodic Acid Solution. Run two blanks by adding 50.0 ml of this reagent solution to two 500 ml glass-stoppered Erlenmeyer flasks, each containing 75 ml of water and allow to stand for at least 30 min, but no longer than 90 min. To each flask, add 20 ml of potassium iodide TS, and allow to stand at least 1 min, but no longer than 5 min, before titrating. Add 100 ml of water, and titrate with 0.1N sodium thiosulfate, using a magnetic stirrer to keep the solution thoroughly mixed, to the disappearance of the brown iodine color, then add 2 ml of starch TS and continue the titration to the disappearance of the blue color.

Calculation:

Calculate the percentage of free propylene glycol by the formula:

$$\frac{(b - S) \times N \times 3.81}{W}$$

in which b is the number of ml of sodium thiosulfate consumed in the blank determination; S is the number of ml required in the titration of the aqueous extracts from the sample; N is the exact normality of the sodium thiosulfate; W is the weight, in g, of the original sample taken and 3.81 is the molecular weight of propylene glycol divided by 20.

Note: If the aqueous extract contains more than 30 mg of propylene glycol, dilute the extract in a volumetric flask and transfer a suitable aliquot into a 500 ml glass-stoppered Erlenmeyer flask before proceeding with the test. The weight of the sample should be corrected in the calculation.

Total propylene glycol and glycerol

A. Sample preparation

Transfer about 15 g of sample, accurately weighed, into a 500-ml flask, add 250 ml of ethanol and 7.5 g of potassium hydroxide and mix. Reflux the solution for 2 h, transfer into an 800-ml beaker rinsing the flask with about 100 ml of water and adding the rinse water to the beaker. Heat on a steam or water bath, adding water occasionally to replace the ethanol and evaporate until the odour of ethanol can no longer be detected. Adjust the volume to about 250 ml with hot water, neutralize with diluted sulfuric acid (1 in 2), add a slight excess of acid, heat with gentle stirring until the fatty acid layer separates. Transfer the fatty acids into a warm 500-ml separatory funnel, wash with four 20-ml portions of hot water and combine the washings with the original aqueous layer from the saponification. Extract the combined aqueous layer with three 20 ml portions of petroleum ether. Neutralize the aqueous layer with sodium hydroxide TS to pH 7. Transfer the solution to a 500-ml volumetric flask and dilute to the mark with water.

B. Total Propylene glycol

Pipette 5.0 ml of the solution into a 125 ml Erlenmeyer flask, add 5.0 ml of 1M periodic acid, swirl and let stand 15 min. Add 10 ml of a saturated solution of sodium bicarbonate, followed by 15.0 ml of 0.1N sodium arsenite and 1 ml of potassium iodide solution (1 in 20) and mix. Add enough sodium bicarbonate so that at the end point some remains undissolved, and titrate with 0.1N iodine, using a 10-ml microburette and continuing the titration to a faint yellow colour. Perform a blank determination and make the appropriate corrections. Each ml of 0.1N iodine is equivalent to 3.805 mg of propylene glycol.

g propylene glycol/100 g of esters =

$$\frac{38.05 \times \text{ml } 0.1\text{N iodine solution}}{\text{sample weight (g)}}$$

If the qualitative test for glycerol included under Identification Test (Positive test for propylene glycol) showed the product to contain glycerol, it becomes necessary to correct for the glycerol content of the polyol solution obtained after saponification and separation of liberated fatty acids.

C. Glycerol

Pipette 50 ml of the solution prepared in "A. Sample preparation" into a 600-ml beaker, add bromothymol blue TS and acidify with 0.2N sulfuric acid to a definite greenish-yellow colour. Neutralize with 0.05N sodium hydroxide to a definite blue end point free of green colour. Prepare a blank containing 50 ml of water and neutralize in the same manner. Pipette 50 ml of sodium periodate TS into each beaker, mix by swirling, cover with a watch glass and allow to stand for 30 min at room temperature (not above 35°) in the dark or in subdued light. Add 10 ml of a mixture of equal volumes of ethylene glycol and water and allow to stand 20 min. Dilute each solution to about 300 ml and titrate with 0.1N sodium hydroxide to pH 8.1±0.1 using a calibrated pH meter. Each ml of 0.1N sodium hydroxide, after correction for the blank, is equivalent to 9.210 mg of glycerol.

g glycerol/100 g of esters =

$$\frac{9.210 \times \text{ml } 0.1\text{N NaOH}}{\text{sample weight (g)}}$$

The true propylene glycol content (in g/100 g of esters) is equal to the apparent propylene glycol content (in g/100 g of esters) minus 1.65 x the glycerol content (in g/100 g of esters).

METHOD OF ASSAY

Determine by gas chromatography using the following: Gas chromatograph, with split injection or on-column injection, oven temperature programming and flame ionisation detector. For split injection an injection port with programmable temperature is preferable. For on-column injection, the reaction mixture is diluted 1:50 with pyridine prior to injection.

Column: Fused silica capillary column, surface fully deactivated by silylation agent, 12-25 m, 0.25-0.35 mm i.d., coating 95% methyl- 5% phenyl silicone (or other phase with similar polarity), film thickness 0.1-0.2 μm.

Injection: Volume 1-5μl: split injection (Split ratio 1:10-1:50); direct injection (hold for 1 min)

Temperatures: Injection port 320° (or 60° for on-column injection); column initial 50° (or 60° for on-column injection); programme rate 10°/ min; final temperature 350°, hold 1 min; detector 400°; carrier gas flow 2-5 ml He/ min (at 80°)

N.B. The precise temperature conditions will be dependent on the details of the equipment used.

Reagents:
N,N - bis(trimethylsilyl)fluoroacetamide (BSTFA)
Trimethylchlorosilane (TMCS)
Pyridine, analytical grade, kept over KOH
n-Heptadecane, analytical grade, 99% minimum

Reference materials: Propylene glycol, propylene glycol monostearate.

Internal standard solution: Accurately weigh approximately 100 mg internal standard, n-heptadecane into a 100-ml volumetric flask, dilute with pyridine to the mark.

Reference solution: Accurately weigh approximately 100 mg propylene glycol monostearate into a 25-ml volumetric flask adding internal standard solution to the mark. When pure reference material of other components such as propylene glycol and di-fatty acid esters of propylene glycol are available, the method is suitable for these also.

Procedure:

Accurately weigh approximately 100 mg of the homogenised sample into a 25-ml volumetric flask and dilute to volume with the internal standard solution. Transfer 0.8 ml of the sample solution to a 2.5-ml screw cap vial with Teflon faced septa or 2.0-ml vial for auto sampler. Add 0.3 ml BSTFA and 0.1 ml TMCS. Close the vial and shake vigorously. Heat the reaction mixture in a heating device at 70° for approximately 20 min, inject 1 to 5 µl of the reaction mixture into the gas chromatograph showing a stable baseline. Do not delay GC analysis. Repeat the reaction with a further 100 mg sample. Make two injections per reaction sample. Transfer 0.8 ml of reference solution to a vial and add the silylating agents, 0.3 ml BSTFA and 0.1 ml TMCS . Heat the reaction mixture and inject into the gas chromatograph as described above.

Identification:

Analyse reference solution using the same operating conditions as for the sample solution. Identify peaks by comparison of retention time with known substances or apply coupled GC/MS.

Calculation and expression of results:

Calculate response factor R_x of the reference substance X vs. internal standard using the reference solution chromatogram. The value of the response factor is given by the formula:

$$R_x = (m_{is}/m_x) \times (A_x/A_{is})$$

where:

m_{is} = mass of internal standard in mg
m_x = mass of reference substance X in mg
A_x = peak area of reference substance X
A_{is} = peak area of internal standard

Calculate percentage of mass content m'_x of component X in the sample by the formula:

$$m'_x = 1/R_x \times (m'_{is}/m'_s) \times (A'_x/A'_{is})\%$$

where:
m'_{is} = mass of internal standard in sample in mg
m'_s = mass of sample in mg
A'_x = peak area of component X in the sample
A'_{is} = peak area of internal standard in sample

When calculating the total content of propylene glycol monoesters in the sample the response factor of propylene monostearate is used for all propylene glycol monoesters in the sample. The FID response of propylene glycol monostearate does not differ significantly from that of other fatty acid monoesters of propylene glycol.

SALATRIM

Prepared at the 49th JECFA (1997)

DEFINITION

Salatrim is the acronym for short- and long-chain acyl triglyceride molecules. Salatrim is prepared by interesterification of triacetin, tripropionin, or tributyrin, or their mixtures with either hydrogenated canola, soybean, cottonseed, or sunflower oil. Triglycerides with three short-chain fatty acids are removed in the process.

Salatrim triglyceride molecules typically contain 30-67 mol-% short-chain fatty acids (SCFA) and 33-70 mol-% long-chain fatty acids (LCFA); stearic acid is the predominant LCFA.

Structural formula

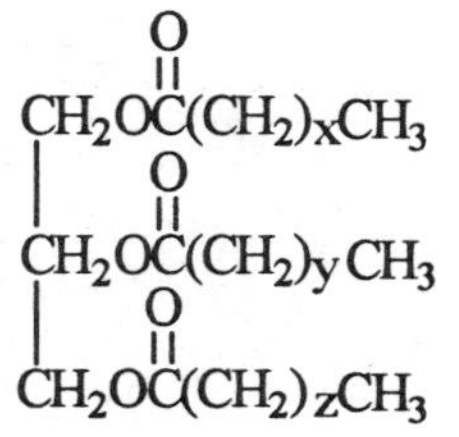

$$\begin{array}{c} O \\ \| \\ CH_2OC(CH_2)_xCH_3 \\ | \quad\; O \\ \quad\;\; \| \\ CH_2OC(CH_2)_y\,CH_3 \\ | \quad\; O \\ \quad\;\; \| \\ CH_2OC(CH_2)_z\,CH_3 \end{array}$$

where $(x + y + z)$ is between 14 and 42

Assay

Not less than 87% triglycerides. Not less than 90% of the triglycerides with a SCFA-to-LCFA mole ratio in the range 0.5-2.0.

DESCRIPTION

Clear, slightly amber liquid to a light-coloured waxy solid at room temperature. Free of particulate matter and of foreign or rancid odour.

FUNCTIONAL USES

Reduced-energy replacement for conventional fats and oils.

CHARACTERISTICS

IDENTIFICATION

Solubility

Soluble in hexane, cyclohexane, acetone, ether, tetrahydrofuran, and liquid triglyceride oils. Insoluble in water.

Melting range

16-71°, depending on triglyceride composition.

Infrared absorption

The infrared absorption spectrum of the sample, contained in a sodium chloride cell or between salt plates, corresponds to the infrared spectrum in the Appendix.

PURITY

Free fatty acids

Not more than 0.5% (as oleic acid). An equivalence factor (e) of 28.2 should be used.

Monoglycerides

Not more than 2%

See description under METHOD OF ASSAY

Sulphated Ash	Not more than 0.1% Test 2 g sample as directed in Method I for solid samples and as directed in Method II for liquid samples.
Lead	Not more than 0.1 mg/kg See description under TESTS.
Peroxide value	Not more than 2.0 See description under TESTS.
Unsaponifiable matter	Not more than 1.0% See description under TESTS.
Water	Not more than 0.3% (Karl Fischer method)

TESTS

PURITY TESTS

Lead

I. Principle:

Determination by graphite furnace atomic absorption spectrophotometry.
(Food Chemicals Codex, 4th Ed. (1996), National Academy of Sciences, Washington, DC, pp. 765-766)

II. Apparatus:

An atomic absorption spectrophotometer (Perkin-Elmer Model 3100 or equivalent) fitted with a graphite furnace (Perkin-Elmer HGA 600 or equivalent), a lead hollow cathode lamp (Perkin-Elmer or equivalent) with argon as the carrier gas.

Follow the manufacturer's directions for setting the appropriate instrument parameters for lead determination. (NOTE: Use reagent-grade chemicals with as low a lead content as practicable, as well as high-purity water and gases.) Prior to this analysis, rinse all glassware and plasticware twice with 10% nitric acid and twice with 10% hydrochloric acid. Then rinse thoroughly with high-purity water, preferably obtained from a mixed-bed strong acid/strong base ion-exchange cartridge capable of producing water with an electrical resistivity of 12 to 15 megohms.

III. Solutions:

Hydrogen Peroxide-Nitric Acid Solution: Mix together equal volumes of 10% hydrogen peroxide and 10% nitric acid (NOTE: use extreme caution; gloves and protective eyeware).

Butanol-Nitric Acid Solution: Introduce approximately 500 ml of n-butanol in a 1000-ml volumetric flask. Slowly add 50 ml nitric acid. Dilute to volume with n-butanol and mix.

Lead Nitrate Stock Solution: Using glassware that is free of lead salts, dissolve 159.8 mg of reagent-grade lead nitrate in 100 ml of Hydrogen Peroxide-Nitric Acid Solution. Dilute to 1000.0 ml with Hydrogen Peroxide-Nitric Acid Solution and mix. Each ml of this solution contains the equivalent of 100 µg of lead ion.

Standard Lead Solution. On the day of use, pipet 10.0 ml of Lead Nitrate Stock Solution into a 100.0 ml volumetric flask, add Hydrogen Peroxide-Nitric Acid Solution to the mark and mix. Each ml of Standard Lead Solution contains the equivalent of 10 µg of lead ion.

Standard Solutions. Into separate 100-ml volumetric flasks, pipet 0.2, 0.5, 1, and 2 ml, respectively, of Standard Lead Solution; dilute to volume with Butanol-Nitric Acid Solution. These solutions contain 0.02, 0.05, 0.1, and 0.2 µg lead per ml, respectively.

Sample Solution. (NOTE: Perform this procedure in a fume hood). Accurately weigh 1 g of the sample, and transfer to a large test tube. Add 1 ml of nitric acid. Place the test tube in a rack in a boiling water bath. As soon as the rusty tint (reddish-brown colour) is gone, add 1 ml of 30% hydrogen peroxide dropwise (in order to avoid a vigorous reaction) and wait for bubbles to form. Stir with an acid-washed plastic spatula if necessary. Remove the test tube from the water bath and let it cool. Transfer the solution to a 10-ml volumetric flask and dilute to volume with Butanol-Nitric Acid Solution. Use this solution for analysis.

Tungsten Solution. Transfer 0.1 g of tungstic acid (H_2WO_4) and 5 g of sodium hydroxide pellets into a 50-ml plastic bottle. Add 5.0 ml of high-purity water (distilled water may be redistilled from an all-glass apparatus or may be passed down a column of cation exchange resin, e.g., Amberlite IR 120(H)), and mix. Heat the mixture in a hot water bath until completely dissolved. Cool, and store at room temperature.

IV. Procedure:

Place the graphite tube in the furnace. Inject a 20-µl aliquot of Tungsten Solution into the graphite tube, using a 300-ml/min argon flow and the following sequence of conditions: dry at 110° for 20 sec, char at 700° to 900° for 20 sec, and, with the argon flow stopped, atomize at 2700° for 10 sec; repeat again using a second 20-µl aliquot. Clean the quartz windows.

(NOTE: The sample injection technique is the most crucial step in controlling the precision of the analysis; the volume of the sample must remain constant. Rinse the µl pipet tip (Eppendorf or equivalent) three times with either the Standard Solutions or Sample Solution before injection. Use a fresh pipet tip for each injection, and start the atomization process immediately after injecting the sample. Between injections, flush the graphite tube to eliminate any residual lead by purging at a high temperature as recommended by the manufacturer.)

With the hollow cathode lamp aligned for maximum absorbance, and the wavelength set at 283.3 nm, atomize 20-µl aliquots of the four Standard Solutions, using a 300-ml/min argon flow and the following sequence of conditions: dry at 110° for 30 sec (20 sec ramp period and 10 sec hold time), char at 700° for 42 sec (20 sec ramp period and 22 sec hold time), and, with the argon flow stopped, atomize at 2300° for 7 sec.

Plot a standard curve of concentration, in μg/ml, of each Standard Solution versus its maximum absorbance value compensated for background correction, as directed for the particular instrument. Atomize 20 μl of the Sample Solution under conditions identical to those for the Standard Solution, and measure its background-corrected maximum absorbance. From the standard curve, determine the concentration of lead in the Sample Solution, C, in μg/ml, Calculate the concentration of lead in the Salatrim sample, in mg/kg, using:

10C/W

where

W is the mass, in g, of the sample

Peroxide value

Reagents:

-Acetic acid-chloroform solution: Mix 3 volumes of acetic acid with 2 volumes of chloroform.
- Potassium iodide solution, saturated: Dissolve excess potassium iodide in freshly boiled water. Excess solid must remain. Store in the dark. Test daily by adding 0.5 ml to 30 ml of the acetic acid-chloroform solution, then add 2 drops of starch TS. If the solution turns blue, requiring more than 1 drop of 0.1 N sodium thiosulfate to discharge the colour, prepare a fresh solution.

Procedure:

Weigh accurately about 5 g of the sample into a 250-ml Erlenmeyer flask. Add 30 ml of the acetic acid-chloroform solution and swirl to dissolve. Add 0.5 ml of the saturated potassium iodide solution, allow to stand with occasional shaking for 1 min, and add 30 ml of water. Slowly titrate with 0.01 N sodium thiosulfate with vigorous shaking until the yellow colour is almost gone. Add about 0.5 ml of starch TS, and continue the titration, shaking the flask vigorously to release all the iodine from the chloroform layer, until the blue colour disappears.

Perform a blank determination and make any necessary correction.

$$\text{Peroxide value} = \frac{S \times N \times 1000}{W}$$

where

S = ml of N sodium thiosulfate
N = normality of sodium thiosulfate
W = weight of the sample (g)

Unsaponifiable matter   Maxwell, R.J., Reimann, K.A., and Percell, K. (1981) Determination of the Unsaponifiable Matter in Fatty Acids by a Rapid Column Method, JAOCS 58:1002-1004.

I. Reagents:

Calcium Chloride-Celite Mixture: Using a mortar and pestle, grind 1 part anhydrous calcium chloride with 1 part water; add 3 parts Celite 545 (grade: not acid-washed, C-212). Grind to a uniform consistency. The mixture may be stored in a covered amber jar for up to one month.

Potassium Hydroxide-Celite Mixture: For multiple analyses, prepare in lots of 75 g or more. Using a mortar and pestle, grind 2 parts potassium hydroxide pellets with 1 part water (CAUTION: considerable heat is generated; wear eye protection and gloves); add 4 parts Celite 545. Grind to uniform consistency. The mixture may be stored in a covered amber jar for up to 10 days.

II. Procedure:

Saponification: Place 10 g Potassium Hydroxide-Celite mixture in a 400-ml mortar; accurately weigh 5 g of sample (W_S) and transfer to the mortar. Grind the mixture until the sample is uniformly distributed. Add another 10 g of Potassium Hydroxide-Celite mixture; grind to uniform consistency. Transfer the mixture to a jar. Transfer any residual sample by sweeping 5 g Celite 545 along the sides of the mortar with the pestle and into the jar. Shake until the mixture is uniform. Heat for 20-30 min in a 130° oven.

Gravimetric Extraction: Transfer the cooled mixture to the mortar; regrind (approximately 30 s) to a uniform granular consistency. Loosely fit a plug of glass wool into the tip of a glass chromatography column (30 mm i.d.; 30 cm long overall, with a drip tip 5 cm x 8 mm o.d.). Pack the column with 5 g of Calcium Chloride-Celite mixture. Transfer the contents of the mortar to the column. Pack to a total bed height of 50-60 mm. Place a 150-ml tared flask under the column. Qualitatively transfer residue from the mortar to the column with about 25 ml dichloromethane. Once this solution has percolated into the column bed, add sufficient dichloromethane so that the column bed is wet and a few drops of eluate have been collected in the flask. Charge the column with 150 ml dichloromethane, and collect the entire volume in the flask (approximately 25 min). Remove the solvent under a stream of nitrogen with gentle heating while the eluate is being collected. Take the contents of the flask to constant weight under vacuum. Determine the weight of the residue (W_R).

To check for completeness of extraction, add 20 ml dichloromethane to the column and collect in a second tared flask. Evaporate the contents of the second flask to dryness, and examine for residue. Determine the weight of the residue (W_{R1}), if present. If residue is observed, repeat the procedure with an additional 20 ml of dichloromethane.

The total residue weight and the weight of the original sample are used to calculate the percent unsaponifiable matter:

$$[(W_R + W_{R1} + ...)/W_S] \times 100$$

METHOD OF ASSAY   Characterization of Triacylglycerols in Saturated Lipid Mixtures with Application to Salatrim 23CA (Huang *et al*, J. Agric. Food Chem., (1994) 42, 453).

I. DETERMINATION OF MONOACYLGLYCERIDE AND TRIACYLGLYCERIDE CONTENT

A. Principle

This method permits the quantitation of monoglycerides (MAG) with one LCFA, and triglycerides (TAG) with the same acyl carbon number (ACN) in Salatrim by high-temperature capillary gas chromatography (HTCGC). (The ACN is the sum of the number of carbons of each carboxylic acid sidechain of each TAG. (e.g., the ACN for tristearin is 54 (i.e., 3 x 18); the ACNs for both dipropionylstearoylglycerol and diacetylarachidoylglycerol are 24 (i.e., [(2 x 3) + 18] and [(2 x 2) + 20], respectively). MAG and TAG are identified by comparison with standards. The weight percent of each MAG and TAG in Salatrim is determined from the peak areas and calibration curves constructed from data from analyses of standard solutions.

B. Materials

MAG Standard: Monopentadecanoin (mono-C15) and monostearin (mono-C18); purity: 99% minimum (available from Nu Check Prep., Inc., Elysian, MN, USA).

TAG Standards: Tricaproin (tri-C6), triheptanoin (tri-C7), tricaprylin (tri-C8), trinonanoin (tri-C9), tricaprin (tri-C10), triundecanoin (tri-C11), trilaurin (tri-C12), tritridecanoin (tri-C13), trimyristin (tri-C14), tripentadecanoin (tri-C15), tripalmitin (tri-C16), triheptadecanoin (tri-C17), and tristearin (tri-C18); purity: 99% minimum (available from Nu Check Prep., Inc., Elysian, MN, USA).

C. Sample Preparation

Internal Standard Stock Solution: Dissolve 200 mg tri-C11 in 2 litres of undecane/toluene (95/5, v/v; spectroscopic grade).

Standard Solutions:

Standard Solution (Group 1): To each of 22 10-ml volumetric flasks, add the thirteen TAG Standards so that each flask, respectively, will contain 1600, 800, 400, 200, 100, 50, 32, 25, 20, 18, 16, 14, 12, 10, 9, 8, 7, 6, 5, 4, 3, and 2 mg/l of each TAG when filled to the mark with the Internal Standard Stock Solution (tri-Cll; 100 mg/l).

Standard Solution (Group 2): To each of 7 10-ml volumetric flasks, add the two MAG Standards so that each flask, respectively, will contain 500, 250, 125, 62.5, 31, 15.6, and 7.8 mg/l of each MAG when filled to the mark with the Internal Standard Stock Solution (tri-C11; 100 mg/l).

Salatrim Solution: Accurately weigh 2 g Salatrim into a 1-L volumetric flask. Dilute to volume with Internal Standard Stock Solution.

D. Procedure

1. Instrumentation and Analysis Parameters

Instrument: Hewlett-Packard 5890 Series II GC equipped with flame-ionization detector (FID), pressure programmable on-column injector, HF 7673 auto-sampler, and HP Series II integrator; or equivalent.

GC Column: Chrompack SIM-DIST CB fused-silica column (Chrompack Inc., Raritan, NJ, USA) 5 m x 0.32 mm i.d.; 0.1 μm film thickness, or equivalent. A deactivated fused-silica pre-column (0.5 m x 0.53 mm i.d.) coupled to the analytical column via a butt connector (Quadrex Corp., New Haven, CT, USA) or equivalent.

Oven temperature: 140° to 350° at 10°/min; total run time 21.0 min. Injector temperature: Track mode "ON" (injector temperature follows the oven temperature conditions).

Injection Mode: On-column injection.
Sample Size: Inject 0.5 μl.
FID Temperature: 375°.
Flow Rate: Hydrogen gas constant flow mode "ON"; pressure: 5.5 psi (140°).

2. Quantitation of MAG

a. Calibration Curve and Response Factor (RF) Determination for Mono-C15 and Mono-C18.

Analyze each of the Standard Solutions of Group 2 using a sample injection volume of 0.5 μl. From each chromatogram, establish the response factors (RF_i) for the two MAG using the following formula:

$$RF_i = (C_{IS}/C_i) \times (A_i/A_{IS})$$

where A_{IS} is the peak area of the Internal Standard (tri-C11); A_i is the peak area of a MAG; C_{IS} is the concentration of the Internal Standard (100 mg/l); and C_i is the concentration (mg/l) of a MAG.

For each MAG, construct a calibration curve by plotting the peak area ratios of (A_i/A_{IS}) (x-axis) versus the RF_i (y-axis) for each solution.

b. Weight Percent of MAG

Analyze the Salatrim sample using a sample injection of 0.5 μl. From the chromatograms, obtain the peak area of each MAG (A_i), and of the Internal Standard (A_{IS}). Example chromatograms of Salatrim are provided in the Appendix to this monograph. Calculate the peak area ratio (A_i/A_{IS}) and determine the RF for each MAG (RF_i) from the calibration curve. The concentration (μg/ml) of each MAG (C_i) in the Salatrim sample is:

$$C_i = (C_{IS}/RF_i) \times (A_i/A_{IS})$$

where C_{IS} is the concentration of the Internal Standard (tri-C11; 100 mg/l). The weight percent of each MAG in the Salatrim sample ($(W\%)_i$) is:

$$(W\%)_i = (C_i/C_T) \times 100$$

where C_T is the concentration of Salatrim Solution (2000 mg/l). The total weight percent of MAG in the Salatrim sample is:

$$\Sigma_i (W\%)_i.$$

3. Quantitation of TAG with the Same ACN

a. Determination of RF for TAG Standards

Analyze each of the Standard Solutions of Group 1 using a sample injection volume of 0.5 μl. The RF for each TAG standard, j, is:

$$RF_{n,j} = (C_{IS}/C_{n,j}) \times (A_{n,j}/A_{IS})$$

where A_{IS} is the peak area of the Internal Standard; $A_{n,j}$ is the peak area of the TAG standard with ACN = n (where n = 18-54 and the ACN of the TAG standards is as follows: tri-C6, 18; tri-C7, 21; tri-C8, 24; tri-C9, 27; tri-C10, 30; tri-C11, 33; tri-C12, 36; tri-C13, 39; tri-C14, 42; tri-C15, 45; tri-C16, 48; tri-C-17, 51; and tri-C18, 54) and concentration $C_{n,j}$ (mg/l); C_{IS} is the concentration of the Internal Standard (100 mg/l).

The relative peak area of each TAG standard with ACN = n and concentration $C_{n,j}$ to that of the Internal Standard is given by:

$$RA_{n,j} = A_{n,j}/A_{IS}$$

The RF and relative peak areas for each TAG with ACN = (n + 1) and with ACN = (n + 2) are calculated from the measured RF and RA values for TAG standards with ACN = n and (n + 3) at the same concentration, $C_{n,j}$, according to the following:

$$RF_{n+1,j} = RF_{n,j} + (RF_{n+3,j} - RF_{n,j}) \times 1/3$$
$$RA_{n+1,j} = RA_{n,j} + (RA_{n+3,j} - RA_{n,j}) \times 1/3$$
$$RF_{n+2,j} = RF_{n,j} + (RF_{n+3,j} - RF_{n,j}) \times 2/3$$
$$RA_{n+2,j} = RA_{n,j} + (RA_{n+3,j} - RA_{n,j}) \times 2/3$$

b. Determination of RF for Salatrim

For the Salatrim Sample, the RF for the TAG with a relative peak area $RA_{n,j}$ is calculated from:

$$RF_{n,j} = RF_{n,j-1} + (RF_{n,j+1} - RF_{n,j-1}) \times [(RA_{n,j} - RA_{n,j-1})/(RA_{n,j+1} - RA_{n,j-1})]$$

where $RF_{n,j+1}$ and $RF_{n,j-1}$ are the RFs, and $RA_{n,j+1}$ and $RA_{n,j-1}$ are the relative peak areas, respectively, of the TAG standard with the same ACN value. $RA_{n,j+1}$ and $RA_{n,j-1}$ must meet the following condition:

$$RA_{n,j-1} \leq RA_{n,j} < RA_{n,j+1}$$

where $RA_{n,j}$ is the ratio of the peak area of the TAG in Salatrim with ACN = n, ($A_{n,j}$), to the peak area for the Internal Standard (A_{IS}). (NOTE: The notation "j+1", "j", and "j-1" denotes consecutive concentration values in the series of standard solutions. For example, for a TAG standard with ACN = n and concentrations of 100, 200, and 400 mg/L, the relative peak areas $RA_{n,j+1}$ and $RA_{n,j-1}$ correspond to data for standards with concentrations of 400 mg/l and 100 mg/l, respectively)

c. Weight Percent Determination of Salatrim TAG Components

The concentration (mg/l) of TAG in the Salatrim Sample with ACN = n is given by

$$C_{n,j} = (C_{IS}/RF_{n,j}) \times (A_{n,j}/A_{IS})$$

where C_{IS} is the concentration of the Internal Standard (tri-C11; 100 mg/l).

The weight percent of TAG with ACN = n in Salatrim is:

$$(W\%)_n = (C_{n,j}/C_T) \times 100$$

where C_T is the concentration of the Salatrim sample (2000 mg/l).

The total weight percent of TAG in the Salatrim sample is:

$$\Sigma_n (W\%)_n.$$

II. DETERMINATION OF THE SCFA/LCFA MOLE RATIO

Either of the two methods given below may be used.

METHOD I

A. Principle: Triglycerides are converted to fatty acid butyl esters and determined by capillary column FID gas chromatography.

B. Apparatus: Gas chromatograph with FID (Hewlett Packard HP 5890 capillary columns, equipped with 5 µl syringe for 0.32 mm i.d. columns. Automatic sampler (HP 7673, or equivalent). Chromatographic data system or integrator (HP 3365 Series II software, or equivalent). Retention gap, deactivated fused silica, 1 mm x 0.32 mm i.d. with capillary column connectors. DB 5-HT, 15 m x 0.32 mm i.d. fused silica capillary column (J&W Scientific, Inc., 91 Blue Ravine Road, Folsom, California 95630-4714, USA; catalog no. 123-5711 or equivalent). Crimp caps and vials (HP 5181-3375, or equivalent) for on-line autosampler.

C. Reagents: Sodium butoxide (50% in butanol); hexane (HPLC grade, 95%); hydrochloric acid (0.5 N volumetric standard); butyl butyrate (98%); n-butyl acetate (99%); butyl propionate; butyl palmitate; butyl stearate (93%); 1-butanol (anhydrous, 99%).

D. Solutions:

0.5 N Sodium Butoxide: Transfer 9.62 g of 50% sodium butoxide solution into a 100-ml volumetric flask, dilute to the mark with 1-butanol, and mix.

Standard Reference Solution: Weigh accurately approximately 50 mg of each butyl ester standard (5 standards) into a single 100-ml volumetric flask. Dilute to volume with hexane and mix. More than one Standard Reference Solution may be necessary if impurities co-elute with standard peaks. (NOTE: Melt butyl stearate standard before sampling.)

Sample Solution: Weigh accurately approximately 50 mg of Salatrim (melt, sample is solid) into a 100-ml volumetric flask. Dilute to volume with hexane and mix.

Butyl Ester Conversion: For each sample to be assayed (hexane blank, Standard Reference Solutions, Sample Solutions), pipet 5.0 ml of solution into a clean 2 dram (8 ml) clear glass vial. Add 0.5 ml of 0.5 N Sodium Butoxide, seal and shake vigorously (solution will turn yellow). Allow the solution to stand for 2 minutes (for hexane blank and Sample Solutions, only); then, neutralize by pipetting 1.0 ml of 0.5 N hydrochloric acid into the solution. Seal and shake well until the solution is clear. Check pH with pH paper. The solution should be acidic. If it is not, the column will degrade. (NOTE: For the Standard Reference Solution, 1-butanol and water may be substituted for 0.5 N Sodium Butoxide and 0.5 N hydrochloric acid, respectively.)

E. Chromatography

-Carrier gas/flow:	Helium/2.0 psi (constant flow)
-Injection volume:	0.5 μl
-Injection temperature:	Temp. track mode (3° above oven temp.)
-Oven temperature:	40° (6 min), 15°/min to 280° (5 min)
-Detector temperature:	380°

Allow the butyl ester sample phases to separate (centrifugation may be used to hasten the separation). Transfer approximately 1 ml of the hexane layer into an autosampler vial. Run the gas chromatography program.

F. Calculations

Response Factors for Butyl Ester Standards (RF_i):

$$RF_i = A_i/(W_i \times (\%purity)_i/100)$$

where A_i is the average peak area counts for the ith standard; W_i is the weight (μg) of the ith standard in the reference solution; and (% purity)$_i$ is the purity of the ith standard expressed as a percentage.

Weights of Butyl Esters in the Sample:

$$W_i = A_i/RF_i$$

where W_i is the weight (µg) of the ith ester in the sample; A_i is the peak area counts for the ith ester in the sample; RF_i is the response factor for the ith ester standard (average area counts/µg).

Weights of Fatty Acids in the Sample:

$$(W_i)_{fatty\ acid} = (W_i)_{butyl\ ester} \times (MW_i)_{fatty\ acid}/(MW_i)_{butyl\ ester}$$

where $(W_i)_{fatty\ acid}$ and $(W_i)_{butyl\ ester}$ are, respectively, the weights (µg) of the ith fatty acid and its butyl ester in the sample; and $(MW_i)_{fatty\ acid}$ and $(MW_i)_{butyl\ ester}$ are their respective molecular weights.

Calculation of Short/Long (S/L) Mole Ratio:

$$(mmoles_i)_{fatty\ acid} = (W_i)_{fatty\ acid}/ (1000x(MW_i)_{fatty\ acid})$$

$$S/L\ mole\ ratio = \Sigma_i\ (mmoles_i)_{SCFA}/\Sigma_i\ (mmoles_i)_{LCFA}$$

where $(W_i)_{fatty\ acid}$ is in µg, (MW_i) is in mg/mmole, and $\Sigma_i(mmoles_i)_{SCFA}$ and $\Sigma_i\ (mmoles_i)_{LCFA}$ are the respective sums of the millimoles of the short chain fatty acids (C_2 - C_4) and the long chain fatty acids (C_{14} -C_{18}).

METHOD II

1. Principle: Fatty acid residues are identified using proton nuclear magnetic resonance spectrometry.

2. Apparatus: A nuclear magnetic resonance spectrometer (e.g., Varian VXR-300 or equivalent).

3. Reagents: Deuterated chloroform.

4. Sample Solutions: Place a small amount of cotton in a Pasteur pipet and pack it down. Place this pipet in an NMR tube. Place 10 mg of sample in a clean 2 dram (8 ml) vial. Add deuterated chloroform to a height of about 1 cm and dissolve the sample completely. Pass the sample solution through the Pasteur pipet filter into the NMR tube so that the height of the sample solution reaches the bottom of the pitet. Remove the pipet and cap the tube.

5. Procedure:

Instrument settings: Delay time, 10 s; number of transients, 16; sweep width, 5000 Hz; transmitter nucleus, H1; acquisition time, 3.74 sec.

Operating parameters: Place the NMR sample tube into the magnet and maintain spinning at 20 Hz. Obtain the deuterium lock frequency by adjusting the 20 shim gradient. Obtain the homogeneous magnetic environment for the sample by adjusting the Z1, Z2, Z3, and Z4 gradients. Obtain the proton spectrum. Phase the data and integrate the following peaks:

	ppm	Values
-CH₃ (stearate/LCFA)	-0.90	D=stearate/LCFA methyl integral
-CH₃ (butyrate)	-0.95	C=butyrate methyl integral
-CH₃ (propionate)	-1.15	B=propionate methyl integral
-CH₃ (acetate)	-2.00	A=acetate methyl integral
		E=total integrals (A+B+C+D)

Mole Ratio of Short Chain to Long Chain Fatty Acids (S/L) = (A+B+C)/D

APPENDIX

Representative infrared absorption spectrum: Salatrim

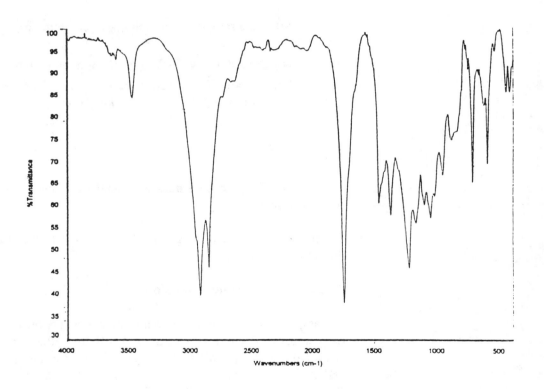

METHOD OF ASSAY

A) Representative HTCGC chromatograms of Salatrim (approximately 2000 mg/l). From top to bottom:

Salatrim derived from tributyrin, tripropionin, and hydrogenated soybean oil - 54% dibutyrylstearoylglycerol (ACN 26); 12% butyryldistearoylglycerol (ACN 40); 8.5% butyrylpropionylstearoylglycerol (ACN 25); 7.3% dibutyrylpalmitoylglycerol (ACN 24); 5.1% butyrylstearoylglycerol (ACN 22); and 4.4% butyrylpalmitoylstearoylglycerol (ACN 38). Note: The percentages are only representative and will vary from batch to batch.

Salatrim derived from triacetin, tripropionin, and hydrogenated soybean oil - 60% diacetylstearoylglycerol (ACN 22); 11% acetylpropionylstearoylglycerol (ACN 23); 9.2% acetyldistearoylglycerol (ACN 38); 6.8% diacetylpalmitoyiglycerol (ACN 20); and 2.3% acetylstearoylglycerol (ACN 20). Note: The percentages are only representative and will vary from batch to batch.

Salatrim derived from tributyrin and hydrogenated soybean oil - 86% dibutyrylstearoylglycerol (ACN 26); 10% dibutyrylpalmitoylglycerol (ACN 24); and 1.9% butyrylstearoylglycerol (ACN 22). Note: The percentages are only representative and will vary from batch to batch.

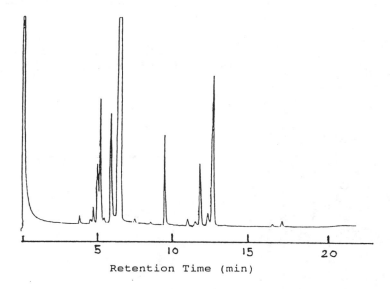

Retention Time (min)

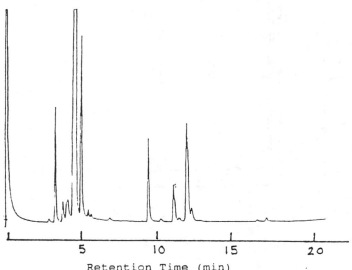

Retention Time (min)

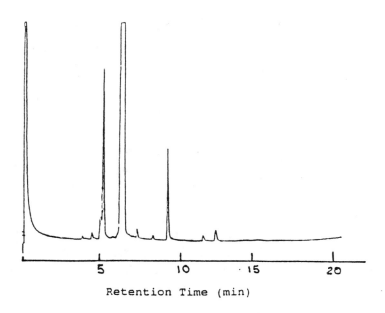

Retention Time (min)

B) Representative capillary gas chromatograms of butyl esters of Salatrim fatty acids for determination of SCFA/LCFA mole ratio.

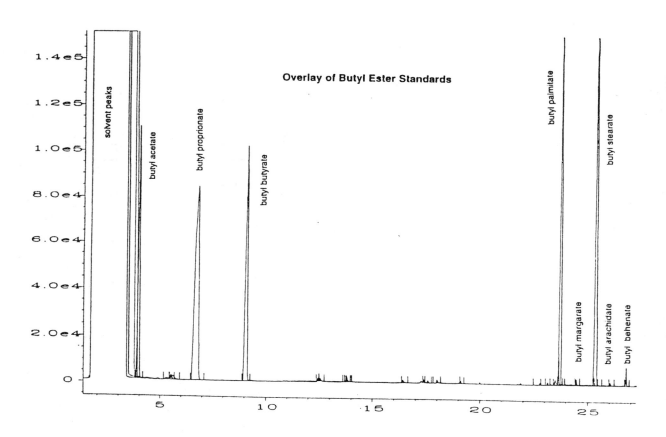

SODIUM ALGINATE

Prepared at the 49th JECFA (1997)
superseding specifications prepared at the 44th JECFA (1995),
published in FNP 52 Addendum 3 (1995)

SYNONYMS   INS No. 401

DEFINITION   Sodium alginate is the sodium salt of alginic acid.

C.A.S. number   9005-38-3

Chemical formula $(C_6H_7NaO_6)_n$

Structural formula   Structural formula from Phillips, Wedlock and Williams: Gums and Stabilizers for the Food Industry 5 (1990) by permission of Oxford University Press.

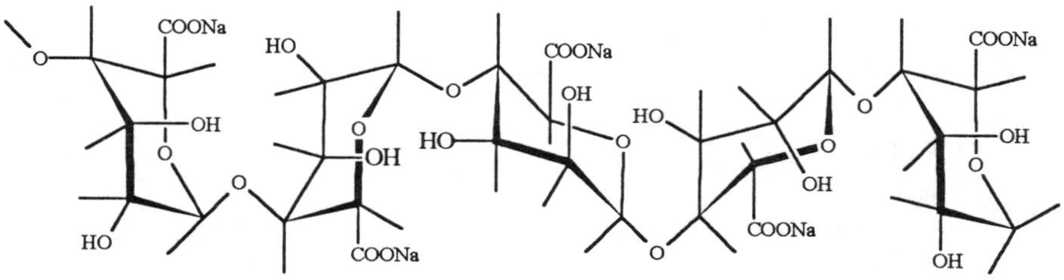

$$\underline{\quad\quad} G({}^1C_4) \underline{\quad\quad} G({}^1C_4) \underline{\quad\quad} M({}^4C_1) \underline{\quad\quad} M({}^4C_1) \underline{\quad\quad} G$$

$$\alpha\text{-}1,4 \quad\quad\quad \alpha\text{-}1,4 \quad\quad\quad \beta\text{-}1,4 \quad\quad\quad \beta\text{-}1,4$$

The number and sequence of the Mannuronate and Glucuronate residues shown above vary in the naturally occurring alginate. The water molecules associated with the alginate molecule are not shown in the above structural formula.

Formula weight   Structural unit :   198.11 (theoretical)
                                         222 (actual average)
                       Macromolecule :   10,000 - 600,000 (typical average)

Assay   Yields, on the dried basis, not less than 18.0% and not more than 21.0% of carbon dioxide (CO_2), equivalent to not less than 90.8% and not more than 106.0% of sodium alginate $(C_6H_7NaO_6)_n$.

DESCRIPTION   Occurs as white to yellowish brown filamentous, grainy, granular or powdered forms

FUNCTIONAL USES   Stabilizer, thickener, gelling agent, emulsifier

CHARACTERISTICS

IDENTIFICATION

Solubility   Dissolves slowly in water, forming a viscous solution; insoluble in ethanol and ether

Precipitate formation with calcium chloride
                                                       Passes test
                                                       See description under TESTS

Precipitate formation with ammonium sulphate
                                                       Passes test
                                                       See description under TESTS

Test for alginate   Passes test
                                                       See description under TESTS

Sodium   Passes test

PURITY

Loss on drying   Not more than 15% (105°, 4 h)

Water-insoluble matter   Not more than 2% on the dried basis
                                                       See description under TESTS

Arsenic   Not more than 3 mg/kg (Method II)

Lead   Not more than 5 mg/kg
                                                       Prepare a sample solution as directed for organic compounds in the Limit
                                                       Test, using 5 µg of lead ion (Pb) in the control.

Microbiological criteria   Total plate count: Not more than 5,000 colonies per gram.

                                                       Initially prepare a 10^{-1} dilution by adding a 50 g sample to 450 ml of
                                                       Butterfield's phosphate buffered dilution water and homogenizing in a high
                                                       speed blender.

                                                       Yeasts and moulds: Not more than 500 colonies per gram

                                                       Coliforms: Negative by test

                                                       Salmonella: Negative by test

TESTS

IDENTIFICATION TESTS

Precipitate formation with calcium chloride
                                                       To a 0.5% solution of the sample in sodium hydroxide TS add one-fifth of its
                                                       volume of a 2.5% solution of calcium chloride. A voluminous, gelatinous

precipitate is formed. This test distinguishes sodium alginate from gum arabic, sodium carboxymethyl cellulose, carrageenan, gelatin, gum ghatti, karaya gum, carob bean gum, methyl cellulose and tragacanth gum.

Precipitate formation with ammonium sulphate

To a 0.5% solution of the sample in sodium hydroxide TS add one-half of its volume of a saturated solution of ammonium sulfate. No precipitate is formed. This test distinguishes sodium alginate from agar, sodium carboxymethyl cellulose, carrageenan, de-esterified pectin, gelatin, carob bean gum, methyl cellulose and starch.

Test for alginate

Moisten 1-5 mg of the sample with water and add 1 ml of acid ferric sulfate TS. Within 5 min, a cherry-red colour develops that finally becomes deep purple.

PURITY TESTS

Water-insoluble matter

Disperse 2 g of the sample, weighed to the nearest 0.1 mg, in 800 ml of water in a 2,000-ml flask. Neutralize to pH 7 with sodium hydroxide TS and then add 3 ml in excess. Add 40 ml of hydrogen peroxide solution containing 30% by weight H_2O_2, cover the flask and boil for 1 h with frequent stirring. Filter while hot through a tared Gooch crucible provided with a glass fibre filter (2.4 cm, No 934 AH, Reeve Angel & Co, Clifton, N.Y.,USA, or equivalent). If slow filtration is caused by high viscosity of the sample solution, boil until the viscosity is reduced enough to permit filtration. Wash the crucible thoroughly with hot water, dry the crucible and its contents at 105° for 1 h, cool and weigh. Calculate as percentage of the dry weight.

METHOD OF ASSAY

Proceed as directed under Carbon Dioxide Determination by Decarboxylation in the *General Methods*. Each ml of 0.25 N sodium hydroxide consumed is equivalent to 5.5 mg of carbon dioxide (CO_2) or 27.75 mg of sodium alginate (equivalent weight 222).

TENTATIVE

SODIUM CARBOXYMETHYL CELLULOSE, ENZYMATICALLY HYDROLYZED

Prepared at the 49th JECFA (1997)

Information required on the physical state of the substance as manufactured, on tests which distinguish the substance from sodium carboxymethyl cellulose, and on the nature and proportion of low molecular weight material present in the substance.

SYNONYMS   Enzymatically hydrolyzed carboxymethyl cellulose, CMC-ENZ, INS No. 469

DEFINITION   The product is the sodium salt of a carboxymethyl ether of cellulose, which has been partially hydrolyzed by enzymatic treatment with food-grade *Trichoderma reesei* cellulase.

Chemical names   Carboxymethyl cellulose, sodium, partially enzymatically hydrolyzed

Chemical formula   Sodium salts of polymers containing substituted anhydroglucose units with the general formula:

$$[C_6H_7O_2(OH)_x(OCH_2COONa)_y]_n$$

where n is the degree of polymerization
$x = 1.50$ to 2.80
$y = 0.20$ to 1.50
$x + y = 3.0$
(y = degree of substitution)

Structural formula

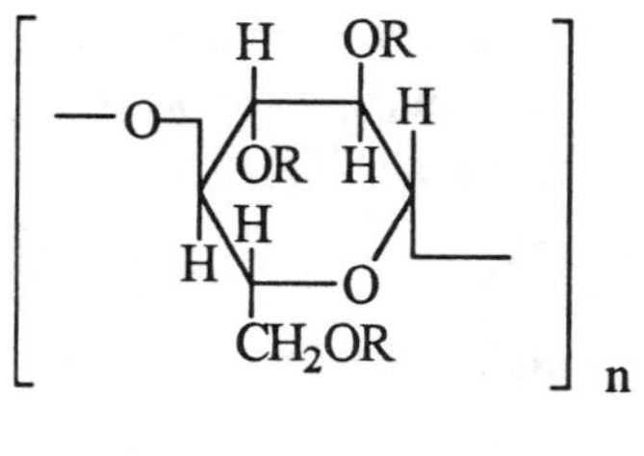

where R = H, CH_2COONa or CH_2COOH

Formula weight   178.14 where $y = 0.20$
282.18 where $y = 1.50$
800 (n about 4) (macromolecules)

Assay   Not less than 99.5%, including mono- and disaccharides, on the dried basis

DESCRIPTION   White or slightly yellowish or greyish, odourless, slightly hygroscopic granular or fibrous powder, or an amber, odourless syrup

FUNCTIONAL USES   Carrier, glazing agent, stabilizer, thickener

CHARACTERISTICS

IDENTIFICATION

Solubility	Freely soluble in water, insoluble in ethanol
Foam test	Passes test See description under TESTS
Precipitate formation	Passes test See description under TESTS
Colour reaction	Passes test See description under TESTS
Viscosity (60% solids)	Not less than 2500 mPas corresponding to an average molecular weight of 5000 D See description under TESTS

PURITY

Loss on drying	Not more than 12% ($105°$ to constant weight)
pH	Not less than 6.0 and not more than 8.5 (1 in 100 solution)
Sodium chloride and sodium glycolate	Not more than 0.5%, singly or in combination See descriptions under TESTS
Degree of substitution	Not less than 0.2 and not more than 1.50 carboxymethyl groups (CH_2COOH) per anhydroglucose unit on the dried basis See description under TESTS
Residual enzyme activity	Passes test See description under TESTS
Lead	Not more than 3 mg/kg Prepare a sample solution as directed for organic compound in the Limit Test and determine the lead content by atomic absorption spectrometry

TESTS

IDENTIFICATION TESTS

Foam test	Vigorously shake a 0.1% solution of the sample. No layer of foam appears. This test distinguishes sodium carboxymethyl cellulose, whether hydrolysed or not, from other cellulose ethers and from alginates and natural gums.
Precipitate formation	To 5 ml of an 0.5% solution of the sample add 5 ml of a 5% solution of copper sulfate or of aluminium sulfate. A precipitate appears. This test distinguishes sodium carboxymethyl cellulose, whether hydrolysed or not, from other cellulose ethers, and from gelatine, carob bean gum and tragacanth gum.

Colour reaction	Add 0.5 g of the powdered sample to 50 ml of water, while stirring to produce a uniform dispersion. Continue the stirring until a clear solution is produced. Dilute 1 ml of the solution with 1 ml of water in a small test tube. Add 5 drops of 1-naphthol TS. Incline the tube, and carefully introduce down the side of the tube 2 ml of sulphuric acid so that it forms a lower layer. A red-purple colour develops at the interface.
Viscosity (60% solids)	To 40 ml of water, add 60 g of the sample, stirring continuously. To ensure the formation of a clear solution without air bubbles, leave the solution to stand in a refrigerator (+4°) for several hours. Using a Bohlin viscometer or an equivalent instrument, measure the viscosity of the solution at 25° using a shear rate of 147 sec^{-1}.

PURITY TESTS

Sodium chloride	Heat 5 g of the sample, weighed to the nearest 0.1 mg, in a platinum or porcelain crucible, first with a small flame so that the sample does not ignite and then, when the charring is complete, heat further in an electric oven for 15 min at about 500°. After cooling, pulverize the ashes thus obtained and extract several times with warm water. Filter the extracts into a 500-ml volumetric flask, acidify with nitric acid and dilute to the mark with water. Determine the NaCl content of 100 ml of this extract by the method of Volhard, using 0.2 N silver nitrate and 0.02 N ammonium thiocyanate. Each ml of 0.02 N silver nitrate is equivalent to 1.169 mg of NaCl. Calculate the sodium chloride content by the formula:

$$\% \, NaCl \; = \; [(a \times 0.001169 \times 5)/b] \times 100$$

where

a = 0.02 N silver nitrate consumed (ml)
b = dry weight of the sample (g)

Sodium glycolate	Proceed as directed under the method for *Chromatography (High Performance Liquid Chromatography)* using the following conditions and using pure glycolic acid as the reference substance:

Column:	Two cation exchange columns in the H$^+$-form in series, e.g. two Fast Fruit Juice columns, 15 cm x 7.8 mm, Waters, or equivalent
Elution:	Isocratic
Mobile phase:	Aqueous 0.05% phosphoric acid
Flow:	0.5 ml/min
Detector type:	UV or diode array, 205 nm
Sample size:	50 µl of a solution of 200.0 mg of the sample in 20 ml of eluent

Degree of substitution	Weigh accurately about 200 mg of the sample, previously dried at 105° to constant weight, and transfer it into a 250 ml, glass-stoppered Erlenmeyer flask. Add 75 ml of glacial acetic acid, and connect the flask with a water-cooled condenser, and reflux gently on a hot plate for 2 h. Cool, transfer the solution to a 250-ml beaker with the aid of 50 ml of glacial acetic acid, and titrate with 0.1 N

perchloric acid in dioxane while stirring with a magnetic stirrer. Determine the endpoint potentiometrically with a pH meter equipped with a standard glass electrode and a calomel electrode modified as follows: Discard the aqueous potassium chloride solution, rinse and fill with the supernatant liquid obtained by shaking thoroughly 2 g each of potassium chloride and silver chloride (or silver oxide) with 100 ml of methanol, then add a few crystals of potassium chloride and silver chloride (or silver oxide) to the electrode.

Record the ml of 0.1 N perchloric acid versus mV (0 to 700 mV range), and continue the titration to a few ml beyond the endpoint. Plot the titration curve, and read the volume (A), in ml, of 0.1 N perchloric acid at the inflection point.

Calculate the degree of substitution (DS) by the formula

$$(16.2 A/G)/[1.000 - (8.0\ A/G)],$$

where

A = the volume of 0.1 N perchloric acid required (ml)
G = weight of the sample taken (mg)
16.2 = one-tenth of the formula weight of one anhydroglucose unit
8.0 = one-tenth of the formula weight of one sodium carboxymethyl group

Residual enzyme activity

Prepare a 5% solution of sodium carboxymethyl cellulose having a viscosity of 25-50 mPas as a 2% solution. To 20 g of this solution, add 2 g of a 20% aqueous solution of the sample. Using a Bohlin viscometer or an equivalent instrument, follow the viscosity of the mixture for 10 minutes at 25°, using a shear rate of 147 sec^{-1}. No change in viscosity (indicating hydrolysis of the sodium carboxymethyl cellulose), occurs.

As a control, measure the viscosity of 2 g of water and 20 g of the same sodium carboxymethyl cellulose solution.

METHOD OF ASSAY

Calculate the percentage of enzyme treated sodium carboxymethyl cellulose by subtracting from 100 the sum of the percentages of sodium chloride and sodium glycolate, determined separately by the procedures above.

SODIUM PROPIONATE

Prepared at the 49th JECFA (1997)
superseding specifications prepared at the 44th JECFA (1995),
published in FNP 52 Addendum 3 (1995)

SYNONYMS   Sodium propanoate, INS No. 281

DEFINITION

    Chemical name   Sodium propionate

    C.A.S. number   137-40-6

    Chemical formula $C_3H_5NaO_2$

    Structural formula $CH_3CH_2COO^-Na^+$

    Formula weight   96.06

    Assay   Not less than 99.0% on the dried basis

DESCRIPTION   White or colourless, hygroscopic crystals with not more than a faint characteristic odour

FUNCTIONAL USES   Preservative, antimould and antirope agent

CHARACTERISTICS

    IDENTIFICATION

    Solubility   Freely soluble in water, soluble in ethanol

    Positive test for sodium   Passes test

    Positive test for propionate
        Warm the sample with sulfuric acid. The propionic acid evolved may be recognized by its odour.

    Positive test for alkali salt of organic acid
        Ignite the sample at a relatively low temperature. The alkaline residue effervesces with acid.

    PURITY

    Loss on drying   Not more than 4 % (105°, 2 h)

    Water-insoluble matter   Not more than 0.1%
        See description under TESTS

    pH   7.5 - 10.5 (1 in 10 soln)

    Iron   Not more than 50 mg/kg

Test 0.5 g of the sample as described in the Limit Test using 2.5 ml of Iron Standard Solution (25 µg Fe) in the control.

Lead

Not more than 5 mg/kg

Prepare a sample solution as directed for organic compounds in the Limit Test, using 5 µg of lead ion (Pb) in the control.

TESTS

PURITY TESTS

Water-insoluble matter

Weigh 5 g of the sample to the nearest mg, transfer into a 100-ml beaker and add 50 ml of water. Stir until all the sample appears to be completely dissolved. Filter through a Gooch crucible, tared to an accuracy of ± 0.2 mg. Rinse the beaker with 20 ml of water. Dry the crucible with its contents in a 60° oven to constant weight. Cool in a desiccator, weigh, and calculate as percentage.

METHOD OF ASSAY

Weigh, to the nearest mg, 3 g of the sample previously dried at 105° for 1 h, into a distillation flask and add 200 ml of 50% phosphoric acid. Boil for 2 h and collect the distillate. During distillation keep the volume in the flask at about 200 ml by adding water using a dropping funnel. Titrate the distillate with 1N sodium hydroxide using phenolphthalein TS as indicator. Each ml of 1N sodium hydroxide corresponds to 96.06 mg of $C_3H_5NaO_2$.

SUCROGLYCERIDES

Prepared at the 49th JECFA (1997)
superseding specifications prepared at the 27th JECFA (1983),
published in FNP 28 (1983)

SYNONYMS	INS No. 474

DEFINITION   Sucroglycerides are obtained by reacting sucrose with an edible fat or oil with or without the presence of a solvent. They consist of a mixture of mono- and di-esters of sucrose and fatty acids together with mono-, di- and triglycerides from the fat or oil. Only the following solvents may be used in the production: dimethyl formamide, cyclohexane, isobutanol, isopropanol and ethyl acetate.

Assay   Not less than 40% and not more than 60% of sucrose esters

DESCRIPTION   Odourless, soft, solid masses, white to off-white powders, or stiff gels

FUNCTIONAL USES   Emulsifier

CHARACTERISTICS

IDENTIFICATION

Solubility   Insoluble in cold water; soluble in ethanol

Test for fatty acids   Passes test
See description under TESTS

Test for sugar   Passes test
See description under TESTS

PURITY

Sulfated ash   Not more than 2%
Proceed as directed under the test for Ash (Sulfated ash, Method I) using 1 g of the sample

Acid value   Not more than 6

Free sucrose   Not more than 5%
See description under TESTS

Dimethyl formamide   Not more than 1 mg/kg
See description under TESTS

Cyclohexane and isobutanol
Not more than 10 mg/kg, singly or in combination
See description under TESTS

Ethyl acetate and isopropanol

Not more than 350 mg/kg, singly or in combination

Lead

Not more than 10 mg/kg
Prepare a sample solution as described for organic compounds in the Limit Test, using 10 µg of lead ion (Pb) in the control

TESTS

IDENTIFICATION TESTS

Test for fatty acids

Add 1 ml of ethanol to 0.1 g of the sample, dissolve by warming, add 5 ml of dilute sulfuric acid TS, heat in a water bath for 30 min and cool. A yellowish white solid or oil is formed, which is soluble in 3 ml of ether.

Test for sugar

To 2 ml of the solution separated from the solid or oil in the Test for fatty acids add 1 ml of anthrone TS carefully down the inside of the test tube. The boundary surface of the two layers turns to blue or green.

PURITY TESTS

Free sucrose

Determine by *gas liquid chromatography* using the following conditions:

Reagents:
- Internal Standard: 5 mg/ml cholesterol in chloroform or 10 mg/ml tetracosane in chloroform
- Pyridine (dried over molecular sieve)
- N,O-Bis-(Trimethylsilyl)-acetamide (BSA)
- Trimethylchlorosilane (TMCS)

Procedure:
Weigh accurately 20-50 mg of the sample into a silylation vial, add 1 ml internal standard solution, 1 ml pyridine, and 0.5 ml each of BSA and TMCS. Seal vial, and heat at 70° for 30 min. Inject 1 µl into the gas liquid chromatograph.

Conditions:
Column:
- length: 0.3 m
- diameter: 4 mm (i.d.)
- material: glass
- packing: Dexil
Carrier gas: Nitrogen
Flow rate: 40 ml/min
Detector: FID
Temperature programme: Hold for 1 min at 160°, then 160-375° at 15°/min.

Measure peak areas for sucrose and internal standard. The response factor (RF) is calculated from a number of gas liquid chromatography runs with standard solutions of sucrose containing internal standard.

Calculation:

$$RF = \frac{\text{mg of internal standard} \times \text{area sucrose}}{\text{area internal standard} \times \text{mg sucrose}}$$

and

$$\% \text{ free sucrose} = \frac{\text{mg internal standard} \times \text{area sucrose} \times 100}{RF \times \text{area internal standard} \times \text{mg sample}}$$

Dimethyl formamide

Determine by hydrolysis to dimethylamine and analysis by *gas liquid chromatography* using the following conditions:

Reagents:
- Dimethyl formamide
- Dimethylamine hydrochloride
- Methanol
- Ethanol
- Hydrochloric acid
- Sodium hydroxide

Standard solutions:
Prepare 4.47 mg/ml (equivalent to 4.0 mg/ml of dimethyl formamide) stock solution of dimethylamine hydrochloride in ethanol, and prepare standard solutions equivalent to 4, 2 and 1 µg/ml of dimethyl formamide, respectively, by dilution of the stock solution with 0.1% sodium hydroxide solution in ethanol.

Sample preparation:
The apparatus for the hydrolysis is shown in the Appendix. Weigh accurately about 40 g of the sample into a 1000-ml round-bottomed flask. Add 500 ml of 5% methanolic solution of sodium hydroxide, and attach the flask to the apparatus. Set an Erlenmeyer flask containing 10 ml of 1% methanolic solution of hydrochloric acid to the apparatus. Heat the round-bottomed flask and let the content reflux for 1 hour, then distil to collect about 50 ml of the distillate while cooling water of the reflux condenser is stopped. Evaporate the distillate to almost dryness on a boiling water bath. Dissolve the residue with a small amount of ethanol, add 2.5 ml of 5% ethanolic solution of sodium hydroxide, and dilute to 25 ml with ethanol to prepare a sample solution.

Procedure:
Inject 2 µl of the sample solution into the gas liquid chromatograph under the conditions below.

Calibration curve:
Prepare a calibration curve by injecting each 2 µl of the standard solutions into the gas chromatograph.

Conditions:
Column:
- length: 2 m
- diameter: 2 mm (i.d.)
- material: glass
- packing: 10% amine 220 and 10% KOH on 80/100 weak acid washed Chromosorb W
- conditioning: Heat to 130° overnight with 5 ml/min of nitrogen flow rate
Carrier gas: Nitrogen
Flow rate: 17 ml/min
Detector: FID
Temperatures
- injection port: 198±5°
- column: 60°

Calculation:

$$C_{DFA} \ (mg / kg) = \frac{C \ (microg / ml) \times 25 \ (ml)}{W \ (g)}$$

where

C_{DFA} = Concentration of dimethyl formamide
C = Concentration of dimethyl formamide detected
W = weight of sample taken

Cyclohexane and isobutanol

Determine by *gas liquid chromatography* using the following conditions:

Reagents:
- Dimethylformamide (GLC purity grade)
- Cyclohexane (UV spectrophotometric grade)
- Isobutanol (analytical grade)

Standard solutions:
Prepare a 0.1% stock solution of cyclohexane and isobutanol in dimethylformamide by pipetting 130 µl of cyclohexane and 125 µl of isobutanol into dimethylformamide and making up the volume to 10 ml.

Prepare by dilution a range of solutions containing 5, 10 and 20 mg/kg of cyclohexane and isobutanol. Prepare a response curve by injecting 5 µl of these diluted standard solutions into the gas chromatograph under the conditions below.

Sample preparation:
Weigh 5 g of sample to the nearest 10 mg into a flask with a ground glass stopper, add 5 g of dimethylformamide and warm to dissolve. Cool and inject 5 µl into the gas chromatograph under the conditions below.

Column:
- length: 3 m
- diameter: 4.5 mm
- material: stainless steel
- packing: 20% Carbowax 20 M on Chromosorb G 60/80
Carrier gas: Helium (1.6 bar)
Detector: Flame ionization
Temperatures
- injection port: 130°
- column: 130°
- detector: 200°

Determine the concentration of cyclohexane and isobutanol in the sample solution (50%) by comparison with the standard solutions and multiply the concentration by two to convert the results to correspond to the original sucroglycerides.

Isopropanol and ethyl acetate

Determine by *gas chromatography* with a head space sampler using the following conditions:

Reagents:
- Isopropanol
- Ethyl acetate

Standard solutions:
Take each 1 g of isopropanol and ethyl acetate in a volumetric flask and add water to total volume of 100 ml, and prepare 0.02-0.4 g/100 ml solutions by dilution of this solution.

If necessary, prepare standard solutions containing up to 7 g/100 ml of isopropanol and ethyl acetate.

Procedure:
Place 1 g (1.0 ± 0.1 g) of powdered sample in a sample vial. Add 5 µl of water to the sample vial and seal it quickly with a septum. Set the sample vial in a pre-conditioned gas chromatograph and start the analysis under the below-mentioned conditions.

Calibration curve:
Take 1 g of powdered sucrose esters of fatty acids, solvent free or known residual solvent contents, in a sample vial, add 5 µl of the standard solution and seal it quickly with a septum. Set the sample vial in a pre-conditioned gas chromatograph and start the analysis under the following conditions and obtain calibration curves for each solvent.

Column:
- length: 30 m
- diameter: 0.53 mm (i.d.)
- material: Silica capillary
- film: 100% methyl polysiloxane

- conditioning: Heat to 60° for 2-3 h with approximately 10 ml/min of nitrogen
Carrier gas: Nitrogen
Flow rate: 5 ml/min

Detector: Flame ionization
Temperatures:
- injection port: 110°
- column: 40°
- detector: 110°

Head space sampler:
- Sample volume: 1.0 g ± 0.1 g + 5 µl
- Sample heating temp.: 80°
- Sample heating time: 40 min
- Syringe temperature: 85°0
- Sample gas injection: 0.4 ml

Calculation:

$$C_i = A_i \times Cf_i \times 1000$$

where

C_i = Concentration of solvent i (mg/kg)
A_i = Peak area of solvent i (µv.sec.)
Cf_i = Conversion coefficient for solvent i (slope of the calibration curve) (µg/µv.sec)

METHOD OF ASSAY Determine by *high pressure liquid chromatography* using the following conditions:

Sample preparation:
Add about 250 mg of the sample, accurately weighed to a 50 ml volumetric flask. Dilute to volume with tetrahydrofuran, and mix. Filter through a 0.5-µm membrane filter.

Procedure:
Inject 100 µl of the sample into the pre-stabilized high pressure liquid chromatograph.

Conditions:
Column: Styrene-divinylbenzene copolymer for gel permeation chromatography (TSK-GEL G2000 (Supelco) or equivalent)
Mobile phase: HPLC-grade degassed tetrahydrofuran
Flow rate: 0.7 ml/min
Detector: Refractive index detector
Temperatures:
Column: 38°
Detector: 38°

Record the chromatogram for about 90 min. Calculate the percentage of sucrose ester content in the sample taken by the formula:

100 A/T

where

A = the sum of peak areas for the three main components, the mono-, di- and triesters, eluting at about 65, 68 and 73 min, respectively

T = the sum of all peak areas eluting within 90 min

APPENDIX

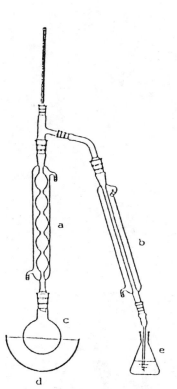

Apparatus for hydrolysis

a: Reflux condenser
b: Condenser
c: Round bottomed flask
d: Water bath
e: Erlenmeyer flask

SUCROSE ESTERS OF FATTY ACIDS

Prepared at the 49th JECFA (1997)
superseding specifications prepared at the 44th JECFA (1995),
published in FNP 52 Addendum 3 (1995)

SYNONYMS   INS No. 473

DEFINITION   Mono-, di- and tri-esters of sucrose with food fatty acids, prepared from sucrose and methyl and ethyl esters of food fatty acids or by extraction from sucroglycerides. Only the following solvents may be used for the production: dimethyl formamide, dimethyl sulfoxide, ethyl acetate, isopropanol, propylene glycol, isobutanol and methyl ethyl ketone.

Assay   Not less than 80%

DESCRIPTION   Stiff gels, soft solids or white to slightly greyish white powders

FUNCTIONAL USES   Emulsifier

CHARACTERISTICS

IDENTIFICATION

Solubility   Sparingly soluble in water, soluble in ethanol

Test for fatty acids   Passes test
See description under TESTS

Test for sugar   Passes test
See description under TESTS

PURITY

Sulfated ash   Not more than 2%
Test 1 g of the sample as directed under the Test for Ash (Sulfated ash, Method I)

Acid value   Not more than 6

Free sucrose   Not more than 5%
See description under TESTS

Dimethyl formamide   Not more than 1 mg/kg
See description under TESTS

Dimethyl sulfoxide   Not more than 2 mg/kg
See description under TESTS

Ethyl acetate, isopropanol and propylene glycol
Not more than 350 mg/kg, singly or in combination
See description under TESTS

Isobutanol	Not more than 10 mg/kg See description under TESTS

Methanol — Not more than 10 mg/kg
See description under TESTS

Methyl ethyl ketone — Not more than 10 mg/kg
See description under TESTS

Lead — Not more than 10 mg/kg
Prepare a sample solution as described for organic compounds in the Limit test, using 10 µg of lead ion (Pb) in the control

TESTS

IDENTIFICATION TESTS

Test for fatty acids — Add 1 ml of ethanol to 0.1 g of the sample, dissolve by warming, add 5 ml of dilute sulfuric acid TS, heat in a water bath for 30 min and cool. A yellowish white solid or oil is formed which is soluble in 3 ml of ether and has no odour of isobutyric acid.

Test for sugar — To 2 ml of the solution separated from the solid and oil in the test for fatty acids, add 1 ml of anthrone TS carefully down the inside of the test tube; the boundary surface of the two layers turns to blue or green.

PURITY TESTS

Free sucrose — Determine by *gas liquid chromatography* using the following conditions:

Reagents:
- Internal Standard: 5 mg/ml cholesterol in chloroform or 10 mg/ml tetracosane in chloroform
- Pyridine (dried over molecular sieve)
- N,O-Bis-(Trimethylsilyl)-acetamide (BSA)
- Trimethylchlorosilane (TMCS)

Procedure:
Weigh accurately 20-50 mg of the sample into a silylation vial, add 1 ml internal standard solution, 1 ml pyridine, and 0.5 ml each of BSA and TMCS. Seal vial, and heat at 70° for 30 min. Inject 1 µl into the gas liquid chromatograph.

Conditions:
Column:
- length: 0.3 m
- diameter: 4 mm (i.d.)
- material: glass
- packing: Dexil
Carrier gas: Nitrogen
Flow rate: 40 ml/min

Detector: FID
Temperature programme: Hold for 1 min at 160°, then 160-375° at 15°/min

Measure peak areas for sucrose and internal standard. The response factor (RF) is calculated from a number of gas liquid chromatography runs with standard solutions of sucrose containing internal standard.

Calculation:

$$RF = \frac{\text{mg of internal standard} \times \text{area sucrose}}{\text{area internal standard} \times \text{mg sucrose}}$$

and

$$\% \text{ free sucrose} = \frac{\text{mg internal standard} \times \text{area sucrose} \times 100}{RF \times \text{area internal standard} \times \text{mg sample}}$$

Dimethyl formamide

Determine by hydrolysis to dimethylamine and analysis by *gas liquid chromatography* using the following conditions:

Reagents:
- Dimethyl formamide
- Dimethylamine hydrochloride
- Methanol
- Ethanol
- Hydrochloric acid
- Sodium hydroxide

Standard solutions:
Prepare 4.47 mg/ml (equivalent to 4.0 mg/ml of dimethyl formamide) stock solution of dimethylamine hydrochloride in ethanol, and prepare standard solutions equivalent to 4, 2 and 1 µg/ml of dimethyl formamide, respectively, by dilution of the stock solution with 0.1% sodium hydroxide solution in ethanol.

Sample preparation:
The apparatus for the hydrolysis is shown in the Appendix. Weigh accurately about 40 g of the sample into a 1000-ml round-bottomed flask. Add 500 ml of 5% methanolic solution of sodium hydroxide, and attach the flask to the apparatus. Set an Erlenmeyer flask containing 10 ml of 1% methanolic solution of hydrochloric acid to the apparatus. Heat the round-bottomed flask and let the content reflux for 1 hour, then distil to collect about 50 ml of the distillate while cooling water of the reflux condenser is stopped. Evaporate the distillate to almost dryness on a boiling water bath. Dissolve the residue with a small amount of ethanol, add 2.5 ml of 5% ethanolic solution of sodium hydroxide, and dilute to 25 ml with ethanol to prepare a sample solution.

Procedure:
Inject 2 µl of the sample solution into the gas liquid chromatograph under the conditions below.

Calibration curve:
Prepare a calibration curve by injecting each 2 μl of the standard solutions into the gas chromatograph.

Conditions:
Column:
- length: 2 m
- diameter: 2 mm (i.d.)
- material: Glass
- packing: 10% amine 220 and 10% KOH on 80/100 weak acid washed Chromosorb W
- conditioning: Heat to 130° overnight with 5 ml/min of nitrogen flow rate
Carrier gas: Nitrogen
Flow rate: 17 ml/min
Detector: FID
Temperatures
- injection port: 198±5°
- column: 60°

Calculation:

$$C_{DFA} \ (mg/kg) = \frac{C \ (microg/ml) \times 25 \ (ml)}{W \ (g)}$$

where

C_{DFA} = Concentration of dimethyl formamide
C = Concentration of dimethyl formamide detected
W = weight of sample taken

Dimethyl sulfoxide

Determine by *gas liquid chromatography* under the following conditions:

Reagents:
- Tetrahydrofuran
- Dimethyl sulfoxide
- Sucrose esters of fatty acids (dimethyl sulfoxide free, i.e. sucrose esters of fatty acids prepared without using dimethyl sulfoxide)

Standard solutions (prepared fresh monthly):
- Prepare a 0.25 mg/ml stock solution of dimethyl sulfoxide in tetra-hydrofuran
- Dissolve 40 g of dimethyl sulfoxide free sucrose esters of fatty acids into tetrahydrofuran and dilute to 200 ml (Sucrose esters of fatty acids solution)
- Prepare a range of solutions containing 0.5, 1 and 5 μg/ml of dimethyl sulfoxide by dilution of the stock solution with the sucrose esters of fatty acids solution, respectively

Procedure:
Weigh accurately about 5 g of the sample, dissolve and dilute it with tetrahydrofuran to 25 ml to prepare a sample solution. Inject 3 µl of the sample solution into the gas chromatograph under the conditions below.

Calibration curve (prepared daily):
Prepare a calibration curve by injecting each 3 µl of the standard solutions into the gas chromatograph

Conditions:
Column:
- length: 2 m
- diameter: 3 mm (i.d.)
- material: Glass
- packing: 10% PEG 20M and 3% KOH on Gas Chrom Z
- conditioning: Raise the oven temperature to 180° at a rate of 10°/min and let stand for 24 to 48 h with 30 to 40 ml/min of nitrogen
Carrier gas: Nitrogen
Flow rate: 50 ml/min
Detector: Flame photometric (using 394 nm sulfur filter)
Temperatures
- injection port: 210°
- column: 160° (do not exceed 200°)

Calculation

$$C_{DMSO} \; (mg/kg) = \frac{C \; (microg/ml) \times 25 \; (ml)}{W \; (g)}$$

where

C_{DMSO} = Concentration of dimethyl sulfoxide
C = Concentration of dimethyl sulfoxide detected
W = weight of sample taken

Propylene glycol

Determine by *gas liquid chromatography* using the following conditions:

Reagents:
- Propylene glycol
- 1,2-Butylene glycol
- Acetic anhydride
- Toluene
- Acetone

Standard solutions:
- Internal standard solution: Prepare 1000 mg/l solution of 1,2-butylene glycol in acetone. 200 µl of the solution contains 0.2 mg of 1,2-butylene glycol.
- Standard solution of propylene glycol: Prepare 1000 mg/l solution of propylene glycol in acetone.

Sample preparation:
Weigh accurately about 2 g of the sample in a 100-ml flat-bottomed flask, and add 10 ml of acetic anhydride and 200 µl of the internal standard solution. Attach a reflux condenser and heat the flask in a boiling water bath for 1 hour. Add 50 ml of water and heat the flask for another 10 min in a boiling water bath. After heating, let it cool to room temperature. Transfer the content to a 100-ml separating funnel and extract with 10 ml of toluene. After separation, discharge the lower layer (aqueous phase). Add 50 ml of water to the separating funnel and wash the extract. The upper layer (toluene phase) is used as a sample solution.

Procedure:
Inject 2 µl of the sample solution into the gas chromatograph under the following conditions. (Note: Since there would be a component of high boiling point, which may have a longer retention time, it is necessary at the end of each measurement to raise the oven temperature to 200° and to evacuate it from the column).

Calibration curve:
Follow the same procedure using 100, 200 and 500 µl of the standard solution of propylene glycol in place of the sample, and prepare a calibration curve.

Column:
- length: 2 m
- diameter: 3 mm (i.d.)
- material: Glass
- packing: 5% Alkyleneglycol phthalate on 80/100 Chromosorb W
- conditioning: Heat to 150° overnight with approximately 50 ml/min of nitrogen
Carrier gas: Nitrogen
Flow rate: 40 ml/min
Detector: Flame ionization
Temperatures:
- injection port: 230°
- column: 110°

Calculation:

$$C = \frac{\dfrac{A_{PG}}{A_{IS}} \times C_{fPG} \times 0.2}{W_{SPL}} \times 1000$$

where

C = Concentration of propylene glycol (mg/kg)
A_{PG} = Peak area of propylene glycol
A_{IS} = Peak area of internal standard
W_{SPL} = Weight of sample (g)
C_{fPG} = Sensitivity correction factor for propylene glycol (slope of the calibration curve)

Methanol, isopropanol, isobutanol, ethyl acetate and methyl ethyl ketone

Determine by *gas chromatography* with a head space sampler using the following conditions:

Reagents:
- Methanol
- Isopropanol
- Isobutanol
- Ethyl acetate
- Methyl ethyl ketone

Standard solutions:
Take each 1 g of methanol, isopropanol, isobutanol, methyl ethyl ketone and ethyl acetate in a volumetric flask and add water to total volume of 100 ml, and prepare 0.02-0.4 g/100 ml solutions by dilution of this solution.

If necessary, prepare standard solutions containing up to 7 g/100 ml of isopropanol and ethyl acetate.

Procedure:
Place 1 g (1.0 ± 0.1 g) of powdered sample in a sample vial. Add 5 µl of water to the sample vial and seal it quickly with a septum. Set the sample vial in a pre-conditioned gas chromatograph and start the analysis under the below-mentioned conditions.

Calibration curve:
Take 1 g of powdered sucrose esters of fatty acids, solvent free or known residual solvent contents, in a sample vial, add 5 µl of the standard solution and seal it quickly with a septum. Set the sample vial in a pre-conditioned gas chromatograph and start the analysis under the following conditions and obtain calibration curves for each solvent.

Column:
- length: 30 m
- diameter: 0.53 mm (i.d.)
- material: Silica capillary
- film: 100% methyl polysiloxane
- conditioning: Heat to 60° for 2-3 h with approximately 10 ml/min of nitrogen
Carrier gas: Nitrogen
Flow rate: 5 ml/min
Detector: Flame ionization
Temperatures
- injection port: 110°
- column: 40°
- detector: 110°

Head space sampler:
- Sample volume: 1.0 g ± 0.1 g + 5 µl
- Sample heating temp.: 80°
- Sample heating time: 40 min
- Syringe temperature: 85°
- Sample gas injection: 0.4 ml

Calculation:

$$C_i = A_i \times Cf_i \times 1000$$

where

C_i = Concentration of solvent i (mg/kg)
A_i = Peak area of solvent i (µv.sec.)
Cf_i = Conversion coefficient for solvent i (slope of the calibration curve) (µg/µv.sec)

METHOD OF ASSAY

Determine by *high pressure liquid chromatography* using the following conditions:

Sample preparation:
Add about 250 mg of the sample, accurately weighed to a 50 ml volumetric flask. Dilute to volume with tetrahydrofuran, and mix. Filter through a 0.5-µm membrane filter.

Procedure:
Inject 100 µl of the sample into the pre-stabilized high pressure liquid chromatograph.

Conditions:
Column: Styrene-divinylbenzene copolymer for gel permeation chromatography (TSK-GEL G2000 (Supelco) or equivalent)
Mobile phase: HPLC-grade degassed tetrahydrofuran
Flow rate: 0.7 ml/min
Detector: Refractive index detector
Temperatures:
Column: 38°
Detector: 38°

Record the chromatogram for about 90 min. Calculate the percentage of sucrose ester content in the sample taken by the formula:

100 A/T

where
A = the sum of peak areas for the three main components, the mono-, di- and triesters, eluting at about 65, 68 and 73 min, respectively
T = the sum of all peak areas eluting within 90 min

APPENDIX

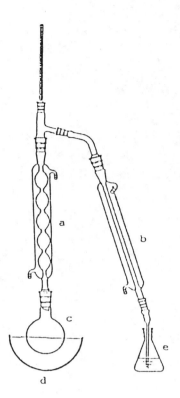

Apparatus for hydrolysis

a: Reflux condenser
b: Condenser
c: Round bottomed flask
d: Water bath
e: Erlenmeyer flask

SULFUR DIOXIDE

Prepared at the 49th JECFA (1997)
superseding specifications prepared at the 30th JECFA (1986),
published in FNP 37 (1986)

SYNONYMS   INS No. 220

DEFINITION

C.A.S. number   7446-09-5

Chemical formula SO_2

Formula weight   64.07

Assay   Not less than 99% SO_2 by weight

DESCRIPTION   Colourless, non-flammable gas, with strong, pungent, suffocating odour. Its vapor density is 2.26 times that of air at atmospheric pressure and 0°. The specific gravity of the liquid is about 1.436 at 0°/4°. At 20° the solubility is about 10 g of SO_2 per 100 g of solution. It is normally supplied under pressure in containers in which it is present in both liquid and gaseous phases.

Caution: Sulfur dioxide gas is intensely irritating to the eyes, throat, and upper respiratory system. Liquid sulfur dioxide may cause skin burns, which result from the freezing effect of the liquid on tissue. Safety precautions to be observed in handling of the material are specified in technical brochures from liquid sulfur dioxide manufacturers, suppliers or organizations of gas manufacturers or suppliers (For example, "Pamphlet G-3" published by the Compressed Gas Association, Suite 1004, 1725 Jefferson Davis Highway, Arlington, VA 22202, USA).

FUNCTIONAL USES   Preservative, bleaching agent

CHARACTERISTICS

IDENTIFICATION

Solubility   Soluble in water (36 v in 1 v) and ethanol (114 v in 1 v).

Positive test for sulfurous substances
                        Passes test
                        The sample blackens filter paper moistened with mercurous nitrate TS.

Oxidizing activity   Passes test
                        Expose a filter paper, treated with potassium iodate and starch TS, to the sample. A blue colour is developed that fades on continued exposure.

PURITY

Water   Not more than 0.05%

Transfer about 50 ml of liquid sulfur dioxide into a Karl Fischer titration jar, determine the weight of the sample taken, and determine the water content by the *Water Determination*

Non-volatile residue

Not more than 0.05%
Measure out 200 ml of sulfur dioxide (288 g) into a 250-ml Erlenmeyer flask, and determine the weight of sample taken by the loss in weight of the sample bomb. Evaporate to dryness on a steam bath, and displace the residual vapors with dry air. Wipe the flask dry, cool in a desiccator, and weigh.

Selenium

Not more than 20 mg/kg
A 2.0-ml portion of the Sample Solution meets the requirements of the Selenium Limit Test, Method II. For sampling and sample preparation, see TESTS.

Lead

Not more than 5 mg/kg
A 7.0-ml portion of the Sample Solution, diluted to 40 ml with water, meets the requirements of the Lead Limit Test using 5 µg of lead ion (Pb) in the control. For sampling and sample preparation, see TESTS.

TESTS

Sampling:

Samples of sulfur dioxide may be safely withdrawn from a tank or transfer lines, either of which should be equipped with a 1-cm nozzle and valve. Samples should be taken in bombs constructed of 316 stainless steel, designed to withstand 7 MPa (1000 psig) and equipped with 316 stainless steel needle valves on both ends. To draw a sample, the bomb is first flushed with dry air to remove any sulfur dioxide, remaining from previous sample drawings, and then attached to the tank or transfer lines with a solid pipe connection. A hose is connected to the other end of the bomb and submerged in either a weak caustic solution or water. Any gas in the bomb is discharged into the caustic or water by first opening the valve at the pipe end, followed by slowly opening at the valve at the hose end. When all of the gas is dispelled and liquid sulfur dioxide begins to emerge into the solution, the valve at the hose end is blocked off. The other valves are then tightly closed, and the bomb is detached from the pipe connecting it to the tank or transfer line. Approximately 15% of the liquid sulfur dioxide in the bomb is then discharged into the water or caustic solution. The bomb is then capped at its end and transferred to the laboratory for analysis.

Caution: The bomb should never be stored with more than 85% of the total water capacity of the bomb.

Sample Solution for the Determination of Lead, and Selenium: Measure out 100 ml of sulfur dioxide (144 g) into a 125-ml Erlenmeyer flask, and determine the weight of sample taken by the loss in weight of the sample bomb. Evaporate to dryness on a steam bath, add 3 ml of nitric acid and 10 ml of water to the dry flask, and warm gently on a hot plate for 15 min. Transfer the contents of the flask to a 100-ml volumetric flask, dilute to volume with water, and mix. Transfer a 10.0-ml aliquot into a second 100-ml volumetric flask, dilute to volume with water, and mix.

Note: The tests in which this solution is to be used will be accurate assuming a 144 g sample has been taken; if not, the weight of sample actually taken must be considered in the calculations.

METHOD OF ASSAY   Subtract from 100 the percentages of non-volatile residue and of water, as determined herein, to obtain the percentage of SO_2.

TALC

Prepared at the 49th JECFA (1997)
superseding specifications prepared at the 39th JECFA (1992),
published in FNP 52 Addendum 1 (1992)

SYNONYMS	Talcum; INS No.553(iii)

DEFINDEFINITION Naturally occuring form of hydrous magnesium silicate containing varying proportions of such associated minerals as alpha-quartz, calcite, chlorite, dolomite, kaolin, magnesite, and phlogopite. Talc derived from deposits that are known to contain associated asbestos is not food grade.

C.A.S. number   14807-96-6

DESCRIPTION Odourless, very fine, white or grayish white, crystalline powder. It is unctuous, adheres readily to the skin, and is free from grittiness.

FUNCTIONAL USES Anticaking agent, filtering aid, coating agent, lubricating and release agent, surface-finishing agent, texturizing agent, filter aid, dusting powder.

CHARACTERISTICS

IDENTIFICATION

Solubility   Insoluble in water and ethanol

Positive test for magnesium

Passes test
See description under TESTS

Infrared adsorption   The infrared absorption spectrum of a potassium bromide dispersion of the sample exhibits major peaks at approximately 1015 cm^{-1} and 450 cm^{-1}.

X-ray diffraction   The X-ray diffraction pattern of a random powder sample exhibits reflections at the following d values of 9.34 Å, 4.66 Å and 3.12 Å.

PURITY

Loss on ignition   Not more than 9%
See description under TESTS

Loss on drying   Not more than 0.5%

Water-soluble substances

Not more than 0.2%
See description under TESTS

Acid-soluble iron   Passes test
Slightly acidify with hydrochloric acid the remaining half of the filtrate obtained in the test for water-soluble substances (above) and add 1 ml of potassium ferrocyanide TS. The solution does not turn blue.

Acid-soluble substances	Not more than 1% See description under TESTS
Arsenic	Not more than 3 mg/kg See description under TESTS
Lead	Not more than 10 mg/kg See description under TESTS

TESTS

IDENTIFICATION TESTS

Positive test for magnesium

Mix 0.5 g sample with 0.2 g of anhydrous sodium carbonate and 2 g of anhydrous potassium carbonate, and heat the mixture in a platinum crucible until fusion is complete. Cool, and transfer the fused mixture to a dish or beaker with the aid of about 50 ml of hot water. Add hydrochloric acid to the liquid until effervescence ceases, then add 10 ml more of the acid, and evaporate the mixture on a steam bath to dryness. Cool, add 20 ml of water, boil and filter the mixture, an insoluble residue of gel remains. Dissolve in the filtrate about 2 g of ammonium chloride, and add 5 ml of ammonia TS. Filter if necessary, and add sodium phosphate TS to the filtrate. A white crystalline precipitate separates.

PURITY TESTS

Loss on ignition

Transfer a 1 g sample, accurately weighed, to a tared platinum crucible. Cover, apply heat gradually, and ignite for at least 3 h to a constant weight.

Water-soluble substances

Boil a 10 g sample with 50 ml of water and from time to time, add water to maintain approximately the original volume, and filter. The filtrate is neutral to litmus paper. Evaporate one-half of filtrate to dryness, and dry further at 105° for 1 h. The weight of the residue does not exceed 10 mg.

Acid-soluble substances

Digest a 1 g sample with 20 ml of dilute hydrochloric acid at 50° for 15 min, add water to restore the original volume, mix and filter. To 10 ml of the filtrate add 1 ml of dilute sulfuric acid TS, evaporate to dryness, and ignite to constant weight. The weight of the residue does not exceed 10 mg.

Arsenic

To a 1 g sample, accurately weighed, add 5 ml of dilute hydrochloric acid TS and boil while stirring; cool, and filter. Wash the residue with 5 ml of dilute hydrochloric acid TS and subsequently with 25 ml of water. Combine the washings with the filtrate. This solution meets the requirement of the Arsenic Limit Test (Method II).

Lead

10 ml of solution prepared for the determination of arsenic meets the requirements of the Limit Test using 10 µg of lead ion (Pb) in the control.

TENTATIVE

TARTARIC, ACETIC AND FATTY ACID ESTERS OF GLYCEROL, MIXED

Prepared at the 49th JECFA (1997)
superseding specifications prepared at the 46th JECFA (1996),
published in FNP 52 Addendum 4 (1996)

Information required on analytical methods in order to distinguish this material from diacetyltartaric and fatty acid esters of glycerol (DATEM). Unless such data is provided by 31 March 1998 the Committee will consider combining the two specifications.

SYNONYMS

Mixed acetic and tartaric acid esters of mono- and diglycerides of fatty acids
INS No. 472f

DEFINITION

The product consists of esters of glycerol with fatty acids of food fats, acetic acid and tartaric acid. It may contain small amounts of free glycerol, free fatty acids, free acetic acid, free tartaric acid and free glycerides.

Structural formula

$$
\begin{array}{l}
CH_2-OR_1 \\
| \\
CH-OR_2 \\
| \\
CH_2-OR_3
\end{array}
$$

where

1) one or two of the R groups is a fatty acid moiety
2) the other R groups are either
- tartaric acid moiety
- acetic acid moiety
- hydrogen
- diacetylated tartaric acid moiety
- monoacetylated tartaric acid moiety

DESCRIPTION

The esters range in appearance from sticky, viscous liquids through a fat-like consistency to yellow waxes which hydrolyse in moist air to liberate acetic acid

FUNCTIONAL USES

Emulsifier

CHARACTERISTICS

IDENTIFICATION

Solubility

Dispersible in water, soluble in methanol, ethanol and acetone

Test for 1,2-diols

To a solution of 500 mg in 10 ml methanol, add dropwise, lead acetate TS. A white flocculent, insoluble precipitate is formed.

Test for fatty acids

Passes test

Test for acetic acid

Passes test

Test for tartaric acid

Passes test

Test for glycerol

Passes test

PURITY

Acids   Acids other than acetic, tartaric and fatty acids, shall not be detectable

Total acetic acid   Not less than 10% and not more than 20%, after hydrolysis
                   See description under TESTS

Total tartaric acid   Not less than 20% and not more than 40%, after saponification
                     See description under TESTS

Free fatty acids   Not more than 3% as oleic acid

Free glycerol   Not more than 2%

Total glycerol   Not less than 12% and not more than 27%, after saponification
               See description under TESTS

Sulfated ash   Not more than 0.5% determined at 800±25°
               Proceed as directed under the test for Ash (Sulfated Ash, Method I, if the sample is solid, and Method II, if liquid), using 5 g of sample

Heavy metals   Not more than 10 mg/kg
               Test 2 g of the sample as directed in the Limit Test (Method II)

TESTS

PURITY TESTS

Total acetic acid   Apparatus:

Assemble a modified Hortvet-Sellier distillation apparatus as shown in the figure, using a sufficiently large (approximately 38- x 203-mm) inner Sellier tube and large distillation trap.

Procedure:

Transfer 4 g of sample, accurately weighed into the inner tube of the assembly, and insert the tube in the outer flask containing about 300 ml of recently boiled hot water. To the sample add 10 ml of approximately 4N perchloric acid [35 ml (60 g) of 70% perchloric acid in 100 ml of water], and connect the inner tube to a water-cooled condenser through the distillation trap. Distil by heating the outer flask so that 100 ml of distillate is collected within 20 to 25 min. Collect the distillate in 100-ml portions, add phenolphthalein TS to each portion, and titrate with 0.5N sodium hydroxide. Continue the distillation until a 100-ml portion of the distillate requires no more than 0.5 ml of 0.5N sodium hydroxide for neutralization. (Caution: Do not distil to dryness.) Calculate the weight, in mg, of volatile acids in the sample taken by the formula V x e, in which V is the total volume, in ml, of 0.5N sodium hydroxide consumed in the series of titrations and e is the equivalence factor 30.03.

Total tartaric acid   Standard curve:

Transfer 100 mg of reagent-grade tartaric acid, accurately weighed, into a 100-ml volumetric flask, dissolve it in about 90 ml of water, add water to volume, and mix well. Transfer 3.0-. 4.0-, 5.0-, and 6.0-ml portions into separate 19- x 150-mm matched cuvettes, and add sufficient water to make 10.0 ml. To each cuvette add 4.0 ml of a freshly prepared 1 in 20 solution of sodium metavanadate and 1.0 ml of acetic acid. (Note: Use these solutions within 10 min after colour development.) Prepare a blank in the same manner, using 10 ml of water in place of the tartaric acid solutions. Set the instrument at zero with the blank, and then determine the absorbance of the four solutions of tartaric acid at 520 nm with a suitable spectrophotometer or a photoelectric colorimeter equipped with a 520-nm filter. From the data thus obtained, prepare a standard curve by plotting the absorbances on the ordinate against the corresponding quantities, in mg, of the tartaric acid on the abscissa.

Test Preparation:

Transfer about 4 g of the sample, accurately weighed, into a 250-ml Erlenmeyer flask, and add 80 ml of approximately 0.5N potassium hydroxide and 0.5 ml of phenolphthalein TS. Connect an air condenser of at least 65 cm in length to the flask, and heat the mixture on a hot plate for about 2.5 h. Add to the hot mixture approximately 10% phosphoric acid until it is definitely acid to congo red test paper. Reconnect the air condenser, and heat until the fatty acids are liquified and clear. Cool and then transfer the mixture into a 250-ml separator with the aid of small portions of water and chloroform. Extract the liberated fatty acids with three successive 25-ml portions of water, and add the washings to the separator containing the water layer. Transfer the contents of the first separator to a 250-ml beaker, heat on a steam bath to remove traces of chloroform under hood, filter through acid-washed, fine-texture filter paper into a 500-ml volumetric flask, and dilute to volume with water (Solution I). Pipet 25.0 ml of this solution into a 100-ml volumetric flask, and dilute to volume with water (Solution II). Retain the rest of Solution I for the determination of total glycerol.

Procedure:

Transfer 10.0 ml of Solution II prepared under Test Preparation into a 19- x 150-mm cuvette and continue as directed under Standard curve beginning with "To each cuvette add 4.0 ml of ...". From the standard curve determine the weight, in mg, of tartaric acid in the final dilution, multiply this by 20, and divide the result by the weight of the original sample for obtaining the percentage of tartaric acid.

Total glycerol

Procedure:

Transfer 5.0 ml of Solution I prepared in the test for total Tartaric Acid into a 250-ml glass-stoppered Erlenmeyer or iodine flask. Add to the flask 15 ml of glacial acetic acid and 25.0 ml of periodic acid solution, prepared by dissolving 2.7 g of periodic acid (H_5IO_6) in 50 ml of water, adding 950 ml of glacial acetic acid, and mixing thoroughly; protect this solution from light. Shake the mixture for 1 or 2 min, allow it to stand for 15 min, add 15 ml of potassium iodide solution (15 in 100) and 15 ml of water, swirl, let stand 1 min, and then titrate the liberated iodine with 0.1N sodium thiosulfate, using starch TS as the indicator. Perform a Residual Blank Titration using water in place of the sample. The corrected volume is the number of ml of 0.1N sodium thiosulfate required for the glycerol and the tartaric acid in the sample represented by the 5 ml of Solution I. From the percentage determined in the Assay for Tartaric Acid calculate the volume of 0.1N sodium thiosulfate required for the tartaric acid in the titration. The difference between the corrected volume and the calculated volume required for the tartaric acid is the number of ml of 0.1N sodium thiosulfate consumed due to the glycerol in the sample. One ml of 0.1N sodium thiosulfate is equivalent to 2.303 mg of glycerol and to 7.505 mg of tartaric acid.

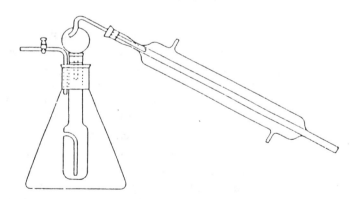

Figure.   Modified Hortvet-Sellier Distillation Apparatus

TERTIARY BUTYLHYDROQUINONE

Prepared at the 49th JECFA (1997)
superseding specifications prepared at the 44th JECFA (1995),
published in FNP 52 Addendum 3 (1995)

SYNONYMS	TBHQ, INS No 319

DEFINITION

Chemical names   Mono-tert-butylhydroquinone, *t*-butylhydroquinone, 2-(1,1-dimethylethyl)-1,4-benzenediol

C.A.S. number   1948-33-0

Chemical formula $C_{10}H_{14}O_2$

Structural formula

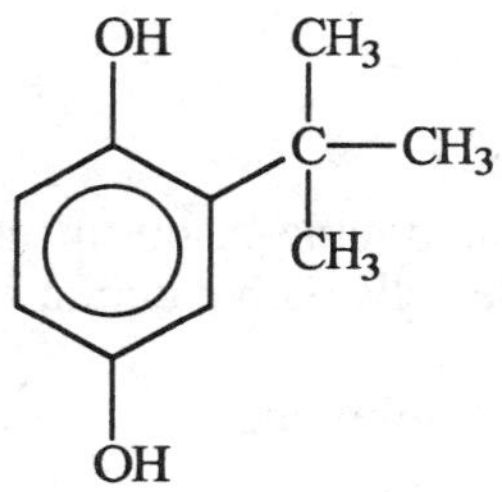

Formula weight   166.22

Assay   Not less than 99.0% of $C_{10}H_{14}O_2$

DESCRIPTION   White, crystalline solid having a characteristic odour.

FUNCTIONAL USES   Antioxidant

CHARACTERISTICS

IDENTIFICATION TESTS

Solubility   Practically insoluble in water
Soluble in ethanol

Melting point   Not less than 126.5°

Phenolics   Passes test
See description under TESTS

PURITY TESTS

Heavy Metals   Not more than 10 mg/kg
Test 2 g of the sample as directed in the Limit Test (Method II)

t-Butyl-p-benzoquinone

     Not more than 0.2%

See description under TESTS

2,5-Di-t-butyl hydroquinone
    Not more than 0.2%
    See description under TESTS

Hydroxyquinone
    Not more than 0.1%
    See description under TESTS

Toluene
    Not more than 25 mg/kg
    See description under TESTS

TESTS

IDENTIFICATION TESTS

Phenolics
Dissolve about 5 mg of the sample in 10 ml of methanol, and add 10.5 ml of dimethylamine solution (1 in 4). A red to pink colour is produced.

PURITY TESTS

t-Butyl-p-benzoquinone

Apparatus:

Use a suitable double-beam infrared spectrophotometer and matched 0.4 mm liquid sample cells with calcium fluoride windows.

Reagents and Solutions:

Standard preparation: Transfer about 10 mg of mono-tertiary-butyl-p-benzoquinone Reference Standard (available from US Pharmacopeial Convention, Inc., 12601 Twinbrook Parkway, Rockville, MD 20852, USA), accurately weighed, into a 10-ml volumetric flask, dissolve in chloroform, dilute to volume with the same solvent and mix.

Sample preparation: Transfer about 1 g of the sample, previously ground to a fine powder in a high-speed blender and accurately weighed, into a 10-ml volumetric flask, dissolve in chloroform, dilute to volume with the same solvent, and mix. Filter through a Millipore filter (UHWPO1300), or equivalent, before use in the Procedure below.

Procedure:

Fill the reference cell with chloroform and the sample cell with the Standard preparation. Place the cells in the respective reference and sample beam of the spectrophotometer, and record the infrared spectrum from 1600 to 1775 cm^{-1}. On the spectrum draw a background line from 1612 to 1750 cm^{-1}, and determine the net absorbence (A_S) of the Standard preparation at 1659 cm^{-1}.

Similarly, obtain the spectrum of the sample preparation, and determine its net absorbence (A_U) at 1659 cm^{-1}.

Calculation:

Calculate the percent of t-butyl-p-benzoquinone in the sample by the formula:

$100 \times A_U/A_S \times W_S/W_U$

in which W_S is the exact weight, in mg, of the mono-tertiary-butyl-p-benzoquinone Reference Standard taken;

W_U is the exact weight, in mg, of the sample taken.

2,5-Di-t-butylhydroquinone and hydroquinone

Apparatus:

Use a suitable gas chromatograph equipped with a thermal conductivity detector (F and M Model 810 or equivalent), containing a 0.61-m (2 ft) × 6.35-mm (outside diameter) stainless steel column packed with 20% Silicone SE-30, by weight and 80% Diatoport S (60/80-mesh), or equivalent materials.

Operating conditions:

The operating parameters may vary, depending upon the particular instrument used, but a suitable chromatogram may be obtained using the following conditions:

- Column temperature: programmed from 100 to 270°, at 15° per min
- Injection port temperature: 300°
- Carrier gas: helium, flowing at a rate of 100 ml per min
- Bridge current: 140 mA
- Sensitivity: 1 × for integrator (Infotronics CRS-100), 2 × for recorder

Reagents and Solutions:

Stock solution: Weigh accurately about 50 mg each of hydroquinone (HQ), 2,5-di-t-butylhydroquinone (DTBHQ), and methyl benzoate (internal standard), transfer into separate 50-ml volumetric flasks, dilute to volume with pyridine, and mix.

Calibration standards: Into separate 10-ml volumetric flasks add 0.50, 1.0, 2.0 and 3.0 ml of the HQ stock solution, then to each flask add 2 ml of the methyl benzoate (internal standard) stock solution, dilute each to volume with pyridine, and mix. In the same manner prepare four DTBHQ calibrating solutions. Prepare the trimethylsilyl derivative of each solution as follows. Add 9 drops of calibration solution to a 2-ml gas syringe, add 250 µl of N,O-bistrimethylsilylacetamide, and heat at about 80° for 10 min Chromatograph 10-µl portions of each standard in duplicate, and plot the concentration ratio of HQ to internal standard (X-axis) against the response ratio of HQ to internal standard (Y-axis). Plot the same relationships between DTBHQ and the internal standard.

Procedure:

Transfer about 1 g of the sample, accurately weighed, into a 10-ml volumetric flask, add 2 ml of the methyl benzoate internal standard stock solution, dilute to volume with pyridine, and mix. Prepare the trimethylsilyl derivative as described above under Calibration standards, and then chromatograph duplicate 10-µl portions to obtain the chromatogram. The approximate peak times, in minutes, are: methyl benzoate, 2.5; TMS derivative of HQ, 5.5; TMS derivative of tert-butylhydroquinone, 7.3; TMS derivative of DTBHQ, 8.4.

Calculation:

Determine the peak areas (response) of interest by automatic integration or manual triangulation. Calculate the response ratio of HQ and DTBHQ to internal standard. From the calibration curves determine the concentration ratio of HQ and DTBHQ to internal standard, and calculate the % HQ and % DTBHQ in the sample by the formula:

$$A = Y \times I \times 10/S$$

in which A is the % HQ or % DTBHQ in the sample; Y is the concentration ratio (X-axis on calibration curve); I is the percentage (w/v) of internal standard in the Sample preparation; S is the weight of sample taken, in g.

Toluene

Apparatus:

Use a suitable gas chromatograph equipped with a flame ionization detector (F and M Model 810 or equivalent), containing a 3.66-m (12-ft) × 3.18-mm (outside diameter) stainless steel column packed with 10% Silicone SE-30, by weight, and 90% Diatoport S (60/80 mesh), or equivalent materials.

Operating conditions:

The operating parameters may vary, depending upon the particular instrument used, but a suitable chromatogram may be obtained using the following conditions:

- Column temperature:	programmed from 70 to 280° at 15° per minute and held
- Injection port temperature:	275°
- Cell temperature:	300°
- H_2 and O_2 (or air) settings:	1.4 atm (20 psi) each

Reagents and solutions:

Standard solution: Prepare a solution of toluene in octanol containing approximately 50 µg per ml, and calculate the exact concentration (C_R) in percent (w/v).

Sample solution: Transfer about 2 g of the sample, accurately weighed, into a 10-ml volumetric flask, dissolve in octanol, dilute to volume with the same solvent, and mix. Calculate the exact concentration of the solution (C_S) in percent (w/v).

Procedure:

Inject a 5-µl portion of the Standard solution into the chromatograph, and measure the height of the toluene peak (H_R) on the chromatogram. The toluene retention time is 3.3 min; other peaks are of no interest in this analysis. Similarly, obtain the chromatogram on a 5-µl portion of the Sample solution and of a blank consisting of octanol, and measure the height of the toluene peak (H_S).

Calculation:

Calculate the mg/kg of toluene in the sample by the formula:

$$H_S / C_R \times C_R / C_S \times 10^6$$

METHOD OF ASSAY

Transfer about 170 mg of the sample, previously ground to a fine powder and accurately weighed, into a 250-ml wide-mouth conical flask, and dissolve in 10 ml of methanol. Add 150 ml of water, 1 ml of N sulfuric acid, and 4 drops of diphenylamine indicator (3 mg of p-diphenylaminesulfonic acid, sodium salt, per ml of 0.1 N sulfuric acid), and titrate with 0.1 N ceric sulfate to the first complete colour change from yellow to red-violet. Record the volume, in ml, of 0.1 N ceric sulfate required as V. Calculate the percent of $C_{10}H_{14}O_2$ in the sample, uncorrected for hydroquinone (HQ) and 2,5-di-tert-butylhydroquinone (DTBHQ), by the formula:

$$(V - 0.1 \text{ ml}) \times N \times 8.311/W$$

in which 0.1 ml represents the volume of ceric sulfate consumed by the primary oxidation products of tert-butylhydroquinone ordinarily present in the sample; N is the normality of the standard ceric sulfate solution; W is the weight of the sample taken, in g.

Record the uncorrected percentage thus calculated as A. If HQ and DTBHQ are present in the sample, they will be included in the titration. Calculate the corrected percentage of $C_{10}H_{14}O_2$ in the sample by the formula:

$$A - (\%HQ \times 1.51) - (\%DTBHQ \times 0.75)$$

using the respective values for % HQ and % DTBHQ as determined by the gas chromatographic procedures given above.

SECTION B.

SPECIFICATIONS

CERTAIN FLAVOURING AGENTS

ORGANIZATION OF THE SECTION FOR SPECIFICATIONS OF FLAVOURING AGENTS

At its 44th meeting JECFA considered a new approach to the safety evaluation of flavouring agents. This approach incorporates a series of criteria whose use enables the evaluation of a large number of these agents in a consistent and timely manner. At the 46th meeting the Committee applied these procedures to the evaluation of 52 flavouring agents. At the current session of the Committee, the procedure was applied to additional 217 flavouring agents. Specifications of identity and purity were prepared for 164 of these 217 flavouring agents and are documented on the following pages.

The specifications are presented in a tabular format because with the number of flavouring agents now being evaluated, the method of presentation becomes a matter of efficiency. Some of the substances have uses additional to that of being a flavouring agent, for example also serving as a carrier solvent. For these substances the specifications are presented both in the traditional format in Section A and in the tabular format in Section B. Section B, in some cases, contains a reference back to Section A so as to avoid repeating some tests which apply to all uses.

Information on specifications is given under the following headings, most of which are self-explanatory: Name; Chemical name; Synonyms; Flavour and Extract Manufacturer's Association of the United States (FEMA) No; Council of Europe (COE) No; Chemical Abstract Service Registry (CAS) No; Molecular weight; Chemical formula; Physical form/odour; Solubility; Solubility in ethanol[*], Boiling point (information only); Identification test (ID), IR infrared spectrum; Assay min%[**]; Acid value max[*]; Refractive index (at 20°, if not otherwise stated)[*]; Specific gravity (at 25°, if not otherwise stated)[*]; Other requirements, e.g. additional tests[*]; and last the JECFA column that indicates the Session at which the specifications were prepared, E means "extraction solvent, C means "also used as carrier solvent" (See Section A), P means "preservative, R means "specifications revised", S means "existing specifications maintained, S,T means "existing tentative specifications maintained, N means "new specifications", and N,T means "new tentative specifications - further information required).

Previous specifications of flavouring agents having no other functional uses have been converted to the new tabular format. The tables were generated using Microsoft Excel 5.0.

The infrared spectra, used for identification and comparison purposes, are provided from page 239 onwards, except for those 52 flavouring agents, evaluated at the 46th session of the Committee. For the IR spectra of these substances, see FNP 52 Addendum 4 (1996).

NOTE: Many of the above IR spectra are of unsatisfactory editorial quality. The FAO JECFA Secretariat is exploring ways and means to produce satisfactory and consistent IR spectra when these specifications are printed again.

---

[*]   **See General Methods (Guide to JECFA Specifications), FAO Food and Nutrition Paper (FNP) 5/Rev. 2 (1991).**

[**]   **See page 233 - Gas chromatographic (GC) Assay of Flavour Chemicals.**

NO	NAME	CHEMICAL NAME	SYNONYMS	FEMA NO	COE NO	CAS NO	MOL WT	CHEMICAL FORMULA	PHYSICAL FORM / ODOUR
1	Allyl proplonate	2-Propenyl propanoate	Allyl propionate	2040	2094	2408-20-0	114.15	$C_6H_{10}O_2$	Colourless liquid with a sharp sour apple/apricot odour
2	Allyl butyrate	2-Propenyl butanoate	Allyl butanoate	2021	280	2051-78-7	128.17	$C_7H_{12}O_2$	Colourless liquid with a peach/apricot odour
3	Allyl hexanoate	2-Propenyl hexanoate	Allyl caproate	2032	2181	123-68-2	156.22	$C_9H_{16}O_2$	Colourless to light yellow stable mobile liquid with fatty-fruity pineapple odour
4	Allyl heptanoate	2-Propenyl heptanoate	Allyl oenanthate	2031	369	142-91-8	170.25	$C_{10}H_{18}O_2$	Colourless to yellow liquid with sweet fruity pineapple odour and a slight banana hint
5	Allyl octanoate	2-Propenyl octanoate	Allyl caprylate	2037	400	4230-97-1	184.28	$C_{11}H_{20}O_2$	Colourless to pale yellow oily liquid with a fruity odour and winey undertone
6	Allyl nonanoate	2-Propenyl nonanoate	Allyl pelargonate	2036	390	7493-72-3	198.31	$C_{12}H_{22}O_2$	Colourless oily liquid with a fruital cognac/pineapple odour
7	Allyl isovalerate	2-Propenyl 3-methylbutanoate		2045	2098	2835-39-4	142.20	$C_8H_{14}O_2$	Colourless to pale yellow liquid with a fruity apple/cherry odour
8	Allyl sorbate	2-Propenyl hexa-2,4-dienoate		2041	2182	7493-75-6	152.19	$C_9H_{12}O_2$	Colourless to light yellow liquid with a fruital pineapple-like odour
9	Allyl 10-undecenoate	2-Propenyl 10-undecenoate	Allyl 10-undecenylate	2044	442	7439-76-7	224.34	$C_{14}H_{24}O_2$	Colourless oily liquid with a fatty coconut/pineapple odour and a rum-like background
10	Allyl tiglate	2-Propenyl trans-2-methyl-2-butenoate	Propenyl tiglate	2043	2183	7493-71-2	140.18	$C_8H_{12}O_2$	Colourless to pale yellow liquid with mild green fruity/green berry odour
11	Allyl 2-ethylbutyrate	2-Propenyl 2-ethylbutanoate	Allyl 2-ethylbutanoate	2029	281	7493-69-8	156.23	$C_9H_{16}O_2$	Colourless liquid with an oily fruity odour
12	Allyl cyclohexane acetate	2-Propenyl cyclohexane acetate		2023	2070	4728-82-9	182.26	$C_{11}H_{18}O_2$	Colourless liquid with an intense sweet long lasting pineapple/peach/apricot odour
13	Allyl cyclohexane propionate	2-Propenyl cyclohexane propionate	Allyl 3-cyclohexane propanoate	2026	2223	2705-87-5	196.29	$C_{12}H_{20}O_2$	Colourless liquid with a pineapple odour
14	Allyl cyclohexane butyrate	2-Propenyl 4-cyclohexane butanoate	Allyl cyclohexyl butyrate	2024	283	7493-65-4	210.31	$C_{13}H_{22}O_2$	Colourless liquid with a fatty pineapple odour
15	Allyl cyclohexane valerate	2-Propenyl 5-cyclohexane pentanoate	Allyl cyclohexyl valerate	2027	474	7493-68-7	224.34	$C_{14}H_{24}O_2$	Colourless liquid with a pineapple/mixed fruity odour
16	Allyl cyclohexane hexanoate	2-Propenyl 6-cyclohexane hexanoate	Allyl cyclohexyl caproate	2025	2180	7493-66-5	238.37	$C_{15}H_{26}O_2$	Colourless liquid with a weak fatty fruity odour
17	Allyl phenylacetate	2-Propenyl phenylacetate	Allyl alpha-toluate	2039	2162	1797-74-6	176.22	$C_{11}H_{12}O_2$	Colourless, slightly viscous liquid with a honey-like odour

NO	SOLUBILITY	SOLUBILITY IN ETHANOL*	BOILING POINT	ID TEST	ASSAY MIN%	ACID VALUE MAX*	REFRACTIVE INDEX*	SPECIFIC GRAVITY*	OTHER REQUIREMENTS	JECFA
1	-	-	122-123°	IR	-	-	1.4105	0.914 at 20°	None	46th/T
2	Insoluble in water and soluble in ethanol and oils	-	44-45° at 15mm Hg	IR	98.0	1.0	1.412 - 1.418	0.897 - 0.902	None	46th
3	Insoluble in water at 260° and in propylene glycol, soluble in ethanol, fixed and organic oils, and soluble in organic solvents	1ml in 6ml 70% ethanol	185°	IR	98.0	1.0	1.422 - 1.426	0.884 - 0.890	Allyl alcohol 0.1% max	46th
4	-	1ml in 1ml 95% ethanol	210°	IR	97.0	1.0	1.426 - 1.430	0.880 - 0.885	Allyl alcohol 0.1% max	46th
5	Insoluble in glycerol & water at 260°, slightly soluble in propylene glycol, and soluble in ethanol and fixed oils	-	222°	IR	97.0	-	1.432 - 1.434	0.872 - 0.880	None	46th
6	Insoluble in water, soluble in essential oils, flavour chemicals, and ethanol	-	241-242°	IR	96.5	-	1.430 - 1.436	0.872 - 0.880	None	46th
7	Insoluble in water and miscible with perfume and flavour materials	1ml in 1ml 95% ethanol	155°	IR	98.0	1.0	1.413-1.418	0.879 - 0.884	Allyl alcohol 0.1% max	46th
8	Soluble in ethanol	-	67°	IR	99.0	-	1.506	0.945 - 0.947	None	46th/T
9	Insoluble in water, soluble in ethanol, propylene glycol and organic solvents	-	180° at 30mm Hg	IR	98.0	1.0	1.448 at 30°	0.8802 at 30°	None	46th
10	Slightly soluble in water, ether and most fixed oils	-	-	-	98.0	1.0	1.451 - 1.454	0.939 - 0.943	None	46th/T
11	Insoluble in water, soluble in ethanol, and miscible with essential oils and flavour materials	-	165-167°	IR	99.0	1.0	1.422 - 1.427	0.882 - 0.887	None	46th
12	Soluble in ethanol and oils	1ml in 4ml 80% ethanol	66° at 1mm Hg	-	96.0	1.0	1.455 - 1.499	0.945 - 0.965	None	46th/T
13	Soluble in ether, higher oils and fatty oils. Insoluble in glycerine and water	1ml in 4ml 80% ethanol	91° at 1mm Hg	IR	98.0	5.0	1.457 - 1.462	0.945 - 0.950	Allyl alcohol 0.1% max	46th, 49th/S
14	Insoluble in water, soluble in ethanol, essential oils and flavour chemicals	-	104° at 1mm Hg	-	-	-	1.4608 at 20.5°	-	None	46th/T
15	Insoluble in water, soluble in ethanol, essential oils and flavour materials, and poorly soluble in propylene glycol	-	119° at 1mm Hg	IR	-	-	1.4605 at 22°	-	None	46th/T
16	Soluble in oils and ethanol, insoluble in water	-	128° at 1.5mm Hg	-	-	-	1.462	-	None	46th/T
17	-	-	89-93° at 3mm Hg	IR	99.0	-	1.5122 at 13.5°	-	None	46th/T

NO	NAME	CHEMICAL NAME	SYNONYMS	FEMA NO	COE NO	CAS NO	MOL WT	CHEMICAL FORMULA	PHYSICAL FORM / ODOUR
18	Allyl phenoxyacetate	2-Propenyl phenoxyacetate		2038	228	7493-74-5	192.22	$C_{11}H_{12}O_3$	Colourless to yellow liquid with honey/pineapple odour
19	Allyl cinnamate	2-Propenyl 3-phenyl-2-propenoate		2022	334	1866-31-5	188.22	$C_{12}H_{12}O_2$	Colourless to light yellow, slightly viscous liquid with a peach/apricot odour
20	Allyl anthranilate	2-Propenyl 2-aminobenzoate		2020	254	7493-63-2	177.21	$C_{10}H_{11}NO_2$	Colourless to pale yellow liquid with a sharp heavy grape-like sweet odour and a green topnote
21	Allyl 2-furoate	2-Propenyl furan-2-carboxylate	Allyl pyromucate	2030	360	4208-49-5	152.15	$C_8H_8O_3$	Colourless or pale straw liquid which darkens when exposed to air and daylight: has a caramelic, fruity odour
22	Benzaldehyde	Benzaldehyde	Benzoic aldehyde	2127	101	100-52-7	106.12	C_7H_6O	Colourless liquid with an almond-like odour
23	Benzyl acetate	Benzyl acetate	Benzyl ethanoate	2135	204	140-11-4	150.18	$C_9H_{10}O_2$	Colourless liquid with a characteristic odour
24	Benzyl benzoate	Benzyl benzoate		2138	262	120-51-4	212.25	$C_{14}H_{12}O_2$	Colourless oily liquid with a faint sweet balsamic odour and a sharp, burning taste
25	Benzyl alcohol	Benzyl alcohol		2137	58	100-51-6	108.14	C_7H_8O	Colourless, clear liquid with a faint aromatic odour and a sharp, burning taste
26	Ethyl formate	Ethyl formate		2434	339	109-94-4	74.08	$C_3H_6O_2$	Colourless liquid with a sharp, rum-like odour
27	Ethyl acetate	Ethyl acetate	Ethyl ethanoate	2414	191	141-78-6	88.11	$C_4H_8O_2$	Colourless liquid, volatile at low temperatures with a fragrant, acetic, ethereal odour
28	Ethyl propionate	Ethyl propanoate		2456	402	105-37-3	102.13	$C_5H_{10}O_2$	Colourless liquid with a fruity, rum-like, ethereal odour
29	Ethyl butyrate	Ethyl butanoate		2427	264	105-54-4	116.16	$C_6H_{12}O_2$	Colourless liquid with a banana, pineapple odour
30	Ethyl pentanoate	Ethyl pentanoate	Ethyl valerate	2462	465	539-82-2	130.19	$C_7H_{14}O_2$	Colourless to pale yellow liquid
31	Ethyl hexanoate	Ethyl hexanoate	Ethyl caproate	2439	310	123-66-0	144.21	$C_8H_{16}O_2$	Colourless liquid with a wine-like odour

NO	SOLUBILITY	SOLUBILITY IN ETHANOL*	BOILING POINT	ID TEST	ASSAY MIN%	ACID VALUE MAX*	REFRACTIVE INDEX*	SPECIFIC GRAVITY*	OTHER REQUIREMENTS	JECFA
18	-	-	100-102° at 1mm Hg	IR	97.5	1.0	1.512 - 1.519	1.00 - 1.11	None	46th
19	Insoluble in water and soluble in ethanol	-	163° at approx. 17mm Hg	IR	-	1.0	1.5661 at 23°	1.046 - 1.058 at 23°	None	46th/T
20	Almost insoluble in water, soluble in essential oils, poorly soluble in propylene glycol	-	105° at 2mm Hg	IR	-	-	-	1.12	None	46th/T
21	-	-	206-209°	IR	-	-	1.495	1.181 at 23°	None	46th/T, 49th/S,T
22	Slightly soluble in water, soluble in ethanol, ether and fixed or volatile oils	-	178°	IR	98.0	-	1.544 - 1.547	1.041 - 1.046	Passes test for chlorinated compounds; passes test for solubility in bisulfite	46th
23	Insoluble in water and glycerol, soluble in acetone, ether, propylene glycol and most fixed oils	1ml in 5ml 60% ethanol	214°	IR	98.0	1.0	1.501 - 1.504	1.052 - 1.056	Passes test for chlorinated compounds	46th/C
24	Insoluble in water and glycerol, soluble in acetone, ether, propylene glycol and most fixed oils	1ml in 2ml 90% ethanol	323°	IR	99.0	1.0	1.568 - 1.570	1.116 - 1.120	Passes test for chlorinated compounds	46th/C
25	Soluble in water (1ml in 30ml), ether and most other organic solvents	1ml in 1.5ml 50% ethanol	206°	IR	98.0	0.5	1.539 - 1.541	1.042 - 1.047	Aldehydes not more than 0.2% v/v; passes test for peroxides; passes test for chlorinated compounds	46th/C
26	Soluble in most fixed oils, propylene glycol, water (with gradual decomposition), slightly soluble in mineral oil. Insoluble in glycerol	1ml in 5ml 50% ethanol	54°	IR	95.0	-	1.359 - 1.363	0.917 - 0.922		46th
27	Slightly soluble in ethanol, ether, glycerol, fixed and volatile oils, soluble in water (1ml in 10ml)	No data	77°	IR	99.0	5.0	1.371 - 1.376	0.894 - 0.898		46th
28	Soluble in most fixed oils and propylene glycol, soluble in water (1ml in 42ml)	No data	99°	IR	97.0	2.0	1.383 - 1.385	0.886 - 0.889	None	46th
29	Soluble in fixed oils and propylene glycol, insoluble in glycerol	1ml in 3ml 60% ethanol	121°	IR	98.0	1.0	1.391 - 1.394	0.870 - 0.877	None	46th
30	Slightly soluble in ethanol, insoluble in water	No data	145°	IR	98.0	1.0	1.399 - 1.404	0.870 - 0.875	None	46th
31	Soluble in most fixed oils and in propylene glycol, insoluble in water and glycerol	1ml in 2ml 70% ethanol	166°	IR	98.0	1.0	1.406 - 1.409	0.867 - 0.871	None	46th

NO	NAME	CHEMICAL NAME	SYNONYMS	FEMA NO	COE NO	CAS NO	MOL WT	CHEMICAL FORMULA	PHYSICAL FORM / ODOUR
32	Ethyl heptanoate	Ethyl heptanoate	Ethyl oenanthate	2437	365	106-30-9	158.24	$C_9H_{18}O_2$	Colourless liquid with a wine, brandy-like odour
33	Ethyl octanoate	Ethyl octanoate	Ethyl caprylate	2449	392	106-32-1	172.27	$C_{10}H_{20}O_2$	Colourless liquid with a wine, brandy, fruity floral odour
34	Ethyl nonanoate	Ethyl nonanoate	Ethyl pelargonate	2447	388	123-29-5	186.29	$C_{11}H_{22}O_2$	Colourless liquid with a fatty, fruity brandy-like odour
35	Ethyl decanoate	Ethyl decanoate	Ethyl caprate	2432	309	110-38-3	200.32	$C_{12}H_{24}O_2$	Colourless liquid with an oily brandy-like odour
36	Ethyl undecanoate	Ethyl undecanoate	Ethyl undecylate	3492	10633	627-90-7	214.35	$C_{13}H_{26}O_2$	Colourless liquid with a wine-like, fatty/fruity, somewhat nutty odour
37	Ethyl dodecanoate	Ethyl dodecanoate	Ethyl laurate	2441	375	106-33-2	228.38	$C_{14}H_{28}O_2$	Colourless, oily liquid with a fruity, floral odour
38	Ethyl tetradecanoate	Ethyl tetradecanoate	Ethyl myristate	2445	385	124-06-1	256.43	$C_{16}H_{32}O_2$	Colourless to pale yellow liquid with a waxy odour reminiscent of orris
39	Ethyl hexadecanoate	Ethyl hexadecanoate	Ethyl palmitate	2451	634	628-97-7	284.49	$C_{18}H_{36}O_2$	Colourless crystals with a waxy odour
40	Ethyl octadecanoate	Ethyl octadecanoate	Ethyl stearate	3490	745	111-61-5	312.54	$C_{20}H_{40}O_2$	Colourless, odourless mass
41	Ethanol	Ethanol	Ethyl alcohol	2419		64-17-5	46.07	C_2H_6O	Clear, colourless, mobile liquid with a characteristic odour and a burning taste
42	Isoamyl formate	3-Methylbutyl formate	Isopentyl formate	2069	500	110-45-2	116.16	$C_6H_{12}O_2$	Colourless liquid with a plum-like odour
43	Isoamyl acetate	3-Methylbutyl acetate	Isoamyl ethanoate	2055	214	123-92-2	130.19	$C_7H_{14}O_2$	Colourless liquid with a fruity, pear, banana-like odour
44	Isoamyl propionate	3-Methylbutyl propanoate	Isoamyl propanoate	2082	417	105-68-0	144.21	$C_8H_{16}O_2$	Colourless liquid with a fruity, apricot, pineapple-like odour
45	Isoamyl butyrate	3-Methylbutyl butanoate	Isoamyl butanoate	2060	282	106-27-4	158.24	$C_9H_{18}O_2$	Colourless liquid with a fruity odour
46	Isoamyl hexanoate	3-Methylbutyl hexanoate	Isoamyl caproate	2075	320	2198-61-0	186.29	$C_{11}H_{22}O_2$	Colourless liquid with a fruity odour
47	Isoamyl octanoate	3-Methylbutyl octanoate	Isoamyl caprylate	2080	401	2035-99-6	214.35	$C_{13}H_{26}O_2$	Colourless liquid with a fruity odour
48	Isoamyl nonanoate	3-Methylbutyl nonanoate	Isoamyl nonylate	2078	391	7779-70-6	228.37	$C_{14}H_{28}O_2$	Colourless oily liquid with a nutty, oily, apricot-like odour

NO	SOLUBILITY	SOLUBILITY IN ETHANOL*	BOILING POINT	ID TEST	ASSAY MIN%	ACID VALUE MAX*	REFRACTIVE INDEX*	SPECIFIC GRAVITY*	OTHER REQUIREMENTS	JECFA
32	Slightly soluble in most fixed oils and in propylene glycol, insoluble in water and glycerol	1ml in 3ml 70% ethanol	189°; 72% azeotrope at 98.5°	IR	98.0	1.0	1.411 - 1.415	0.867 - 0.872	None	46th
33	Soluble in most fixed oils, slightly soluble in propylene glycol, insoluble in water and glycerol	1ml in 4ml 70% ethanol	209°	IR	98.0	1.0	1.417 - 1.419	0.865 - 0.868	None	46th, 49th/S
34	Soluble in propylene glycol, insoluble in water	1ml in 10ml 70% ethanol	229°	IR	98.0	3.0	1.420 - 1.424	0.863 - 0.867	None	46th, 49th/S
35	Soluble in most fixed oils, insoluble in glycerol and propylene glycol	1ml in 4ml 80% ethanol	243°	IR	98.0	1.0	1.424 - 1.427	0.863 - 0.868	None	46th
36	Soluble in ethanol and oils, insoluble in water	No data	255°	IR	-	-	1.438	0.870	None	46th/T
37	Soluble in ether, insoluble in water	1ml in 9ml 80% ethanol	269°	IR	98.0	1.0	1.430 - 1.434	0.858 - 0.863	None	46th
38	Slightly soluble in ether	1ml in 1ml 95% ethanol	178°-180° at 12mm Hg	IR	98.0	1.0	1.434 - 1.438	0.857 - 0.862	None	46th
39	Soluble in ethanol and oils, insoluble in water	No data	303°	IR	99.0	1.0	1.404 - 1.408	0.863 - 0.865	None	46th
40	Soluble in ethanol and oils, insoluble in water	No data	105° at 11mm Hg	IR	93.0	1.0	1.420 - 1.440	0.880 - 0.900	None	46th
41	Soluble in water		78°	IR	94.9	0.003	1.364	< 0.810	None	46th/C
42	Soluble in ethanol, most fixed oils and propylene glycol, slightly soluble in water, insoluble in glycerol	1ml in 40ml 60% ethanol	124°	IR	92.0	3.0	1.396 - 1.400	0.881 - 0.889	None	46th
43	Soluble in ether, ethyl acetate and most fixed oils, slightly soluble in water, insoluble in glycerol and propylene glycol	1ml in 3ml 60% ethanol	145°	IR	95.0	1.0	1.400 - 1.404	0.868 - 0.878	None	46th/C, 49th/R, C
44	Soluble in ethanol and most fixed oils, insoluble in glycerol, propylene glycol and water	1ml in 3ml 70% ethanol	160°	IR	98.0	1.0	1.405 - 1.409	0.866 - 0.871	None	46th
45	Soluble in ethanol and most fixed oils, insoluble in glycerol, propylene glycol and water	1ml in 4ml 70% ethanol	179°	IR	98.0	1.0	1.409 - 1.414	0.861 - 0.866	None	46th, 49th/S
46	Soluble in ethanol and fixed oils, insoluble in glycerol, propylene glycol and water	1ml in 3ml 80% ethanol	222°	IR	98.0	1.0	1.418 - 1.422	0.858 - 0.863	None	46th
47	Slightly soluble in propylene glycol, insoluble in glycerol and water	1ml in 7ml 80% ethanol	267° - 268°	-	98.0	1.0	1.425 - 1.429	0.855 - 0.861	None	46th/T
48	Soluble in ethanol, insoluble in water	-	260° - 265°	IR	-	-	-	0.86	None	46th/T

208

NO	NAME	CHEMICAL NAME	SYNONYMS	FEMA NO	COE NO	CAS NO	MOL WT	CHEMICAL FORMULA	PHYSICAL FORM / ODOUR
49	Isoamyl isobutyrate	3-Methylbutyl 2-methyl propanoate	Isoamyl 2-methyl propanoate	3507	294	2050--01-3	158.24	$C_9H_{18}O_2$	Liquid with a fruity apricot, pineapple-like odour
50	Isoamyl isovalerate	3-Methylbutyl 3-methylbutanoate	Isoamyl isopentanoate	2085	458	659-70-1	172.27	$C_{10}H_{20}O_2$	Colourless liquid with a fruity apple-like odour
51	Isoamyl 2-methylbutyrate	3-Methylbutyl 2-methylbutanoate	Isoamyl 2-methyl butanoate	3505	10721	27625-35-0	172.27	$C_{10}H_{20}O_2$	Colourless liquid with a fruity odour
52	Isoamyl alcohol	3-Methyl-1-butanol	Isobutyl carbinol	2057	51	123-51-3	88.15	$C_5H_{12}O$	Colourless to pale yellow liquid
53	Citronellyl formate	3,7-Dimethyl-6-octen 1-yl formate		2314	345	105-85-1	184.28	$C_{11}H_{20}O_2$	colourless liquid/strong, fruity, floral odour
54	Geranyl formate	trans-3,7-Dimethyl-2,6-octadien-1-yl formate		2514	343	1005-86-2	182.26	$C_{11}H_{18}O_2$	colorless to pale yellow liquid/fresh, leafy, rose-like odour
55	Neryl formate	cis-3,7-Dimethyl-2,6-octadien-1-yl formate		2776	2060	2142-94-1	182.26	$C_{11}H_{18}O_2$	colourless to pale yellow liquid/sweet, herbaceous, green, rose odour
56	Rhodinyl formate	3,7-Dimethyl-7-octen 1-yl formate		2984	346	141-09-3	184.28	$C_{11}H_{20}O_2$	colourless to slightly yellow liquid/leafy, rose-like odour
57	Citronellyl acetate	3,7-Dimethyl-6-octen 1-yl acetate		2311	202	150-84-5	198.31	$C_{11}H_{22}O_2$	colourless liquid/fruity odour
58	Geranyl acetate	trans-3,7-Dimethyl-2,6-octadien-1-yl acetate		2509	201	105-87-3	196.29	$C_{12}H_{20}O_2$	colourless liquid/floral odour
59	Neryl acetate	cis-3,7-Dimethyl-2,6-octadien-1-yl-acetate		2773	2061	141-12-8	196.29	$C_{12}H_{20}O_2$	colourless to pale yellow liquid/sweet, floral odour
60	Rhodinyl acetate	3,7-Dimethyl-7-octen 1-yl acetate		2981	223	141-11-7	198.31	$C_{11}H_{22}O_2$	colourless to slightly yellow liquid/light, fresh, rose-like odour
61	Citronellyl propionate	3,7-Dimethyl-6-octen 1-yl propanoate		2316	410	141-14-0	212.33	$C_{13}H_{24}O_2$	colourless liquid/fruity-rosy odour
62	Geranyl propionate	trans-3,7-Dimethyl-2,6-octadien-1-yl propanoate		2517	409	105-90-8	210.32	$C_{13}H_{22}O_2$	colourless liquid/rosy, fruity odour
63	Neryl propionate	cis-3,7-Dimethyl-2,6-octadien-1-yl propanoate		2777	509	105-91-9	210.31	$C_{13}H_{22}O_2$	colourless, oily liquid/ether, fruity, jasmine, rose odour
64	Rhodinyl propionate	3,7-Dimethyl-7-octen 1-yl propanoate		2986	422	105-89-5	212.26	$C_{13}H_{24}O_2$	colourless, oily liquid/rose, geranium odour

NO	SOLUBILITY	SOLUBILITY IN ETHANOL*	BOILING POINT	ID TEST	ASSAY MIN%	ACID VALUE MAX*	REFRACTIVE INDEX*	SPECIFIC GRAVITY*	OTHER REQUIREMENTS	JECFA
49	No information	-	170°	IR	98.0	0.1	1.407 - 1.411	0.862 - 0.869 at 15°	None	46th, 49th/S
50	Soluble in most fixed oils, slightly soluble in propylene glycol, insoluble in water	1ml in 6ml 70% ethanol	192°	IR	98.0	2.0	1.411 - 1.414	0.851 - 0.857	None	46th, 49th/S
51	Soluble in ethanol and oil, insoluble in water	-	70-71° at 8mm Hg	-	95.0	-	1.4124	-	None	46th/T
52	Soluble in ethanol, water and most organic solvents	-	130°	IR	98.0	-	1.405 - 1.410	0.807 - 0.813	None	46th/T
53	soluble in alcohol, most fixed oils; slightly soluble in propylene glycol; insoluble in glycerin, water	1 ml in 3 ml 80% alcohol remains in soln to 10 ml	235°	IR	86.0	3.0	1.443-1.452	0.890-0.903		49th/N
54	soluble in alcohol, most fixed oils; insoluble in glycerin, propylenen glycol, water	1 ml in 3 ml 80% alcohol	216°	IR	85.0 (total esters)	3.0	1.457-1.466	0.906-0.920		49th/N
55	insoluble in water	1ml in 10 ml 70% alcohol	215 - 225°	IR	85.0		1.456-1.458	0.9163-0.9169 (15°)		49th/N
56	soluble in alcohol, most fixed oils; insoluble in glycerin, propylene glycol, water	1 ml in 2 ml 80% alcohol gives clear solution	220°	IR	85.0 (total esters)	2.0	1.453-1.458	0.901-0.908		49th/N
57	soluble in alochol, most fixed oils; insoluble in glycerin, propylene glycol, water	1 ml in 9 ml 70% alcohol	229°	IR	92.0 (total esters)	1.0	1.440-1.450	0.883-0.893		49th/N
58	soluble in alcohol, most fixed oils; slightly soluble in propylene glycol; insoluble in glycerin, water	1 L in 9 ml 70% alcohol		IR	90.0 (total esters)		1.458-1.464	0.900-0.914		49th/R
59		1 ml in 1 ml 95% alcohol	134° (25 mm Hg)	IR	96.0	1.0	1.458-1.464	0.905-0.914		49th/N
60	soluble in alcohol, most fixed oils; insoluble in glycerin, propylene glycol, water	1 ml in 2 ml 80% alcohol remains in soln to 10 ml	237°	IR	87.0 (total esters	1.0	1.450-1.458	0.895-0.908	Angular Rotation: -2° to -6°	49th/N
61	miscible with alcohol, most fixed oils; insoluble in water	1 ml in 4 ml 80% alcohol gives clear soln	242°	IR	90.0 (total esters)	1.0	1.443-1.449	0.877-0.886		49th/N
62	soluble in alcohol, most fixed oils; insoluble in glycerin, propylene glycol	1 ml in 4 ml 80% alcohol	253°	IR	92.0 (total esters)	1.0	1.456-1.464	0.896-0.913		49th/N
63	very slightly soluble in water; soluble in alcohol	1 ml in 15 ml 70% alcohol	233°	IR	95.0		1.45-1.47	0.89-0.91 (d20/4)		49th/N
64	soluble in alcohol; practically insoluble in water		255°	IR			1.46	0.910 (15.5°)		49th/N,T

NO	NAME	CHEMICAL NAME	SYNONYMS	FEMA NO	COE NO	CAS NO	MOL WT	CHEMICAL FORMULA	PHYSICAL FORM / ODOUR
65	Citronellyl butyrate	3,7-Dimethyl-6-octen 1-yl butanoate		2312	275	141-16-2	226.36	$C_{14}H_{26}O_2$	colourless liquid/strong, fruity-rosy odour
66	Geranyl butyrate	trans-3,7-Dimethyl-2,6-octadien-1-yl butanoate		2512	274	106-29-6	224.34	$C_{14}H_{24}O_2$	colourless to pale yellow liquid/fruity, rose-like odour
67	Neryl butyrate	cis-3,7-Dimethyl-2,6-octadien-1-yl butanoate		2774	505	999-40-6	224.34	$C_{14}H_{24}O_2$	colourless to pale yellow liquid/sweet, leafy, floral odour
68	Rhodinyl butyrate	3,7-Dimethyl-7-octen 1-yl butanoate		2982	284	141-15-1	226.36	$C_{14}H_{26}O_2$	colourless to yellowish or greenish liquid/fruity, rose odour
69	Citronellyl valerate	3,7-Dimethyl-6-octen 1-yl pentanoate		2317	469	7540-53-6	240.39	$C_{15}H_{28}O_2$	liquid/rose, herb, honey-like odour
70	Geranyl hexanoate	trans-3,7-Dimethyl-2,6-octadien-1-yl hexanoate	Geranyl caproate	2515	317	10032-02-7	252.40	$C_{16}H_{28}O_2$	colourless liquid/rose-geranium, pineapple, banana odour
71	Citronellyl isobutyrate	3,7-Dimethyl-6-octen 1-yl 2-methyl propanoate		2313	296	97-89-2	226.36	$C_{14}H_{26}O_2$	colourless liquid/rosy-fruity odour
72	Geranyl isobutyrate	trans-3,7-Dimethyl-2,6-octadienyl 2-methyl propanoate		2513	3061	2345-26-8	224.34	$C_{14}H_{245}O_2$	colourless to pale yellow liquid/rose odour
73	Neryl isobutyrate	cis-3,7-Dimethyl-2,6-octadien-1-yl 2-methyl propanoate		2775	299	2345-24-6	224.34	$C_{14}H_{24}O_2$	colourless liquid/sweet, rose odour
74	Rhodinyl isobutyrate	3,7-Dimethyl-7-octen 1-yl 2-methyl propanoate		2983	297	1338-23-8	226.36	$C_{14}H_{26}O_2$	colourless to pale yellow oily liquid/fruity, floral odour
75	Geranyl isovalerate	trans-3,7-Dimethyl-2,6-octadienyl 3-methylbutanoate		2518	448	109-20-6	238.37	$C_{15}H_{26}O_2$	colourless to pale yellow liquid/rose odour
76	Neryl isovalerate	cis-3,7-Dimethyl-2,6-octadien-1-yl-2-methylbutanoate		2778	508	3915-83-1	238.38	$C_{15}H_{26}O_2$	colourless to pale yellow liquid/fruity, bergamot, clary sage, petitgrain odour
77	Rhodinyl isovalerate	3,7-Dimethyl-7-octen 1-yl 3-methylbutanoate		2987	460	7778-96-3	240.36	$C_{15}H_{28}O_2$	colourless, oily liquid/rose odour
78	Geranyl 2-ethylbutanoate	trans-3,7-Dimethyl-2,6-octadien-1-yl 2-ethylbutanoate		3339	11667	73019-14-4	252.37	$C_{16}H_{30}O_2$	
79	Formic acid	Formic acid		2487	1	64-18-6	46.03	CH_2O_2	colourless, highly corrosive liquid/characteristic pungent odour

NO	SOLUBILITY	SOLUBILITY IN ETHANOL*	BOILING POINT	ID TEST	ASSAY MIN%	ACID VALUE MAX*	REFRACTIVE INDEX*	SPECIFIC GRAVITY*	OTHER REQUIREMENTS	JECFA
65	miscible with alcohol, ether, most fixed oils, chloroform; insoluble in water	1 ml in 6 ml 80% alcohol gives clear soln	245°	IR	90.0 (total esters)	1.0	1.444-1.448	0.873-0.883		49th/N
66	soluble in alcohol, most fixed oils; insoluble inglycerin, propylene glycol, water	1 ml in 6 ml 80% alcohol	243°	IR	92.0 (total esters)	1.0	1.455-1.462	0.889-0.904		49th/N
67	soluble in alcohol; insoluble in water	1 ml in 6 ml 80% alcohol	239 - 240°	IR	98.0	0.7	1.4539-1.4650	0.898-0.910		49th/N
68		1ml in 8ml 80% alcohol; 1ml in 1ml 90% alcohol	137° (13 mm Hg)	IR	90.0	1.0	1.446-1.4560	0.880-0.895 (20°/20°)		49th/N
69			237°	IR			1.44	0.890 (15.5°)		49th/N,T
70			240°	IR			1.45	0.890 (15.5°)		49th/N,T
71	miscible with alcohol, chloroform, ether, most fixed oils; insoluble in water	1 ml in 6 ml 80% alcohol gives clear soln	249°	IR	92.0 (total esters)	1.0	1.440-1.448	0.870-0.880		49th/N
72	soluble in most organic solvents; insoluble in water			IR	90.0		1.451-1.457	0.885-0.893 (d20/4)		49th/N,T
73	practically insoluble in water	1 ml in 5 ml 80% alcohol	232°	IR	92.0		1.451-1.460	0.88-0.90 (d20/4)		49th/N
74	soluble in alcohol; insoluble in water		260°		85.0		1.448-1.453	0.881-0.891 (d20/4)		49th/N,T
75	soluble in alcohol, most fixed oils; insoluble in water			IR	95.0		1.454-1.470	0.878-0.899		49th/N,T
76	insoluble in water	1 ml in 8 ml 80% alcohol	238°	IR	99.0		1.4531-1.460	0.889-0.893		49th/N
77	soluble in alcohol; practically insoluble in water		270°	IR			1.447	0.8829 (15°)		49th/N,T
78				IR						49th/N,T
79	miscible with water, alcohol, glycerin, ether			IR	85.0			1.20	Acetic acid: < 0.4%; Dilution Test: passes test; Heavy Metals: < 10 mg/kg; Sulfate: <0.004%	49th/R,P

NO	NAME	CHEMICAL NAME	SYNONYMS	FEMA NO	COE NO	CAS NO	MOL WT	CHEMICAL FORMULA	PHYSICAL FORM / ODOUR
80	Acetaldehyde	Acetaldehyde	Ethanal; Acetic aldehyde	2003	89	75-07-0	44.05	C_2H_4O	flammable, colourless liquiduid/pungent ethereal odour
81	Acetic acid	Acetic acid		2006	2	64-19-7	60.05	$C_2H_4O_2$	clear, colourless liquid/pungent odour
82	Propyl alcohol	1-Propanol	n-Propanol	2928	50	71-23-8	60.09	C_3H_8O	colourless liquid
83	Propionaldehyde	Propanal		2923	90	123-38-6	58.08	C_3H_6O	colourless, mobile liquid/sharp, pungent odour
84	Propionic acid	Propanoic acid		2924	3	79-09-4	74.08	$C_3H_6O_2$	oily liquid/slightly pungent, rancid odour
85	Butyl alcohol	1-Butanol	Butan-1-ol	2178	52	71-36-3	74.12	$C_4H_{10}O$	colourless, mobile liquid/vinous odour
86	Butyraldehyde	Butanal	Butyl aldehyde	2219	91	123-72-8	72.11	C_6H_8O	colourless, mobile liquid/pungent, nutty odour
87	Butyric acid	Butanoic acid		2221	5	107-92-6	88.11	$C_4H_8O_2$	colourless liquid/strong, rancid, butterlike odour
88	Amyl alcohol	1-Pentanol		2056	514	71-41-0	88.15	$C_5H_{12}O$	colourless to pale yellow liquid
89	Valeraldehyde	Pentanal	Valeric Aldehyde	3098	93	110-62-3	86.13	$C_5H_{10}O$	colourless to pale yellow liquid
90	Valeric acid	Pentanoic acid		3101	7	109-52-4	102.13	$C_5H_{10}O_2$	colourless to pale yellow mobile liquid/unpleasant, penetrating rancid odour
91	Hexyl alcohol	1-Hexanol	Alcohol C-6	2567	53	111-27-3	102.18	$C_6H_{14}O$	colourless, mobile liquid/mild, sweet, green
92	Hexanal	Hexanal	Caproic aldehyde; Hexaldehyde; Aldehyde C-6	2557	96	66-25-1	100.16	$C_6H_{12}O$	almost colourless liquid/fatty-green, grassy odour
93	Hexanoic acid	Hexanoic acid	Caproic acid	2559	9	142-62-1	116.16	$C_6H_{12}O_2$	colourless to very pale yellow, oily liquid/cheesy, sweat-like odour

NO	SOLUBILITY	SOLUBILITY IN ETHANOL*	BOILING POINT	ID TEST	ASSAY MIN%	ACID VALUE MAX*	REFRACTIVE INDEX*	SPECIFIC GRAVITY*	OTHER REQUIREMENTS	JECFA
80	miscible with water, alcohol, organic solvents		21	IR	99.0	5.0		0.804-0.811 (0°/20°)	Res. on Evap.: 0.006%	49th/N
81	miscible with water, alcohol, and glycerin		118	IR	99.5			1.049	Heavy Metals: < 10 mg/kg; Nonvolatile Res.: < 0.005%; Readily Oxid. Sub.: Passes test; Solidification Pt.: > 15.6°	49th/R,A
82		1 ml in 1 ml 95% alcohol	97	IR	99.0		1.383-1.388	0.800-0.805		49th/R, C,E
83	miscible with alcohol, ether, water		49	IR	97.0	5.0		0.800-0.805	Dist. Range: 46° to 50°; Water: 2.5%	49th/N
84	miscible with water, alcohol, organic solvents		138.5-142.5	IR	99.5			0.993-0.997 (20°/20°)	Dist. Range: 138.5° to 142.5°; Heavy Metals: < 10 mg/kg; Nonvolatile Res.: < 0.01%; Water: < 0.15%	49th/N,P
85	miscible with alcohol, ether, organic solvents, 1 ml in 15 ml water		118	IR	99.5	2.0		0.807-0.809	Butyl Ether: 0.15%; Dist. Range: max. 1.5° between beginning and end	49th/R,E
86	soluble in 1 ml in 15 ml water; miscible with alcohol, ether		75	IR	98.0	5.0		0.797-0.802	Dist. Range: 72° to 80°; para-Butyraldehyde: <2.5%; Water: <0.5%	49th/N
87	miscible with alcohol, most fixed oils, propylene glycol, water		164	IR	99.0		1.397-1.399	0.952-0.956	Heavy Metals: <0.004%; Lead: <10 mg/kg; Reducing Subs.: passes test	49th/N
88	miscible with alcohol		136	IR	98.0		1.407-1.412	0.810-0.816		49th/N
89		1 ml in 1 ml 95% alcohol	103	IR	97.0	5.0	1.390-1.395	0.805-0.809		49th/N
90	miscible with alcohol, ether, 1 ml in 40 ml water		186	IR	99.0		1.405-1.414 (25°)	0.935-0.940		49th/N
91	miscible with alcohol, ether, 1 ml in 175 ml water		157	IR	96.5	2.0		0.816-0.821		49th/N
92	very slightly soluble in water; miscible with alcohol, propylene glycol, most fixed oils		131	IR	97.0	10.0	1.402-1.407	0.808-0.817		49th/N
93	miscible with alcohol, most fixed oils, ether, 1 ml in 250 ml water		205	IR	98.0		1.415-1.418	0.923-0.928	Solidification Pt: > -4.5°	49th/N

NO	NAME	CHEMICAL NAME	SYNONYMS	FEMA NO	COE NO	CAS NO	MOL WT	CHEMICAL FORMULA	PHYSICAL FORM / ODOUR
94	Heptyl alcohol	1-Heptanol	Alcohol C-7; Enanthic alcohol	2548	70	111-70-6	116.20	$C_7H_{16}O$	colourless liquid/citrus odour
95	Heptanal	Heptanal	Aldehyde C-7; Heptaldehyde	2540	117	111-71-7	114.19	$C_7H_{14}O$	colourless to slightly yellow liquid/penetrating, oily odour
96	Heptanoic acid	Heptanoic acid	Enanthic Acid; Heptoic acid	3348	28	111-14-8	130.18	$C_7H_{14}O_2$	colourless oily liquid/ disagreeable rancid, sour, fatty odour
97	1-Octanol	1-Octanol	Octyl alcohol; Alcohol C-8; Capryl alcohol	2800	54	111-87-5	130.23	$C_8H_{18}O$	colourless liquid/sharp fatty-citrus odour
98	Octanal	Octanal	Aldehyde C-8; Caprylic aldehyde	2797	97	124-13-0	128.21	$C_8H_{16}O$	colourless to light yellow liquid/fatty-orange odour
99	Octanoic acid	Octanoic acid	Caprylic acid	2799	10	124-07-2	144.21	$C_8H_{16}O_2$	colourless, oily liquid/slight, unpleasant odour
100	Nonyl alcohol	1-Nonanol	Alcohol C-9; Pelargonic alcohol	2789	55	143-08-8	144.26	$C_9H_{20}O$	colourless liquid/rose-citrus odour
101	Nonanal	Nonanal	Aldehyde C-9; Pelargonic aldehyde	2782	114	124-19-6	142.24	$C_9H_{18}O$	colourless to yellow liquid/fruity odour
102	Nonanoic acid	Nonanoic acid		2784	29	112-05-0	158.24	$C_9H_{18}O_2$	colourless to pale yellow liquid
103	1-Decanol	1-Decanol	Alcohol C-10; Decyl alcohol	2365	73	112-30-1	158.28	$C_{10}H_{22}O$	colourless liquid/floral, waxy, fruity odour
104	Decanal	Decanal	Aldehyde C-10; Capraldehyde	2362	98	112-31-2	156.27	$C_{10}H_{20}O$	colourless to light yellow liquid/fatty, floral-orange odour on dilution
105	Decanoic acid	Decanoic acid	Capric acid	2364	11	334-48-5	172.27	$C_{10}H_{20}O_2$	white crystals/unpleasant, rancid odour

NO	SOLUBILITY	SOLUBILITY IN ETHANOL*	BOILING POINT	ID TEST	ASSAY MIN%	ACID VALUE MAX*	REFRACTIVE INDEX*	SPECIFIC GRAVITY*	OTHER REQUIREMENTS	JECFA
94	slightly soluble in water; miscible with alcohol, ether, most fixed oils	1 ml in 2 ml 60% alcohol	175	IR	97.0	1.0	1.423-1.427	0.820-1.824	Aldehydes: 1.0% as heptanal	49th/N
95	slightly soluble in water; miscible with alcohol, ether, fixed oils	1 ml in 2 ml 70% alcohol	153	IR	92.0	10.0	1.412-1.420	0.814-0.819		49th/N
96	slightly soluble in water; soluble in alcohol, ether, acetone, nitric acid, and dimethyl sulfoxide		223	IR	98.0	422-430	1.421-1.425	0.915-0.920 (20°/20°)	Congealing Point: -6.26°; Melting Point: -7.5°	49th/N
97	soluble in most fixed oils, propylene glycol; insoluble in glycerin	1 ml in 5 ml 50% alcohol	195	IR	98.0	1.0	1.428-1.431	0.822-0.830		49th/N
98	soluble in alcohol, most fixed oils, propylene glycol; insoluble in glycerin	1ml in 2ml of 70% alcohol	171	IR	92.0	10.0	1.417-1.425	0.810-0.830		49th/R
99	slightly soluble in water; soluble in most organic solvents		240	IR		366-396		0.910	Heavy Metals: < 10 mg/kg; Iodine Value: < 2.0; Res. on Ignition: < 0.1%; Saponification Value: 366 to 398; Solidification Pt.: 8° to 15°; Unsaponifiable Matter: < 0.2%; Water: < 0.4%	49th/N
100	miscible with alcohol, chloroform, ether; insoluble in water	1 ml in 3 ml 60% alcohol gives clear soln	213	IR	97.0	1.0	1.431-1.435	0.824-0.830		49th/N
101	soluble in alcohol, most fixed oils, propylene glycol; insoluble in glycerin	1 ml in 3 ml of 70% alcohol	93 (23 mm Hg) 191	IR	92.0	10.0	1.422-1.429	0.820-0.830		49th/R
102	soluble inmost organic solvents; Insoluble in water		254	IR	98.0		1.431-1.435	0.901-0.906		49th/N
103	soluble in alcohol, ether, mineral oil, propylene glycol, most fixed oils; Insoluble in glycerin, water	1 ml in 3 ml 60% alcohol	233	IR	98.0	1.0	1.435-1.439	0.826-0.831	Solidification Pt.: > 5°	49th/N
104	miscible with alcohol, fixed oils, propylene glycol (may be turbid); insoluble in glycerin, water	1 ml in 1 ml of 80% alcohol	209	IR	92.0	10.0	1.426-1.430	0.823-0.832		49th/R
105	soluble in most organic solvents; practically insoluble in water		268	IR		320-329			Heavy Metals: < 10 mg/kg; Iodine Value: < 0.6; Res. on Ignition: < 0.1%; Saponification Value: 320-331; Solidification Pt.: 27° to 32°; Unsaponifiable Matter: < 0.2%; Water: < 0.2%	49th/N

NO	NAME	CHEMICAL NAME	SYNONYMS	FEMA NO	COE NO	CAS NO	MOL WT	CHEMICAL FORMULA	PHYSICAL FORM / ODOUR
106	Undecyl alcohol	1-Undecanol	Alcohol C-11	3097	751	112-42-5	172.31	$C_{11}H_{24}O$	colourless liquid/fatty-floral odour
107	Undecanal	Undecanal	Aldehyde C-11 undecyclic; n-Undecyl aldehyde	3092	121	112-44-7	170.30	$C_{11}H_{22}O$	colourless to slightly yellow liquid/sweet, fatty, floral odour
108	Undecanoic acid	Undecanoic acid	n-Undecylic acid	3245	696	112-37-8	186.29	$C_{11}H_{22}O_2$	colourless crystals/ faint fatty, aldehydic odour
109	Lauryl alcohol	1-Dodecanol	Alcohol C-12	2617	56	112-53-8	186.34	$C_{12}H_{26}O$	Colourless liquid above 21°, fatty odour
110	Lauric aldehyde	Dodecanal	Aldehyde C-12; Lauryl aldehyde	2615	99	112-54-9	184.32	$C_{12}H_{24}O$	colourless to light yellow liquid/fatty odour
111	Lauric acid	Dodecanoic acid		2614	12	143-07-7	200.32	$C_{12}H_{24}O_2$	white or faintly yellowish crystalline solid
112	Myristaldehyde	Tetradecanal	Aldehyde C-14	2763	118	124-25-4	212.38	$C_{14}H_{28}O$	colourless to pale yellow liquid/fatty, orris-like odour
113	Myristic acid	Tetradecanoic acid		2764	16	544-63-8	228.38	$C_{14}H_{28}O_2$	hard, white, or faintly yellowish, somewhat glossy, crystalline solid
114	1-Hexadecanol	1-Hexadecanol	Alcohol C-16	2554	57	36653-82-4	242.45	$C_{16}H_{34}O$	white solid/odourless
115	Palmitic acid	Hexadecanoic acid		2832	14	57-10-3	256.43	$C_{16}H_{32}O_2$	hard, white or faintly yellowish crystalline solid

NO	SOLUBILITY	SOLUBILITY IN ETHANOL*	BOILING POINT	ID TEST	ASSAY MIN%	ACID VALUE MAX*	REFRACTIVE INDEX*	SPECIFIC GRAVITY*	OTHER REQUIREMENTS	JECFA
106	soluble in most fixed oils; insoluble in water	1ml in 4 ml of 60% alcohol	146 (30 mm Hg)	IR	97.0		1.437-1.443	0.820-0.840		49th/N
107	soluble in most fixed oils, propylene glycol; insoluble in glycerin, water	1 ml in 5 ml of 70% alcohol	223	IR	92.0	10.0	1.430-1.435	0.825-0.832		49th/N
108	Insoluble in water; very soluble in alcohol, chloroform, acetone		284	IR	99.0	295-301	1.4355 (30°)	0.9948 (20°/20°)		49th/N
109	soluble in most fixed oils, propylene glycol; insoluble in glycerin, water	1 ml in 3 ml 70% alcohol; remains clear to 10 ml	259	IR	97.0	1.0	1.440-1.444	0.830-0.836	Solidification Pt.: > 21°	49th/N
110	soluble in alcohol, most fixed oils, propylene glycol (may be turbid); insoluble in glycerin, water	1 ml in 2 ml of 80% alcohol	249	IR	92.0	10.0	1.433-1.439	0.826-0.836		49th/N
111	practically insoluble in water; soluble in alcohol, chloroform, ether			IR		252-287			Heavy Metals: < 10 mg/kg; Iodine Value: < 3.0; Res. on Ignition: <0.1%; Saponification Value: 253 to 287; Solidification Pt.: 26° to 44°; Unsaponifiable Matter: < 0.3%; Water: < 0.2%	49th/N
112	soluble in most organic solvents; Insoluble in water	1 ml in 1 ml of 80% alcohol	260	IR	85.0	5.0	1.438-1.445	0.825-0.830		49th/N
113	practically insoluble in water; soluble in alcohol, chloroform, ether			IR		242-249			Heavy Metals: < 10 mg/kg; Iodine Value: < 1.0; Residue on Ignition: < 0.1%; Saponification Value: 242 to 251; Solidification Pt.: 48° to 55.5°; Unsaponifiable Matter: < 1%; Water: < 0.2%	49th/N
114	insoluble in water; soluble in ether	1 gm in 3ml 90% alcohol	344	IR	97.0	1.0	1.4283 (78.9°)	0.8152 (55°)	Congealing Pt.: 46°C	49th/N
115	practically insoluble in water; soluble in alcohol, ether, chloroform			IR		204-220			Heavy metals: <10 mg/kg; Iodine Value: < 2.0; Res. on Ignition: <0.1%; Saponification Value: 205 to 221; Solidification Pt.: 53.3 to 62°; Unsaponifiable Matter: <1.5%; Water: <0.2%	49th/N

NO	NAME	CHEMICAL NAME	SYNONYMS	FEMA NO	COE NO	CAS NO	MOL WT	CHEMICAL FORMULA	PHYSICAL FORM / ODOUR
116	Stearic acid	Octadecanoic acid		3035	15	57-11-4	284.48	$C_{18}H_{36}O_2$	hard, white or faintly yellowish crystalline solid/tallow odour
117	Propyl formate	Propyl formate	Propyl methanoate	2943	340	110-74-7	88.10	$C_4H_8O_2$	colourless to pale yellow liquid with a characteristic fruity, rum plum odour
118	Butyl formate	Butyl formate		2196	501	592-84-7	102.13	$C_5H_{10}O_2$	colourless to pale yellow liquid with a fruity, plum-like odour
119	n-Amyl formate	Pentyl formate		2068	497	638-49-3	116.16	$C_6H_{12}O_2$	colourless to pale yellow liquid with a fruit-like odour
120	Hexyl formate	Hexyl formate		2570	499	629-33-4	130.18	$C_7H_{14}O_2$	colourless liquid with an ethereal, fruity, leafy, green odour
121	Heptyl formate	Heptyl formate		2552	341	112-23-2	144.21	$C_8H_{16}O_2$	colourless liquid with a fruity, floral, orris-rose odour
122	Octyl formate	Octyl formate		2809	342	112-32-3	158.24	$C_9H_{18}O_2$	colourless liquid with a fruity, rose-orange odour
123	cis-3-Hexenyl formate	cis-3-Hexen-1-yl formate	3-Hexenyl methanoate	3353	2153	33467-73-1	128.17	$C_7H_{12}O_2$	colourless to pale yellow liquid with a green, vegetable odour
124	Isobutyl formate	2-Methylpropyl formate	Tetryl formate	2197	502	542-55-2	102.13	$C_5H_{10}O_2$	colourless to pale yellow liquid with a fruity, ethereal odour
125	Methyl acetate	Methyl acetate		2676	213	79-20-9	74.08	$C_3H_6O_2$	colourless liquid with a pleasant, fruity odour
126	Propyl acetate	Propyl acetate	n-Propyl acetate	2925	192	109-60-4	102.13	$C_5H_{10}O_2$	colourless mobile liquid with a fruity, pear-raspberry odour
127	Butyl acetate	Butyl acetate	n-Butyl acetate	2174	194	123-86-4	116.16	$C_6H_{12}O_2$	colourless, mobile liquid with a strong fruity odour
128	Hexyl acetate	Hexyl acetate		2565	196	142-92-7	144.21	$C_8H_{12}O_2$	colourless liquid with a fruity odour
129	Heptyl acetate	Heptyl acetate		2547	212	112-06-1	158.24	$C_9H_{18}O_2$	colourless liquid with a herbaceous, green, rose odour
130	Octyl acetate	Octyl acetate		2806	197	112-14-1	172.27	$C_{10}H_{20}O_2$	colourless liquid with a fruity, orange-like, jasmine-like odour

NO	SOLUBILITY	SOLUBILITY IN ETHANOL*	BOILING POINT	ID TEST	ASSAY MIN%	ACID VALUE MAX*	REFRACTIVE INDEX*	SPECIFIC GRAVITY*	OTHER REQUIREMENTS	JECFA
116	practically insoluble in water; soluble in alcohol, ether, chloroform	1 g in 20 ml alcohol		IR		196-211			Heavy metals: < 10 mg/kg; Iodine Value: < 7; Res. on Ignition: < 0.1%; Saponification Value: 197 to 212; Solidification Pt.: 54.5° to 69°; Unsaponifiable Matter: < 1.5%; Water: < 0.2%	49th/N
117	miscible with alcohol, ether, most organic solvents; soluble in 1 ml in 45 ml water		81-82°	IR	94.0		1.369-1.384	0.895-0.905	None	49th/N
118	miscible with alcohol, ether, most organic solvents; slightly soluble inwater		106.8°	IR	95.0	2.0	1.380-1.400	0.877-0.903	None	49th/N
119	miscible with alcohol, ether, most organic solvents		128-130°	IR	92.0	5 (add to ice soln)	1.396-1.402	0.881-0.887	None	49th/N
120	miscible with alcohol, ether; slightly soluble in water		176.7°	IR	95.0		1.404-1.409	0.8789 (20°)	None	49th/N
121	soluble in ether, most organic solvents; insoluble in water	1 ml in 5 ml 70% alcohol	176.7-178°	IR			1.414	0.88277 (15°)	None	49th/N,T
122	soluble in most fixed oils, mineral oil, propylene glycol; insoluble in glycerol	1 ml in 5 ml 70% alcohol	198-200°	IR	96.0	1.0	1.418-1.420	0.869-0.874	None	49th/N
123	soluble in alcohol, propylene glycol, most fixed oils; practically insoluble in water		155°	IR	95.0		1.417-1.437	0.898-0.918	None	49th/N
124	miscible with alcohol, ether; soluble in organic solvents; slightly soluble in water		97-98.2°	IR	94.0		1.383-1.39	0.876-0.886	None	49th/N
125	miscible with alcohol, ether; soluble in water	1 ml in 10ml 50% alcohol	56.9-57.5°	IR	98.0	1.0	1.358-1.363	0.927-0.932	None	49th/N
126	miscible with alcohol, ether; soluble 1ml in 60ml water	1 ml in 1 ml 95% alcohol	102°	IR	97.0	1.0	1.382-1.387	0.880-0.886	None	49th/N
127	miscible with alcohol, ether, propylene glycol; soluble 1 ml in 145 ml water		125-126°	IR	98.0	2.0	1.393-1.396	0.876-0.880	Distillation range 120° to 128°	49th/R
128	soluble in alcohol, ether; insoluble in water	1 ml in 1 ml 95% alcohol	168-172°	IR	98.0	1.0	1.407-1.411	0.868-0.872	None	49th/N
129	soluble in alcohol, ether; insoluble in water		192°	IR	97.5	1.0	1.411-1.417	0.87505 (15°)	None	49th/N
130	miscible with alcohol, most fixed oils, organic solvents; insoluble in water	1 ml in 4 ml 70% alcohol	203-208°	IR	98.0	1.0	1.418-1.421	0.865-0.868	None	49th/N

NO	NAME	CHEMICAL NAME	SYNONYMS	FEMA NO	COE NO	CAS NO	MOL WT	CHEMICAL FORMULA	PHYSICAL FORM / ODOUR
131	Nonyl acetate	Nonyl acetate		2788	198	143-13-5	186.29	$C_{11}H_{22}O_2$	colourless liquid with a floral, fruity odour
132	Decyl acetate	Decyl acetate	Acetate C-10	2367	199	112-17-4	200.32	$C_{12}H_{24}O_2$	colourless to pale yellow liquid with a pear, floral, orange-rose odour
133	Lauryl acetate	Dodecyl acetate	Acetate C-12; Dodecyl acetate	2616	200	112-66-3	228.37	$C_{14}H_{28}O_2$	colourless liquid with a waxy, citrus-rose odour
134	cis-3-Hexenyl acetate	cis-3-Hexen-1-yl acetate		3171	644	3681-71-8	142.20	$C_8H_{14}O_2$	colourless to pale yellow liquid with a powerful green note
135	trans-3-Heptenyl acetate	trans-3-Hepten-1-yl acetate		3493	10662	34942-91-1	156.22	$C_9H_{16}O_2$	colourless liquid
136	10-Undecen-1-yl acetate	10-Undecen-1-yl acetate	Acetate C-11	3096	2062	112-19-6	212.33	$C_{13}H_{24}O_2$	colourless liquid with a rose odour
137	Isobutyl acetate	2-Methylpropyl acetate		2175	195	110-19-0	116.16	$C_6H_{12}O_2$	colourless liquid with a fruity, banana-like odour on dilution
138	2-Methylbutyl acetate	2-Methyl-1-butyl acetate		3644	10762	624-41-9	130.18	$C_7H_{14}O_2$	colourless to pale yellow liquid with an apple peel, banana odour
140	2-Ethylbutyl acetate	2-Ethylbutyl acetate		2425	215	10031-87-5	144.21	$C_8H_{16}O_2$	liquid
141	Methyl propionate	Methyl propanoate		2742	415	554-12-1	88.11	$C_4H_8O_2$	colourless to pale yellow liquid with a fruity, rum odour
142	Propyl propionate	n-Propyl propanoate		2958	403	106-36-5	116.16	$C_6H_{12}O_2$	colourless to pale yellow liquid with a fruity (apple, banana, pineapple) odour
143	Butyl propionate	Butyl propanoate		2211	405	590-01-2	130.18	$C_7H_{14}O_2$	colourless to pale yellow liquid with an earthy, faintly sweet odour
144	Hexyl propionate	n-Hexyl propanoate		2576	420	2445-76-3	158.24	$C_9H_{18}O_2$	colourless to pale yellow liquid with an earthy, acrid odour
145	Octyl propionate	Octyl propanoate		2813	407	142-60-9	186.30	$C_{11}H_{22}O_2$	colourless to pale yellow liquid with a waxy odour
146	Decyl propionate	Decyl propanoate		2369	408	5454-19-3	214.35	$C_{13}H_{26}O_2$	colourless to pale yellow liquid with a slightly fatty, aldehyde odour
147	cis-3 & trans-2-Hexenyl propionate	cis-3 & trans-2-Hexenyl propanoate		3778	10683	33467-74-2/ 53398-80-4	156.23	$C_9H_{16}O_2$	colourless to pale yellow liquid
148	Isobutyl propionate	2-Methylpropyl propanoate		2212	406	540-42-1	130.18	$C_7H_{14}O_2$	colourless to pale yellow liquid with an odour reminiscent of rum & pineapple

NO	SOLUBILITY	SOLUBILITY IN ETHANOL*	BOILING POINT	ID TEST	ASSAY MIN%	ACID VALUE MAX*	REFRACTIVE INDEX*	SPECIFIC GRAVITY*	OTHER REQUIREMENTS	JECFA
131	soluble in alcohol, ether; insoluble in water	1 ml in 6 ml 70% alcohol	208-212°	IR	97.0	1.0	1.422-1.426	0.864-0.868	None	49th/N
132	insoluble in water	1 ml in 2 ml 80% alcohol	272°	IR	98.0	1.0	1.424-1.430	0.861-0.866	None	49th/N
133	soluble in most organic solvents	1 ml in 4 ml 80% alcohol		IR	98.0	1.0	1.410-1.436	0.860-0.865	None	49th/N
134		1 ml in 1 ml 95% alcohol	198°	IR	92.0	1.0	1.425-1.429	0.896-0.901	Minimum assay = 98.0% expressed as the sum of isomers	49th/N
135	soluble in alcohol, fixed oils; insoluble in water		55-57° (3mm Hg)	IR	98.0		1.429-1.432	0.885-0.887 (d20/4)	None	49th/N
136	soluble in most organic solvents	1 ml in 2 ml 80% alcohol	272°	IR	95.0		1.438-1.442	0.876-0.880	None	49th/N
137	soluble in alcohol, most fixed oils, propylene glycol, 1 ml in 180 ml water		116-118°	IR	95.0	1.0	1.389-1.392	0.862-0.871	None	49th/N
138	soluble in fat; slightly soluble in water		141° (720 mmHg)	IR	99.0	1.0	1.399-1.404	0.872-0.877	None	49th/N
140			160-163°	IR			1.4109	0.8784 (20°)	None	49th/N,T
141	miscible with alcohol, ether, propylene glycol; soluble 1 ml in 16 ml water		79°	IR	95.0	3.0	1.373-1.380	0.861-0.867	None	49th/N
142	miscible with alcohol, ether, propylene glycol; soluble 1 ml in 200 ml water	1 ml in 1 ml 95% alcohol	122-124°	IR	98.0	1.0	1.391-1.396	0.873-0.879	None	49th/N
143	miscible with alcohol, ether; slightly soluble in water		145-146°	IR	96.0	1.0	1.3975-1.4045	0.868-0.8825	None	49th/N
144	soluble in alcohol, propylene glycol; insoluble in water		180°	IR	97.0	1.5	1.409-1.415	0.863-0.874	None	49th/N
145	soluble in alcohol, propylene glycol; insoluble in water		225-228°	IR	95.0		1.419-1.430	0.8700-0.87044 (15°)	None	49th/N
146			138-139° (15 mmHg)	IR	95.0		1.426-1.432	0.857-0.867	None	49th/N
147				IR	96.0	3.0	1.424-1.436	0.887-0.910	None	49th/N
148	miscible with alcohol; soluble in most organic solvents; insoluble in water		137-138°	IR	95.0		1.395-1.400	0.861-0.867	None	49th/N

NO	NAME	CHEMICAL NAME	SYNONYMS	FEMA NO	COE NO	CAS NO	MOL WT	CHEMICAL FORMULA	PHYSICAL FORM / ODOUR
149	Methyl butyrate	Methyl butanoate		2693	263	623-42-7	102.13	$C_5H_{10}O_2$	colourless liquid with an apple-like odour
150	Propyl butyrate	n-Propyl-n-butanoate		2934	266	105-66-8	130.18	$C_7H_{14}O_2$	colourless liquid with a pineapple, apricot odour
151	Butyl butyrate	n-Butyl n-butanoate		2186	268	109-21-7	144.21	$C_8H_{16}O_2$	colourless liquid with a fruity, pineapple-like odour on dilution
152	n-Amyl butyrate	Pentyl butanoate		2059	270	540-18-1	158.23	$C_9H_{18}O_2$	colourless to pale yellow liquid
153	Hexyl butyrate	Hexyl butanoate		2568	271	2639-63-6	172.27	$C_{10}H_{20}O_2$	colourless to pale yellow liquid with a fruity, apricot odour
154	Heptyl butyrate	Heptyl butanoate		2549	504	5870-93-9	186.30	$C_{11}H_{22}O_2$	colourless liquid with a camomile odour
155	Octyl butyrate	Octyl n-butanoate		2807	272	110-39-4	200.32	$C_{12}H_{24}O_2$	colourless liquid with a green herbaceous, parsley odour
156	Decyl butyrate	Decyl butanoate		2368	273	5454-09-1	228.37	$C_{14}H_{28}O_2$	oily liquid with an ethereal, apricot odour
157	cis-3-Hexenyl butyrate	cis-3-Hexen-1-yl butanoate	Leaf butyrate	3402	11859	16491-36-4	170.25	$C_{10}H_{18}O_2$	colourless to pale yellow liquid with a green, fruity, buttery odour
158	Isobutyl butyrate	2-Methylpropyl butanoate		2187	269	539-90-2	144.21	$C_8H_{16}O_2$	colourless liquid with a sweet, fruity, apple-like, pineapple-like odour
159	Methyl valerate	Methyl pentanoate		2752	588	624-24-8	116.16	$C_6H_{12}O_2$	colourless to pale yellow, mobile liquid with a green, apple, pineapple odour
160	Butyl valerate	Butyl pentanoate		2217	466	591-68-4	158.24	$C_9H_{18}O_2$	liquid with an apple-raspberry odour
161	Propyl hexanoate	Propyl hexanoate	Propyl caproate	2949	311	626-77-7	158.24	$C_9H_{18}O_2$	colourless to pale yellow liquid with an ethereal, pineapple-blackberry odour
162	Butyl hexanoate	Butyl hexanoate	Butyl caproate	2201	313	626-82-4	172.27	$C_{10}H_{20}O_2$	colourless liquid with a pineapple odour
163	n-Amyl hexanoate	Pentyl hexanoate	Amyl caproate	2074	315	540-07-8	186.29	$C_{11}H_{22}O_2$	colourless liquid with a fruity odour
164	Hexyl hexanoate	Hexyl hexanoate	Hexyl caproate	2572	316	6378-65-0	200.32	$C_{12}H_{24}O_2$	colourless to pale yellow oily liquid with a herbaceous odour
165	cis-3-Hexenyl hexanoate	cis-3-Hexen-1-yl hexanoate	cis-3-Hexenyl caproate	3403	11779	31501-11-8	198.31	$C_{12}H_{22}O_2$	colourless to pale yellow liquid with a fruity green odour

NO	SOLUBILITY	SOLUBILITY IN ETHANOL*	BOILING POINT	ID TEST	ASSAY MIN%	ACID VALUE MAX*	REFRACTIVE INDEX*	SPECIFIC GRAVITY*	OTHER REQUIREMENTS	JECFA
149	miscible with alcohol, ether; soluble 1 ml in 60 ml water		102-103°	IR	98.0	1.0	1.386-1.39	0.892-0.897	None	49th/N
150	miscible with alcohol, ether; slightly soluble in water		140-145°	IR	95.0		1.395-1.405	0.866 - 0.875	None	49th/N
151	miscible with alcohol, ether, most vegetable oils; slightly soluble in propylene glycol, water	1 ml in 3 ml 70% alcohol	165°	IR	98.0	1.0	1.405-1.407	0.867-0.871	None	49th/N
152	soluble in alcohol, ether		185-186°	IR	98.0	1.0	1.409-1.414	0.863-0.866	None	49th/N
153			208°	IR	95.0	1.0	1.413-1.419	0.858-0.869	None	49th/N
154	soluble in alcohol, propylene glycol; insoluble in water		226°	IR			1.4231	0.8555 (30°/30°)	None	49th/N,T
155	soluble in alcohol; practically insoluble in water		244°	IR			1.421-1.434	0.8549 (30°)	None	49th/N,T
156			270°	IR			1.4245-1.43977	0.8617 (20°)	None	49th/N,T
157	soluble in alcohol, propylene glycol; miscible with most fixed oils; insoluble in water		192°	IR	95.0		1.420-1.435	0.860-0.899	None	49th/N
158	soluble in most fixed oils; slightly soluble in water; insoluble in glycerol	1 ml in 8 ml 60% alcohol	157-158°	IR	98.0	1.0	1.402-1.405	0.858-0.863	None	49th/N
159	soluble in propylene glycol, alcohol, most fixed oils; very slightly soluble in water		126-127°	IR	98.0		1.393-1.399	0.883-0.895	None	49th/N
160	soluble in propylene glycol; slightly soluble in water		186.5°	IR	99.0		1.408-1.416	0.861-0.871 (d20/4)	None	49th/N
161	soluble in alcohol; insoluble in water		187°	IR	95.0		1.409-1.413	0.865-0.871	None	49th/N
162			208°	IR	98.0		1.414-1.417	0.8623	None	49th/N
163	soluble in alcohol, propylene glycol, fixed oils: insoluble in glycerol, water	1 ml in 1 ml 80% alcohol	222-227°	IR	98.0	1.0	1.418-1.422	0.858-0.863	None	49th/N
164	insoluble in water	1 ml in 2 ml 70% alcohol	244-246°	IR	97.0	1.0	1.420-1.430	0.855-0.863 (20°)	None	49th/N
165	soluble in alcohol, propylene glycol, most fixed oils; insoluble in water			IR	96.0		1.420-1.440	0.870-0.890	None	49th/N,T

224

NO	NAME	CHEMICAL NAME	SYNONYMS	FEMA NO	COE NO	CAS NO	MOL WT	CHEMICAL FORMULA	PHYSICAL FORM / ODOUR
166	Isobutyl hexanoate	2-Methylpropyl hexanoate	Isobutyl caproate	2202	314	105-79-3	172.27	$C_{10}H_{20}O_2$	clear, colourless to yellowish liquid with a fruity, cocoa odour
167	Methyl heptanoate	Methyl heptanoate	Methyl heptoate	2705	368	106-73-0	144.21	$C_8H_{16}O_2$	colourless liquid with a fruity, orris odour
168	Propyl heptanoate	Propyl heptanoate	Propyl heptoate	2948	367	7778-87-2	172.27	$C_{10}H_{20}O_2$	colourless liquid with an ethereal odour
169	Butyl heptanoate	Butyl heptanoate	Butyl heptoate; butyl heptylate	2199	363	5454-28-4	186.30	$C_{11}H_{22}O_2$	colourless liquid with a herbaceous, slightly fruity odour
170	n-Amyl heptanoate	Pentyl heptanoate		2073	370	7493-82-5	200.32	$C_{12}H_{24}O_2$	colourless to pale yellow liquid with a fruity, unripe banana odour
171	Octyl heptanoate	Heptanoic acid, octyl ester	Octyl heptoate	2810	366	5132-75-2	242.41	$C_{15}H_{30}O_2$	colourless liquid with a fruity, slightly fatty odour
172	Isobutyl heptanoate	2-Methylpropyl heptanoate	Isobutyl heptoate	2200	364	7779-80-8	186.30	$C_{11}H_{22}O_2$	colourless liquid with a green odour
173	Methyl octanoate	Methyl octanoate	Methyl caprylate	2728	398	111-11-5	158.24	$C_9H_{18}O_2$	colourless to pale yellow, oily liquid with a winey, fruity, orange odour
174	n-Amyl octanoate	Pentyl octanoate	Amyl caprylate	2079	393	638-25-5	214.35	$C_{13}H_{26}O_2$	colourless liquid with a fruity, orris odour
175	Hexyl octanoate	Hexyl octanoate	Hexyl caprylate	2575	394	1117-55-1	228.37	$C_{14}H_{28}O_2$	colorless liquid with a fresh vegetable, fruity odour
176	Heptyl octanoate	Heptyl octanoate	Heptyl caprylate	2553	399	4265-97-8	242.41	$C_{15}H_{30}O_2$	colourless, oily liquid with a green odour
177	Octyl octanoate	Octyl octanoate	Octyl caprylate	2811	395	2306-88-9	256.44	$C_{16}H_{32}O_2$	colourless liquid with a faint, green tea odour
178	Nonyl octanoate	Nonyl octanoate	Nonyl caprylate	2790	396	7786-48-3	270.46	$C_{17}H_{34}O_2$	colourless, oily liquid with a sweet, rose, mushroom odour
179	Methyl nonanoate	Methyl nonanoate		2724	389	1731-84-6	172.27	$C_{10}H_{20}O_2$	colourless to pale yellow oily liquid with a wine, coconut odour
180	Methyl laurate	Methyl dodecanoate		2715	377	111-82-0	214.35	$C_{13}H_{26}O_2$	colourless to pale yellow liquid with a fatty, floral, winey odour
181	Butyl laurate	Butyl dodecanoate		2206	376	106-18-3	256.44	$C_{16}H_{32}O_2$	colourless to pale yellow liquid with a fruity, peanut odour
182	Isoamyl laurate	3-Methylbutyl dodecanoate	Isopentyl laurate	2077	379	6309-51-9	270.46	$C_{17}H_{34}O_2$	Colourless, oily liquid with a faint oily, fatty odour

NO	SOLUBILITY	SOLUBILITY IN ETHANOL*	BOILING POINT	ID TEST	ASSAY MIN%	ACID VALUE MAX*	REFRACTIVE INDEX*	SPECIFIC GRAVITY*	OTHER REQUIREMENTS	JECFA
166		1 ml in 2 ml 80% alcohol		IR	98.0	1.0	1.410-1.418	0.854-0.858	None	49th/N
167	soluble in organic solvents		173.8°	IR	99.0		1.4114-1.41334	0.87115 (20°)	None	49th/N
168	soluble in most organic solvents; insoluble in water		206-208°	IR			1.4160-1.41894	0.85705 (20°)	None	49th/N,T
169	soluble in most organic solvents		226.2°	IR			1.4228	0.8555 (20°)	None	49th/N,T
170	soluble in most organic solvents	1 ml in 1 ml 95% alcohol	240-245°	IR	93.0	1.0	1.422-1.426	0.859-0.863	None	49th/N
171	soluble in most organic solvents; insoluble in water		290.8°	IR			1.43488	0.85200 (20°)	None	49th/N,T
172	soluble in most organic solvents		209°	IR				0.8593 (20°)	None	49th/N,T
173	soluble in alcohol; insoluble in water		194-195°	IR	95.0	1.0	1.413-1.422	0.875-0.890	None	49th/N
174	soluble in alcohol, most fixed oils; slightly soluble in propylene glycol; insoluble in glycerol, water	1 ml in 7 ml 80% alcohol	260°	IR	98.0	1.0	1.425-1.429	0.855-0.8562	None	49th/N
175	soluble in alcohol; insoluble in water		277°	IR	98.5		1.428-1.433	0.857-0.864 (d20/4)	Melting Pt.: -31°	49th/N
176	insoluble in water	1 ml in 3 ml 90% alcohol	291°	IR			1.434	0.8520 (30°)	Melthing Pt.: -10°	49th/N,T
177	soluble in alcohol; insoluble in water		306-307°	IR			1.4352-1.4925	0.8554	Melting Pt.: -18°	49th/N,T
178	soluble in alcohol; insoluble in water		315°	IR				0.86	None	49th/N,T
179	soluble in alcohol, ether; insoluble in water		213.5-214°	IR	96.0		1.419-1.428	0.870-0.879	None	49th/N
180	soluble in most organic solvents; insoluble in water		261-262°	IR	94.0		1.430-1.438	0.863-0.872	Melting Pt.: 5°	49th/N
181	soluble in most organic solvents; insoluble in water		154° (4.5 mm Hg)	IR	98.0		1.430-1.438	0.853-0.863	Melting Pt.: -7°	49th/N
182	soluble in alcohol; insoluble in water									49th/N,T

NO	NAME	CHEMICAL NAME	SYNONYMS	FEMA NO	COE NO	CAS NO	MOL WT	CHEMICAL FORMULA	PHYSICAL FORM / ODOUR
183	Methyl myristate	Methyl n-tetradecanoate		2722	387	124-10-7	242.41	$C_{15}H_{30}O_2$	colourless, oily liquid or white, waxy solid with a faint onion, honey, orris odour
184	Butyl stearate	Butyl octadecanoate		2214	2189	123-95-5	340.59	$C_{22}H_{44}O_2$	colourless, waxy solid, odourless or with a faintly fatty odour
185	Methyl isobutyrate	Methyl 2-methyl propanoate		2694	287	547-63-7	102.13	$C_5H_{10}O_2$	colourless liquid
186	Ethyl isobutyrate	Ethyl 2-methyl propanoate		2428	288	97-62-1	116.16	$C_6H_{12}O_2$	colourless liquid/fruity odour
187	Propyl isobutyrate	n-Propyl 2-methyl propanoate		2936	289	644-49-5	130.18	$C_7H_{14}O_2$	colourless liquid/pineapple odour
188	Butyl isobutyrate	Butyl-2-methyl propanoate		2188	291	97-87-0	144.21	$C_8H_{16}O_2$	colourless liquid/fresh fruity,apple-pineapple odour
189	Hexyl isobutyrate	Hexyl 2-methyl propanoate		3172	646	2349-07-7	172.27	$C_{10}H_{20}O_2$	colourless to pale yellow liquid/fruity odour
190	Heptyl isobutyrate	Heptyl 2-methyl propanoate		2550	295	2349-13-5	186.30	$C_{11}H_{22}O_2$	colourless to pale yellow liquid/herbaceous, woody odour
191	trans-3-Heptenyl 2-methyl propanoate	trans-3-Heptenyl 2-methyl propanoate		3494	10663	67801-45-0	184.28	$C_{11}H_{20}O_2$	colourless liquid
192	Octyl isobutyrate	Octyl 2-methyl propanoate		2808	593	109-15-9	200.32	$C_{12}H_{24}O_2$	colourless to pale yellow liquid/refreshing, herbaceous odour
193	Dodecyl isobutyrate	Dodecyl 2-methyl propanoate		3452	10563	6624-71-1	256.43	$C_{16}H_{32}O_2$	liquid/slightly fruity or practically odourless
194	Isobutyl isobutyrate	2-methylpropyl 2-methyl propanoate		2189	292	97-85-8	144.21	$C_8H_{16}O_2$	colourless to pale yellow liquid/pineapple odour
195	Methyl isovalerate	Methyl 3-methylbutanoate		2753	457	556-24-1	116.16	$C_6H_{12}O_2$	colourless liquid/herbaceous, fruity odour
196	Ethyl isovalerate	Ethyl 3-methylbutanoate		2463	442	108-64-5	130.19	$C_7H_{14}O_2$	colourless liquid/strong, fruity, vinous, apple-like odour on dilution
197	Propyl isovalerate	Propyl 3-methylbutanoate	n-Propyl methylbutyrate	2960	443	557-00-6	144.21	$C_8H_{16}O_2$	colourless, mobile liquid/fruity odour
198	Butyl isovalerate	Butyl 3-methylbutanoate		2218	444	109-19-3	158.24	$C_9H_{18}O_2$	colourless to pale yellow liquid/fruity odour

NO	SOLUBILITY	SOLUBILITY IN ETHANOL*	BOILING POINT	ID TEST	ASSAY MIN%	ACID VALUE MAX*	REFRACTIVE INDEX*	SPECIFIC GRAVITY*	OTHER REQUIREMENTS	JECFA
183	soluble in alcohol, most fixed oils; insoluble in water		295-300°	IR	98.0		1.435-1.4875	0.870 (15.5°)	Melting Pt.: 18° to 22°	49th/N
184			343° (220-225° at 25 mmHg)	IR				0.855-0.875	Melting Range: 17° to 21°; Iodine Value: < 1; Saponification Value: 165 to 180	49th/N,T
185		1 ml in 1 ml 95% alcohol	90	IR	97.0	1.0	1.382-1.386	0.884-0.888		49th/N
186	very soluble in ether	1 ml in 1 ml 95% alcohol	112-113	IR	98.0	1.0	1.385-1.391	0.862-0.868		49th/N
187	soluble in organic solvents, alcohol; insoluble in water		134 (752 mm Hg)	IR	98.0		1.395-1.396	0.860-0.864 (20°/20°)		49th/N
188	miscible in alcohol, ether, most fixed oils; insoluble in glycerin, propylene glycol, water	1 ml in 7 ml 60% alcohol	166	IR	97.0	1.0	1.401-1.404	0.859-0.864		49th/N
189	soluble in alcohol, propylene glycol; miscible with most fixed oils; insoluble in water		199	IR	98.0	1.0	1.399-1.421	0.852-0.876		49th/N
190	insoluble in water; soluble in organic solvents		98 (10 mmHg)	IR	95.0		1.417-1.421	0.8625 (15°/15°)		49th/N
191	soluble in alcohol; insoluble in water		85-90 (3mm Hg)	IR	98.0		1.429-1.430			49th/N
192		1 ml in 1 ml 95% alcohol	245	IR	98.0	1.0	1.420-1.425	0.853-0.858		49th/N
193	soluble inorganic solvents; in soluble inwater			IR	97.0	1.0	1.432-1.436	0.854-0.860 (20°/20°)		49th/N
194	soluble in organic solvents; insoluble in water		144-151	IR	98.0	1.0	1.396-1.402	0.850-0.857	Melting Pt.: - 80° to -81°	49th/N
195	soluble in alcohol, most fixed oils; insoluble water		115-117	IR	98.0	2.0	1.413-1.416	0.852-0.857		49th/N
196	soluble in propylene glycol, 1 ml in 350 ml water; miscible with alcohol, most fixed oils		135	IR	98.0	2.0	1.395-1.399	0.862-0.866		49th/R
197	soluble in organic solvents, alcohol; insoluble in water		156-157	IR	99.0	1.0	1.400 - 1.405	0.860 - 0.866		49th/N
198	soluble inorganic solvents, alcohol; insoluble inwater	1 ml in 1 ml 95% alcohol	175	IR	97.0	1.0	1.407-1.411	0.856-0.859		49th/N

NO	NAME	CHEMICAL NAME	SYNONYMS	FEMA NO	COE NO	CAS NO	MOL WT	CHEMICAL FORMULA	PHYSICAL FORM / ODOUR
199	Hexyl 3-methylbutanoate	Hexyl 3-methylbutanoate		3500	10692	10032-13-0	186.29	$C_{11}H_{22}O_2$	colourless liquid/pungent, fruity odour
200	Octyl isovalerate	Octyl 3-methylbutanoate		2814	446	7786-58-5	274.35	$C_{13}H_{26}O_2$	colourless liquid/apple-pineapple odour
201	Nonyl isovalerate	Nonyl 3-methylbutanoate		2791	447	7786-47-2	228.37	$C_{14}H_{28}O_2$	colourless to pale yellow liquid/apple-hazelnut, citrus odour
202	3-Hexenyl 3-methylbutanoate	3-Hexenyl 3-methylbutanoate	cis-3-Hexenyl isovalerate	3498	2344	10032-11-8	184.28	$C_{11}H_{20}O_2$	colourless liquid/swet, apple-like odour
203	2-Methylpropyl 3-methylbutyrate	2-Methylpropyl 3-methylbutanoate	Isobutyl isovalerate	3369	568	589-59-3	158.24	$C_9H_{18}O_2$	colourless to pale yellow liquid
204	2-Methylbutyl 3-methylbutanoate	2-Methylbutyl 3-methylbutanoate		3506	10772	2445-77-4	162.26	$C_{10}H_{20}O_2$	colourless liquid
205	Methyl 2-methylbutyrate	Methyl 2-methylbutanoate		2719	2085	868-57-5	116.16	$C_6H_{12}O_2$	almost colourless liquid/sweet, fruity, apple-like odour
206	Ethyl 2-methylbutyrate	Ethyl 2-methylbutanoate		2443	265	7452-79-1	130.19	$C_7H_{14}O_2$	colourless liquie/strong, green-fruity, apple-like odour
207	n-Butyl 2-methylbuytyrate	Butyl 2-methylbutanoate		3393	10534	15706-73-7	158.23	$C_9H_{18}O_2$	colourless to pale yellow lquid
208	Hexyl 2-methylbutanoate	Hexyl 2-methylbutanoate	Hexyl 2-methylbutyrate	3499	11781	10032-15-2	186.29	$C_{11}H_{22}O_2$	colourless liquid/strong, fresh-green, fruity odour
209	Octyl 2-methylbutyrate	Octyl 2-methylbutanoate		3604	10866	29811-50-5	214.30	$C_{13}H_{26}O_2$	colourless liquid
210	Isopropyl 2-methylbutyrate	1-Methylethyl-2-methylbutanoate		3699	-	66576-71-4	144.21	$C_8H_{16}O_2$	colourless liquid
211	3-Hexenyl 2-methylbutanoate	3-Hexenylethyl 2-methylbutanoate		3497	2345	10094-41-4	184.28	$C_{11}H_{20}O_2$	clear, colourless liquid
212	2-Methylbutyl 2-methylbutyrate	2-Methylbutyl 2-methylbutanoate		3359	10773	2445-78-5	172.27	$C_{10}H_{20}O_2$	colourless to pale yellow lquid
213	Methyl 2-methyl pentanoate	Methyl 2-methyl pentanoate		3707	-	2177-77-7	130.19	$C_7H_{14}O_2$	pale yellow liquid
214	Ethyl 2-methyl pentanoate	Ethyl 2-methyl pentanoate		3488	10616	28959-02-6	144.21	$C_8H_{16}O_2$	colourless to pale yellow liquid
215	Ethyl 3-methyl pentanoate	Ethyl 3-methyl pentanoate		3679	-	5870-68-8	144.21	$C_8H_{16}O_2$	colourless liquid

NO	SOLUBILITY	SOLUBILITY IN ETHANOL*	BOILING POINT	ID TEST	ASSAY MIN%	ACID VALUE MAX*	REFRACTIVE INDEX*	SPECIFIC GRAVITY*	OTHER REQUIREMENTS	JECFA
199	soluble in alcohol, most fixed oils; insoluble in water		215	IR	95.0	2.0	1.417-1.421	0.853-0.857		49th/N
200	soluble in alcohol; insoluble in water		245	IR	98.0		1.418-1.420	0.86 (20°/20°)		49th/N
201	soluble in alcohol; insoluble in water		264	IR	97.0		1.427-1.430	0.853-0.859		49th/N
202	soluble in alcohool, most fixed oils; insolouble- water		199	IR	95.0	2.0	1.429-1.435	0.876-0.874		49th/N
203	miscible with alcohol		170	IR	98.0	1.0	1.404-1.408	0.850-0.854		49th/N
204			113-115	IR			1.394		·	49th/N,T
205	soluble in alcohol, most fixed oils; insoluble in water		115	IR	92.0	2.0	1.393-1.397	0.879-0.883		49th/N
206	soluble in alcohol, propylene glycol; very slightly soluble in water; miscible with most fixed oils		133	IR	95.0	2.0	1.393-1.400	0.863-0.870		49th/N
207				IR	90.0		1.402-1.500	0.856-0.866		49th/N
208	soluble in alcohol, most fixed oils; insoluble in water			IR	95.0	2.0	1.416-1.421	0.854-0.859		49th/N
209				IR	99.5		1.425	0.8577 (20°/20°)		49th/N
210	insoluble in water	soluble			98.0		1.395-1.399			49th/N,T
211				IR	98.0		1.428-1.434			49th/N,T
212			184-187	IR	90.0		1.409-1.509	0.854-0.864		49th/N
213				IR						49th/N,T
214				IR	98.0	1.0	1.401-1.404	0.859-0.865		49th/N
215				IR						49th/N,T

NO	NAME	CHEMICAL NAME	SYNONYMS	FEMA NO	COE NO	CAS NO	MOL WT	CHEMICAL FORMULA	PHYSICAL FORM / ODOUR
216	Methyl 4-methylvalerate	Methyl 4-methylvalerate	Methyl isobutyl acetate	2721	322	2412-24-1	130.18	$C_7H_{14}O_2$	colourless liquid/sweet, pineapple-like odour
217	trans-Anethole	trans-methoxy-4(1-propenyl) benzene	Isoestragole	2086	183	4180-23-8	148.21	$C_{10}H_{12}O$	Colourless to faintly yellow liquid with an aniseed-like odour
218	Citric acid	2-Hydroxy-1,2,3-propane-tricarboxylic acid; 2-Hydroxy-1,2,3-propane-tricarboxylic acid, monohydrate				77-92-9; 5949-29-1	192.13; 210.14	$C_6H_8O_7$; $C_6H_8O_7, H_2O$	White or colourless, odourless, crystalline solid. Monohydrate effloresces in dry air

NO	SOLUBILITY	SOLUBILITY IN ETHANOL*	BOILING POINT	ID TEST	ASSAY MIN%	ACID VALUE MAX*	REFRACTIVE INDEX*	SPECIFIC GRAVITY*	OTHER REQUIREMENTS	JECFA
216	soluble in alcohol, most fixed oils; insoluble in water		142-143	IR	97.0		1.402-1.406			49th/N
217	Slightly soluble in water; miscible with chloroform and ether	1 ml in 2 ml 96% alcohol	234-239.5°	IR	99.0		1.559-1.562	0.983-0.988		49th/R
218	Very soluble in water, slightly soluble in ether	Freely soluble		IR	99.5				Positive test for citrate	49th/R

The following IR-spectra are reprinted from Merck FT-IR Atlas through courtesy of Dr. K.G.R. Pachler, Mr. F. Matlock, and Dr. H-U. Gremlich, and VCH Verlagsgesellschaft, Weinheim, Germany: 79, 80, 81, 82, 83, 84, 85, 86, 87, 91, 92, 93, 95, 96, 97, 98, 99, 101, 102, 103, 104, 105, 108, 110, 111, 113, 114, 116, 117, 118, 119, 125, 126, 127, 128, 137, 141, 142, 143, 148, 149, 179, 183, 184, 185, 186, 206, 217, and 218.

The following IR-spectra are reprinted with the permission from the Food Chemicals Codex , 4th Edition. Copyright 1996 by the National Academy of Sciences. Courtesy of the National Academy Press, Washington, D.C.: 53, 54, 56, 57, 58, 59, 60, 61, 62, 66, 65, 71, 89, 94, 100, 106, 107, 109, 122, 130, 131, 134, 151, 158, 174, 188, 196, and 198.

GAS CHROMATOGRAPHIC (GC) ASSAY OF FLAVOUR CHEMICALS

This procedure applies both to the assay of flavour chemicals and to the quantitation of minor components in flavour chemicals. Analysts following this procedure and performing the test should obtain sufficient resolution of major and even trace components of a mixture to calculate accurately the concentration of the desired component; should be familiar with the general principles, usual techniques, and instrumental variables normally met in gas chromatographic analysis; and should pay particular attention to the following:

1. Stability of baseline, return to baseline before and after each peak of interest, and minimum use of recorder attenuation.

2. Any incompatibility between a sensitive sample component and column support, liquid substrate, or construction material.

3. The response to different components of the same or different detectors. Since sizable errors may be encountered in correlating area percent directly to weight percent, the methods for calculating response factors should be known.

4. Where limits for minor components are specified in the column entitled *Other Requirements* in the above tabular specifications for flavour chemicals, analysts should use authentic materials to confirm the retention times of minor components. Determine the quantity of components following the instructions below under *Calculations and Methods*.

GC CONDITIONS FOR ANALYSIS

Column: open tubular capillary column of fused silica or deactivated glass 30 m long x 0.25 to 0.53 mm id

Stationary phase:

1. For a nonpolar column: methyl silicone gum, or equivalent (preferable a bonded and cross-linked dimethyl polysiloxane)

2. For a polar column: polyethylene glycol, or equivalent (preferable a bonded and cross-linked polyethylene glycol)

3. The stationary phase coating should have a thickness of 1 to 3 μm

Carrier gas: helium flowing at a linear velocity of 20 to 40 ml/s

Sample size: 0.1 to 1.0 μl

Split ratio: (for 0.25 mm to 0.35 mm id columns only) 50:1 to 200:1, typically, making sure that no one component exceeds the capacity of the column

Inlet temperature: 225 to 275°

Detector temperature: 250 to 300°

Detectors: use either a thermal conductivity or flame ionization detector operating both as recommended by the manufacturer

Oven program: 50 to 240°, increasing the temperature by 5°/min, hold at 240° for 5 min

Analysts can also use any GC conditions providing separations equal to (or better than) those obtained with the above method, but in the case of a dispute, the above method must stand.

CALCULATIONS AND METHODS

A.   Peak area integration with total area detected normalized to 100%, using electronic integrators: Use an electronic peak integrator in accordance with the manufacture's recommendations, ensuring that the integration parameters permit proper integration of the peaks of a variety of shapes and magnitudes and do not interpret baseline shifts and noise spikes as area contributed by the sample. Use internal or external standards as needed to confirm that the total GC peak area corresponds to 100% of the components present in the sample.

B.   Results obtained as described above are based on the assumption that the entire sample has eluted and the peaks of all of the components have been included in the calculation. They will be incorrect if any part of the sample does not elute or if all the peaks are not measured. In such cases, and in all methods described above, the internal standard method may be used to determine percentages based on the total sample. For this method, measurements are required of the peaks of the component(s) being assayed and of the internal standard.

An accurately weighed mixture of the internal standard and the sample is prepared and chromatographed, the area ratio(s) of the component(s) to the standard is computed, and the percentage(s) of the component(s) is calculated.

If this calculation is to be applied, the substance used as the standard should be one that meets the following criteria:

a.   Its detector response is similar to that of the component(s) to be determined. In general, the more nearly the chemical structure of the component resembles that of the standard, the closer the response will be.

b.   Its retention time is close to, but not identical with, that of the component(s).

c.   Its elution time is different from that of any other component in the sample so that its peak does not superimpose on any other.

The weight ratio of the internal standard to the sample should be such that the internal standard and the component sought produce approximately equal peaks. This is, of course, not possible if several components of interest are at different levels of concentration.

If the internal standard method is applied properly, it may be assumed that the ratio of the weight of component to the weight of internal standard is exactly proportional to the peak area ratio, and under these conditions no correction factor is needed. The sample is first run by itself to determine whether the internal standard would mask any component by peak superposition. If there is no interference, a mixture is prepared of the sample and of the internal standard in the specified weight ratio, and the percentages of the internal standard and of the sample in the mixture are calculated. The mixture is chromatogrphed, and the areas of the component peak and the internal standard peak are calculated by one of the methods described above.

The calculations are as follows:

1a.   % Component in Mixture/%Internal Standard in Mixture = Component Area/Internal Standard Area, or

1b.   % Component in Mixture = % Int. Std. in Mixture x (Component Area/Internal Standard Area)

2.   % Component in Sample=(%Component in Mixture x 100)/%Sample in Mixture

Should calibration be necessary, mixtures should be prepared of internal standard and component, of either 100% or of known purity. The number of mixtures and the weight ratios to be used depend on the component being analyzed. Usually, three mixtures will be required. The weight ratio of one is chosen so that the heights of component and standard are equal. The ratios of the other two may be two-thirds and four-thirds of their value. Each mixture should be chromatographed at least three times, and areas calculated. The factor for each chromatograph should be calculated as specified below, and the averages taken for each mixture. An overall average factor is calculated from them. The calibration should be performed periodically.

1.   Factor = [(Wt. Component x % Purity)/(Wt. Int. Std. x % Purity)] x [(Int. Std. Area)/Component Area]

2.   % Component in Sample Mixture = (Component Area x Factor x % Int. Std. in Sample Mixture)/Int. Std. Area

3.   % Component in Sample = (% Component in Sample Mixture x 100)/% Sample in Sample Mixture

GC SYSTEM SUITABILITY TEST SAMPLE

The GC system suitability test sample consists of an equal-weight mixture of food-quality acetophenone, benzyl alcohol, benzyl acetate, linalool, and hydroxycitronellal.

Using the test sample described below, periodically test the performance of and resolution provided by the gas chromatograph employed. The test sample must display results comparable in quantitative composition, peak shape, and elution order to those specified herein. The quantitative composition should not deviate from the results listed below by more than 10%. Analyze the GC test sample using the *GC Conditions for Analysis* given above.

Component in Test Sample	Order of Elution Non-polar	Polar	Normalized % Area (FID) Non-polar	Polar
Benzyl alcohol	1	4	22.0	21.3
Acetophenone	2	2	21.1	21.4
Linalool	3	1	20.8	21.0
Benzyl acetate	4	3	18.6	19.1
Hydroxycitronellal	5	5	16.7	16.7

SPECIFICATIONS OF FLAVOURING AGENTS LISTED AS "TENTATIVE" AT THE 49TH MEETING OF JECFA

No	Substance	Information required
21	Allyl 2-furoate	Assay; Acid value
64	Rhodinyl propionate	Assay; Acid value
69	Citronellyl valerate	Assay; Acid value
70	Geranyl hexanoate	Assay; Acid value
72	Geranyl isobutyrate	Boiling point; Acid value
74	Rhodinyl isobutyrate	ID test; Acid value
75	Geranyl isovalerate	Boiling point; Acid value
77	Rhodinyl isovalerate	Assay; Acid value
78	Geranyl 2-ethylbutanoate	Boiling point; Assay; Acid value; Refractive index; Specific gravity
121	Heptyl formate	Assay; Acid value
140	2-Ethylbutyl acetate	Assay; Acid value
154	Heptyl butyrate	Assay; Acid value
155	Octyl butyrate	Assay; Acid value
156	Decyl butyrate	Assay; Acid value
165	cis-3-Hexenyl hexanoate	Boiling point; Acid value
168	Propyl heptanoate	Assay; Acid value
169	Butyl heptanoate	Assay; Acid value
171	Octyl heptanoate	Assay; Acid value
172	Isobutyl heptanoate	Assay; Acid value; Refractive index
176	Heptyl octanoate	Assay; Acid value
177	Octyl octanoate	Assay; Acid value
178	Nonyl octanoate	Assay; Acid value; Refractive index
182	Isoamyl laurate	Boiling point; ID test; Assay; Acid value; Refractive index; Specific gravity
184	Butyl stearate	Assay; Acid value; Refractive index
204	2-Methylbutyl 2-methylbutyrate	Assay; Acid value; Specific gravity
210	Isopropyl 2-methylbutyrate	Boiling point; ID test; Acid value; Specific gravity
211	3-Hexenyl 2-methylbutanoate	Boiling point; Acid value; Specific gravity
213	Methyl 2-methylpentanoate	Boiling point; Assay; Acid value; Refractive index; Specific gravity
215	Ethyl 3-methylpentanoate	Boiling point; Assay; Acid value; Refractive index; Specific gravity

INFRARED (IR) SPECTRA OF CERTAIN FLAVOURING AGENTS

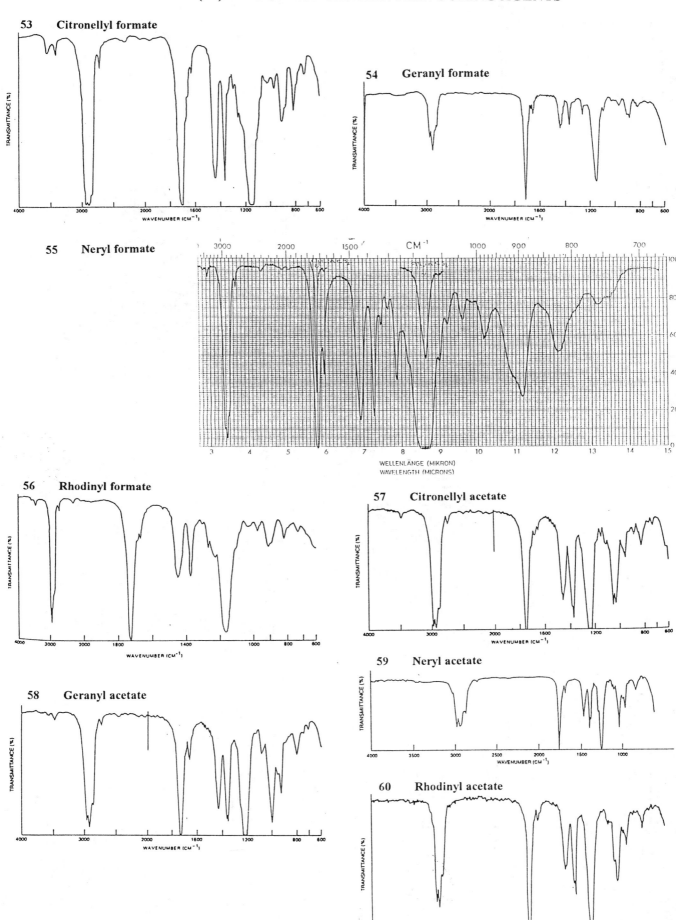

53   Citronellyl formate

54   Geranyl formate

55   Neryl formate

56   Rhodinyl formate

57   Citronellyl acetate

58   Geranyl acetate

59   Neryl acetate

60   Rhodinyl acetate

61 Citronellyl propionate

62 Geranyl propionate

63 Neryl propionate

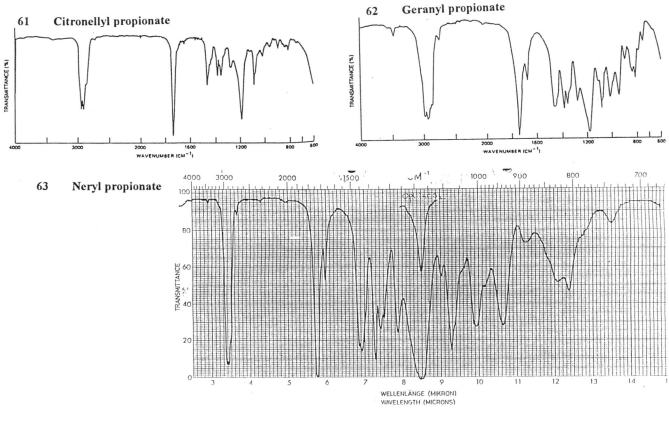

64 Rhodinyl propionate

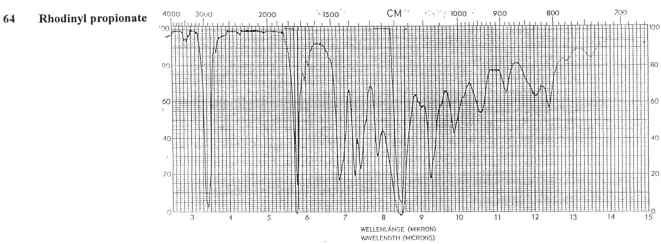

65 Citronellyl butyrate

66 Geranyl butyrate

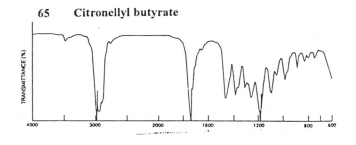

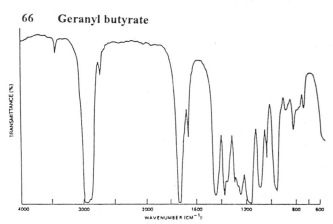

67   Neryl butyrate

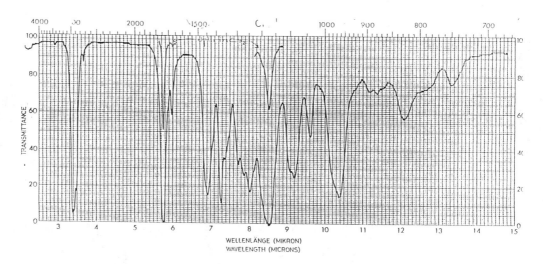

WELLENLÄNGE (MIKRON)
WAVELENGTH (MICRONS)

68   Rhodinyl butyrate

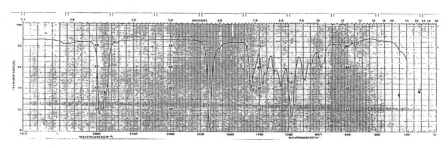

69   Citronellyl valerate

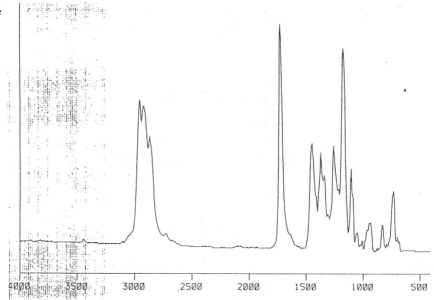

70   Geranyl hexanoate

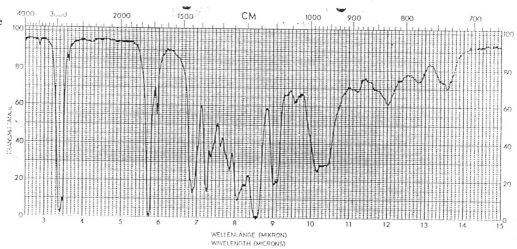

WELLENLÄNGE (MIKRON)
WAVELENGTH (MICRONS)

242

71   Citronellyl isobutyrate

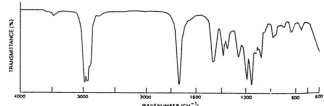

72   Geranyl isobutyrate

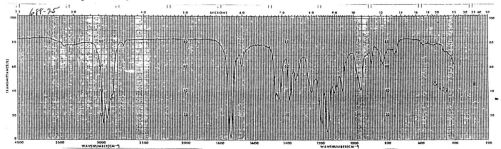

73   Neryl isobutyrate

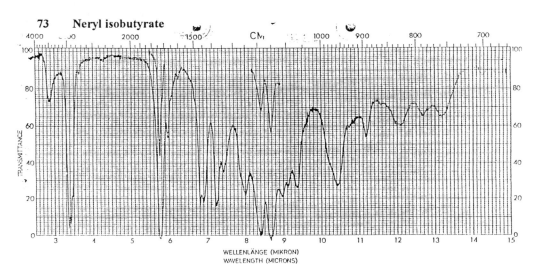

WELLENLÄNGE (MIKRON)
WAVELENGTH (MICRONS)

75   Geranyl isovalerate

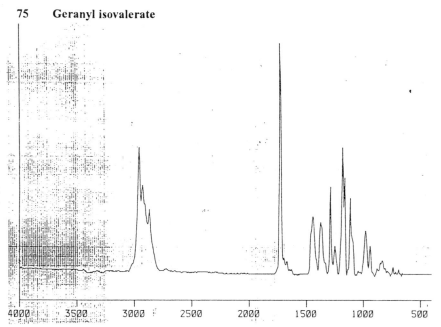

76   Neryl isovalerate

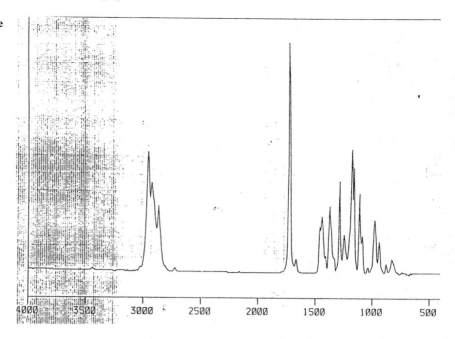

77   Rhodinyl isovalerate

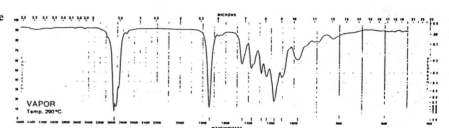

VAPOR
Temp. 290 °C

78   Geranyl 2-ethylbutanoate

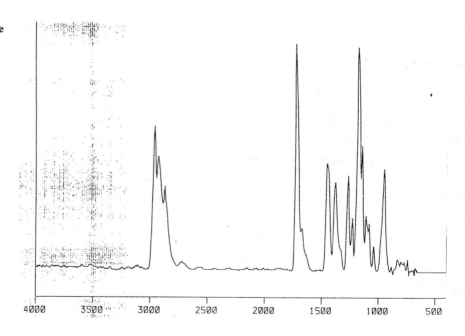

79   Formic acid

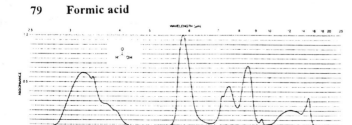

80   Acetaldehyde

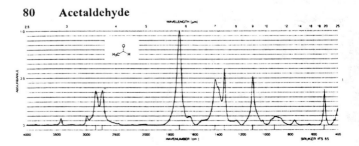

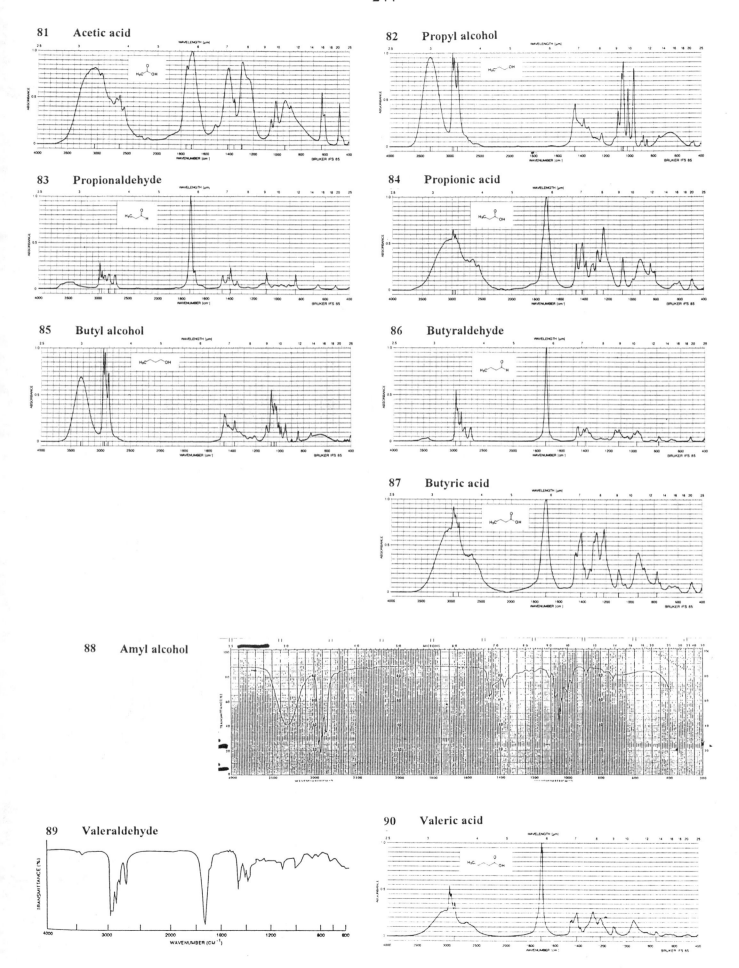

81   Acetic acid

82   Propyl alcohol

83   Propionaldehyde

84   Propionic acid

85   Butyl alcohol

86   Butyraldehyde

87   Butyric acid

88   Amyl alcohol

89   Valeraldehyde

90   Valeric acid

91 Hexyl alcohol

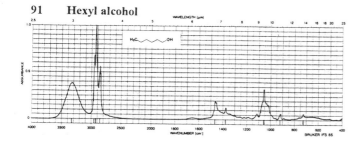

92 Hexanal

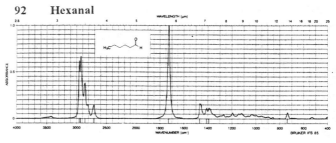

93 Hexanoic acid

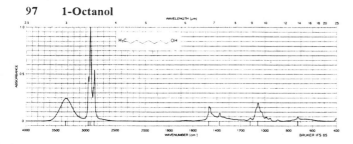

94 Heptyl alcohol

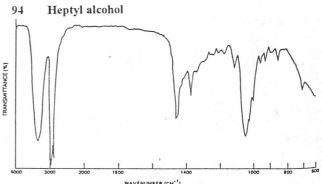

95 Heptanal

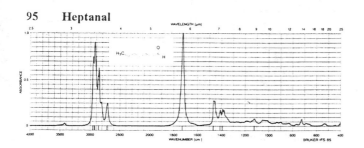

96 Heptanoic acid

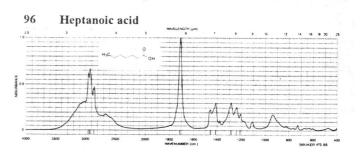

97 1-Octanol

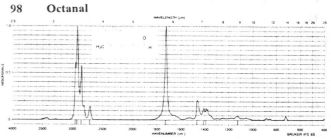

98 Octanal

99 Octanoic acid

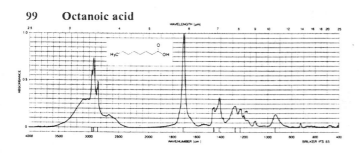

100 Nonyl alcohol

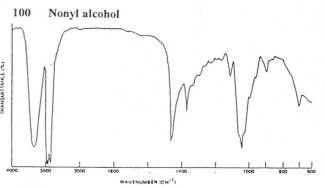

101 Nonanal

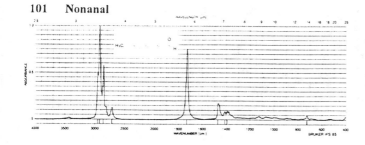

102 Nonanoic acid

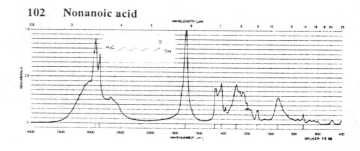

246

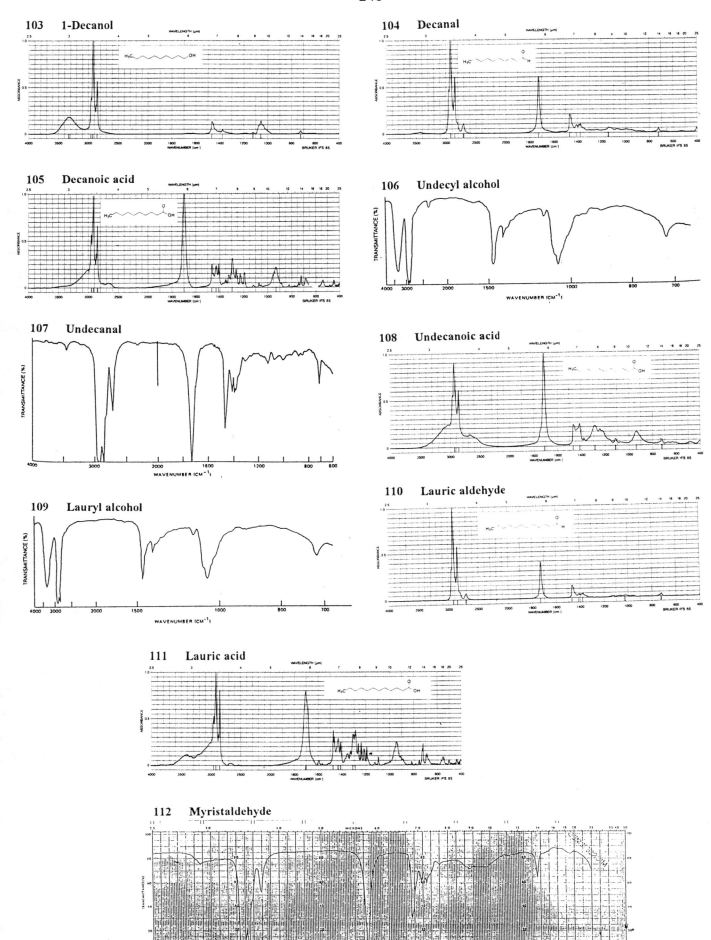

103 1-Decanol

104 Decanal

105 Decanoic acid

106 Undecyl alcohol

107 Undecanal

108 Undecanoic acid

109 Lauryl alcohol

110 Lauric aldehyde

111 Lauric acid

112 Myristaldehyde

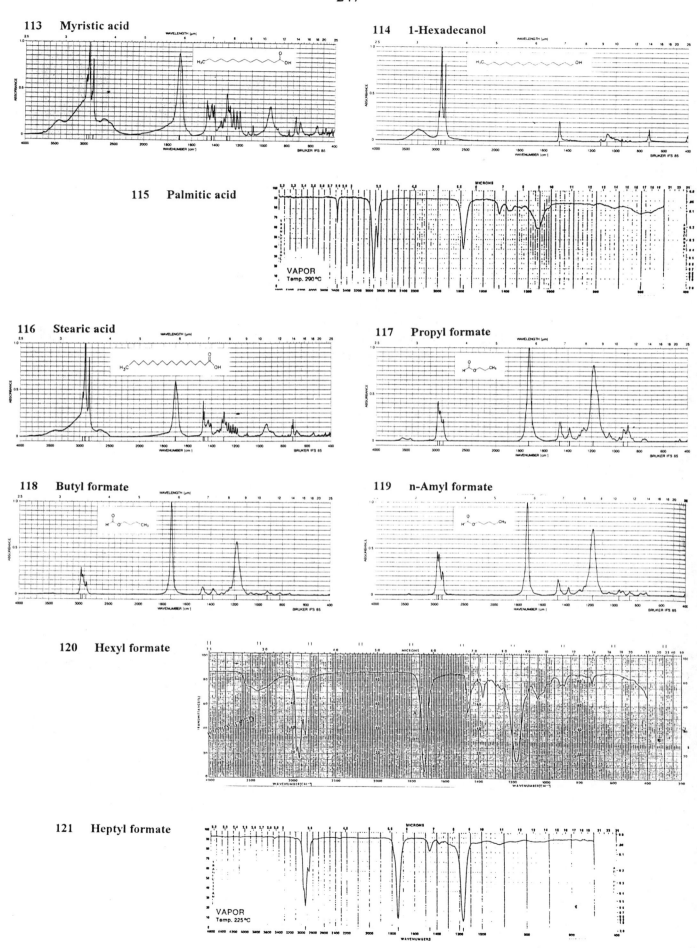

113   Myristic acid

114   1-Hexadecanol

115   Palmitic acid

VAPOR
Temp. 290 °C

116   Stearic acid

117   Propyl formate

118   Butyl formate

119   n-Amyl formate

120   Hexyl formate

121   Heptyl formate

VAPOR
Temp. 225 °C

122   Octyl formate

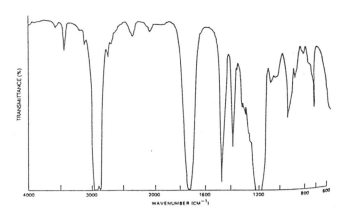

123   *cis*-3-Hexenyl formate

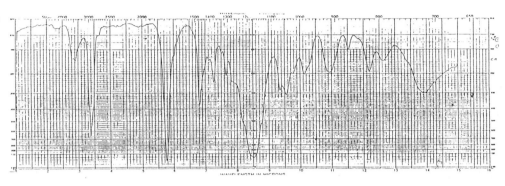

124   Isobutyl formate

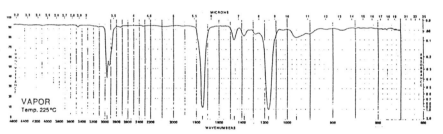

125   Methyl acetate

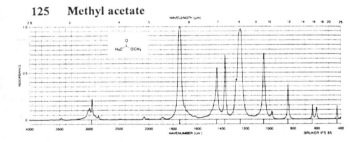

126   Propyl acetate

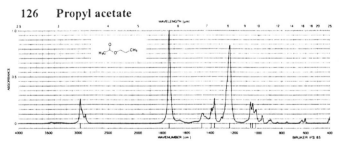

127   Butyl acetate

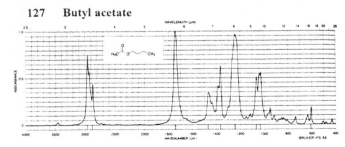

128   Hexyl acetate

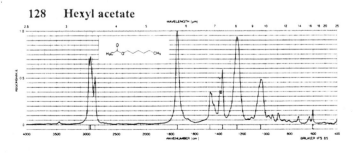

129   Heptyl acetate

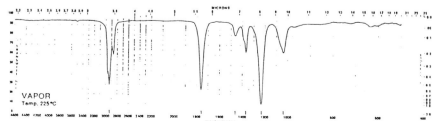

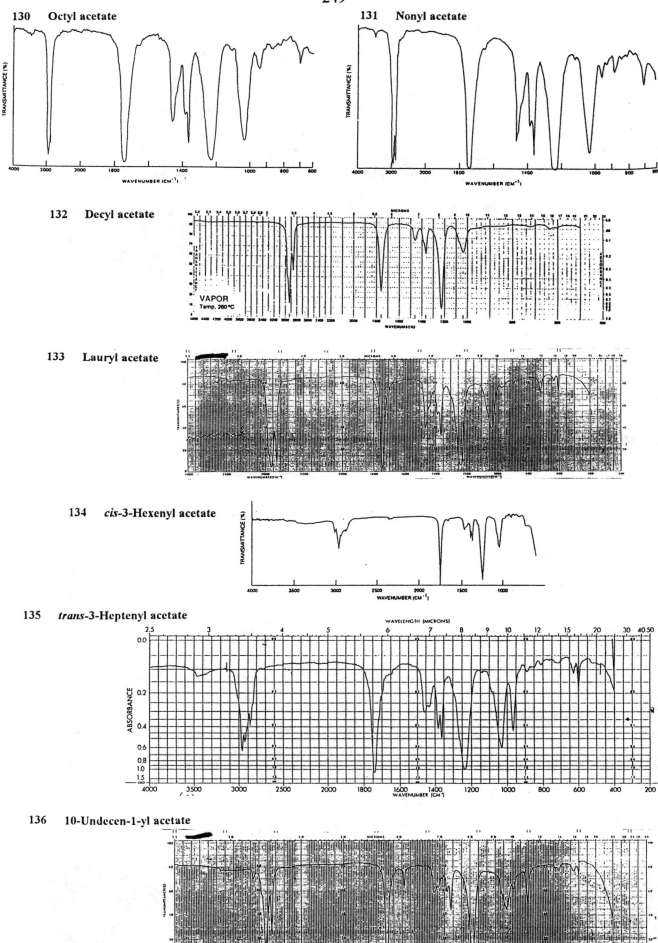

130   Octyl acetate

131   Nonyl acetate

132   Decyl acetate

133   Lauryl acetate

134   *cis*-3-Hexenyl acetate

135   *trans*-3-Heptenyl acetate

136   10-Undecen-1-yl acetate

137   Isobutyl acetate

138   2-Methylbutyl acetate

140   2-Ethylbutyl acetate

141   Methyl propionate

142   Propyl propionate

143   Butyl propionate

144   Hexyl propionate

145   Octyl propionate

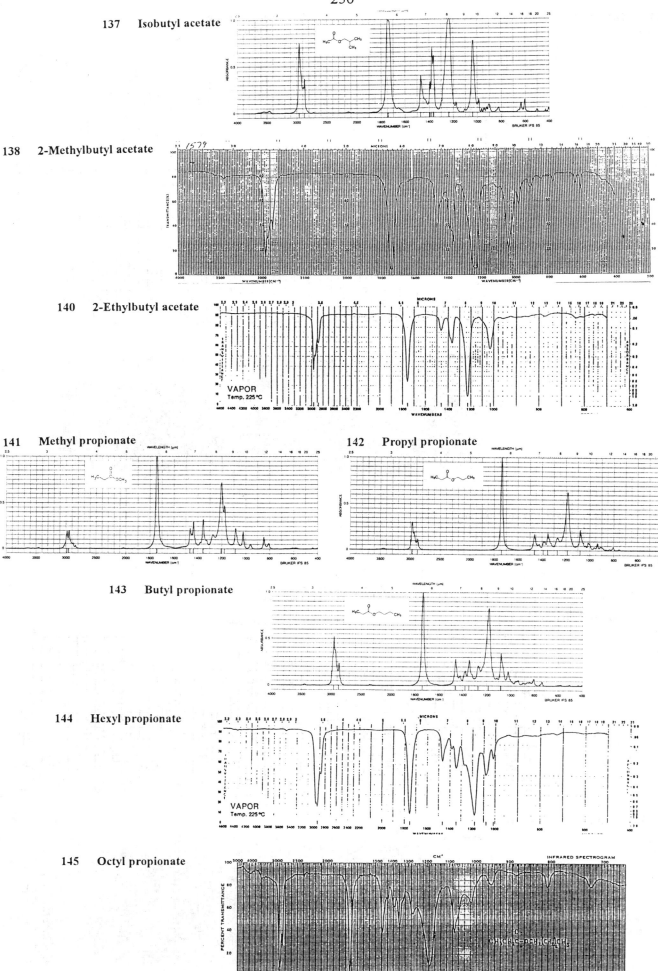

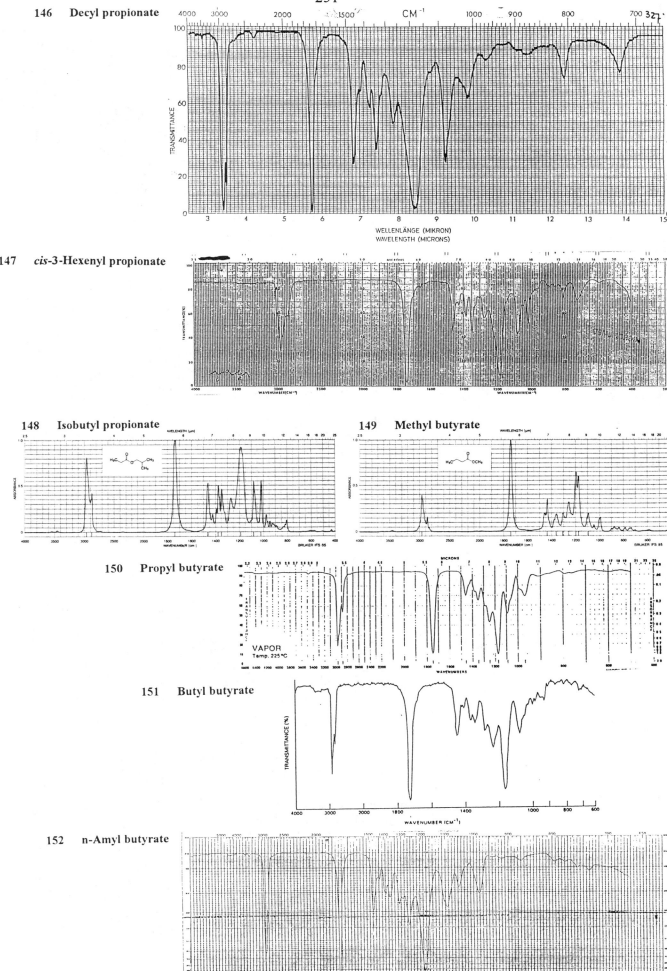

146   Decyl propionate

147   *cis*-3-Hexenyl propionate

148   Isobutyl propionate

149   Methyl butyrate

150   Propyl butyrate

VAPOR
Temp. 225°C

151   Butyl butyrate

152   n-Amyl butyrate

153 **Hexyl butyrate**

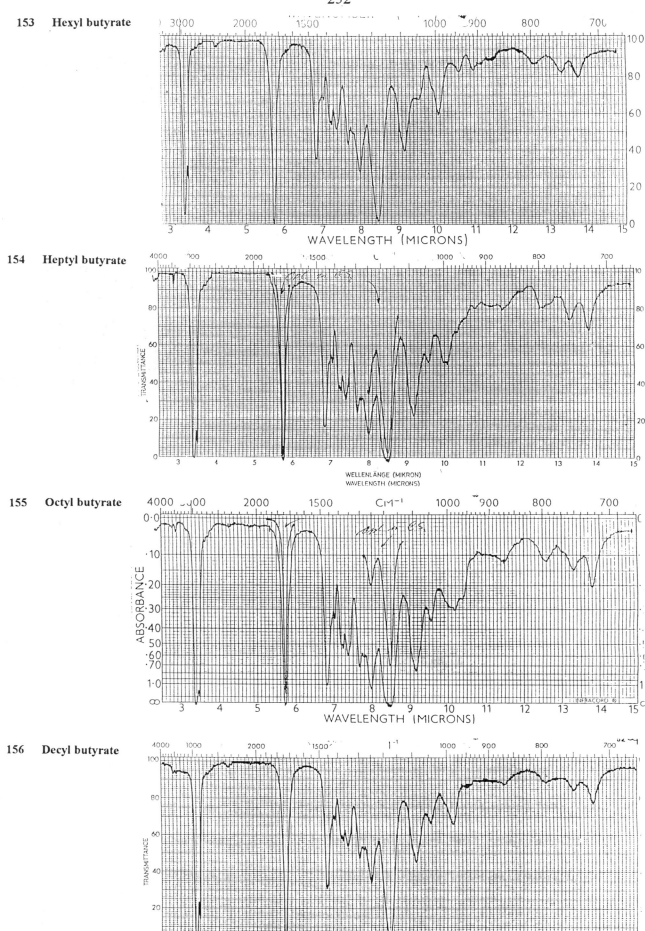

154 **Heptyl butyrate**

155 **Octyl butyrate**

156 **Decyl butyrate**

157   *cis*-3-Hexenyl butyrate

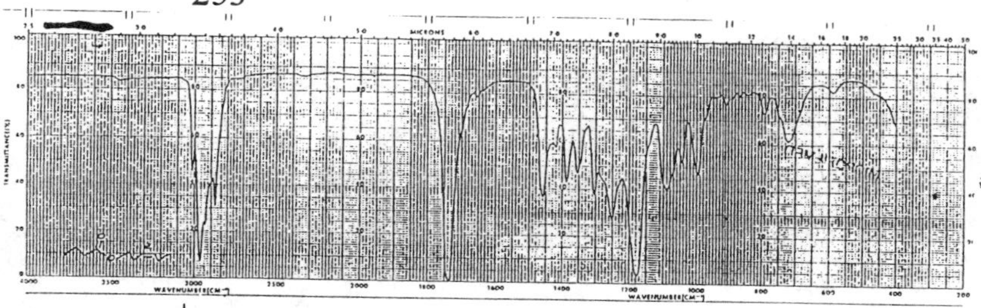

158   Isobutyl butyrate

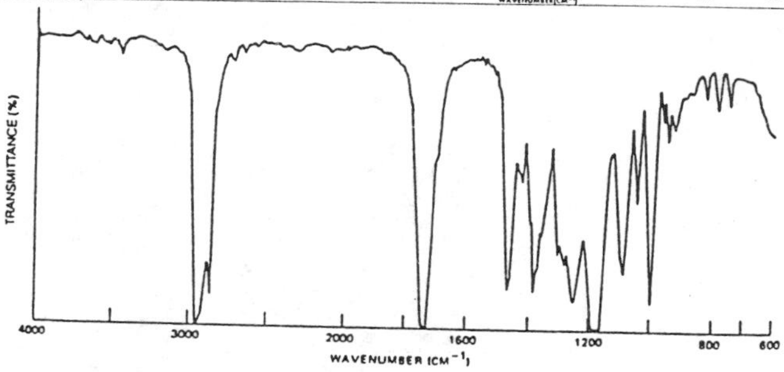

159   Methyl valerate

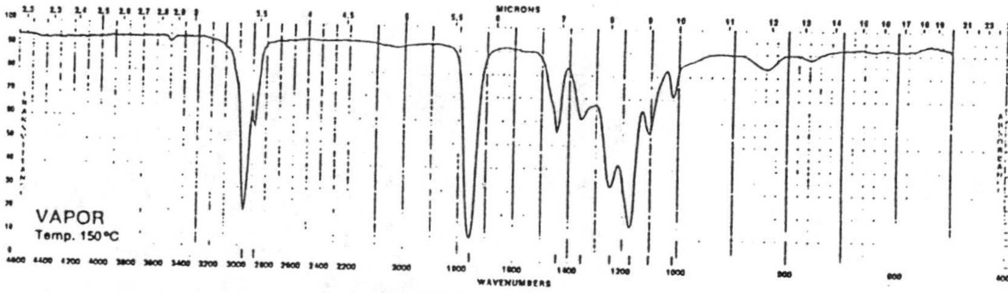

VAPOR
Temp. 150°C

160   Butyl valerate

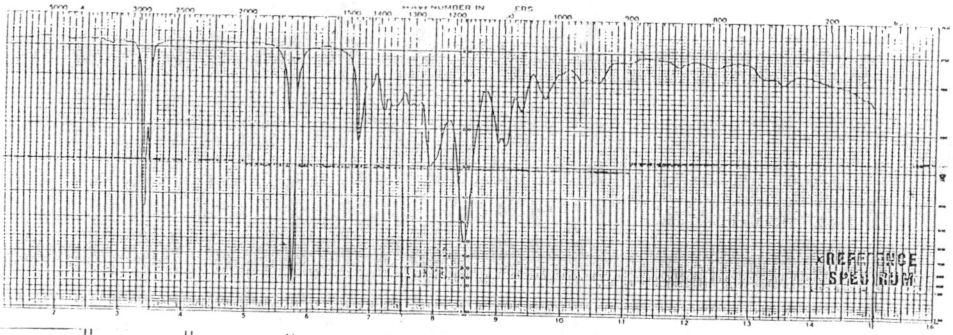

161   Propyl hexanoate

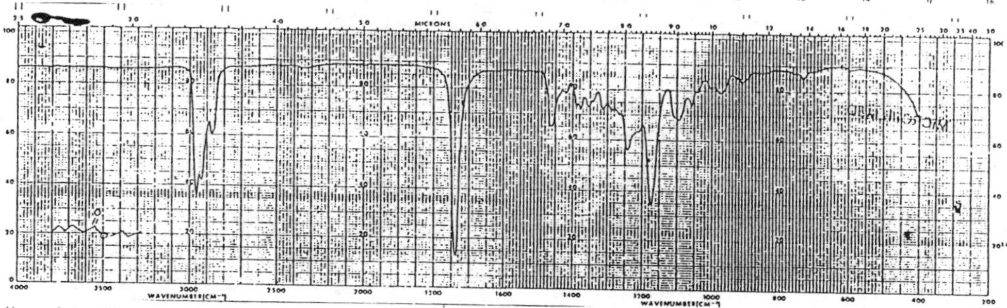

162   Butyl hexanoate

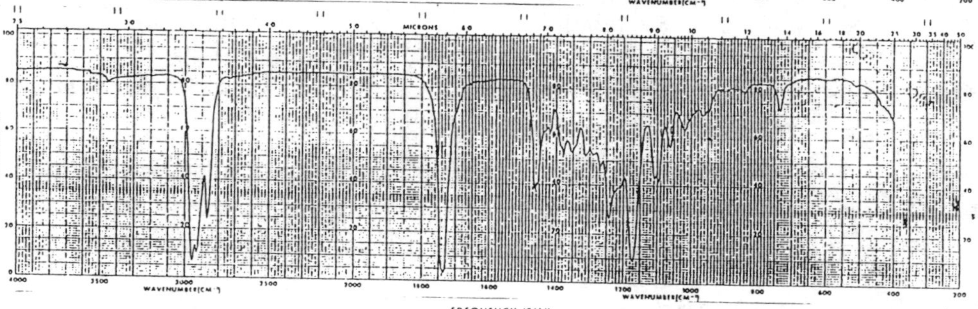

163   n-Amyl hexanoate

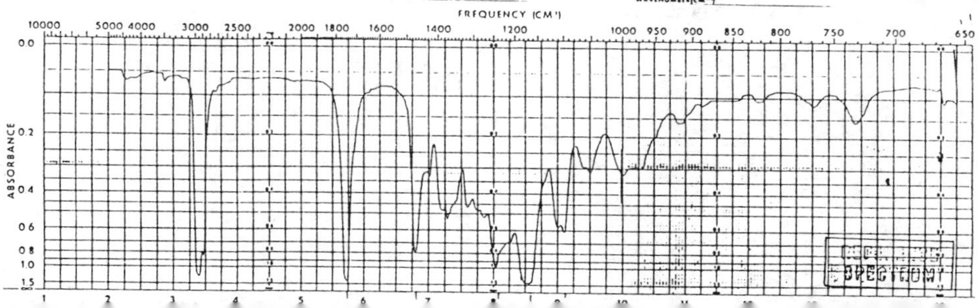

164   Hexyl hexanoate

165   *cis*-3-Hexenyl hexanoate

166   Isobutyl hexanoate

167   Methyl heptanoate

168   Propyl heptanoate

169   Butyl heptanoate

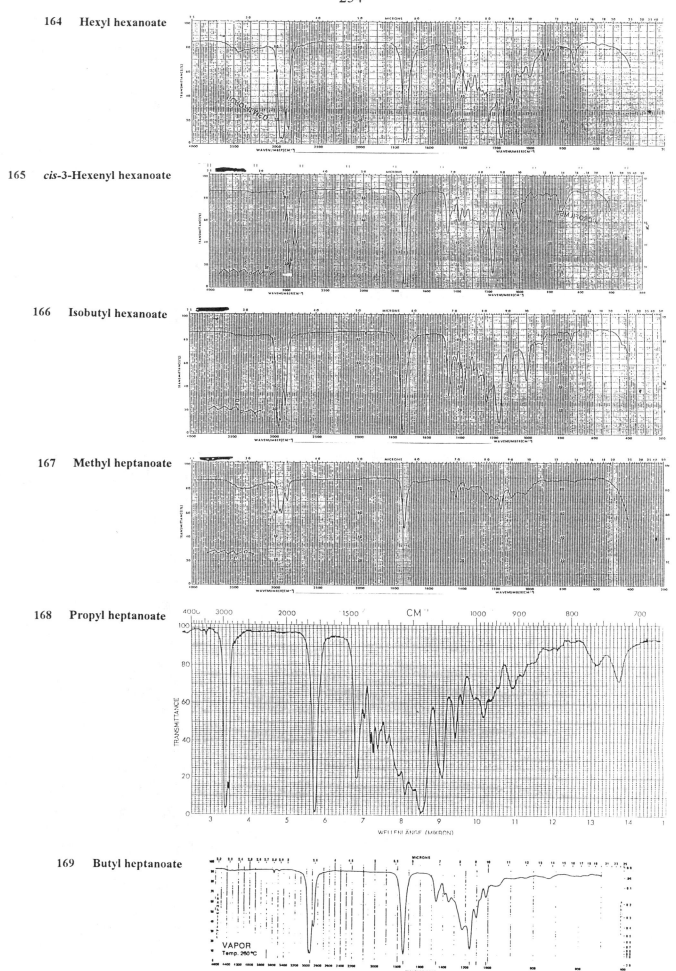

170 n-Amyl heptanoate

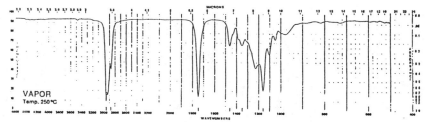

VAPOR
Temp. 250 °C

171 Octyl heptanoate

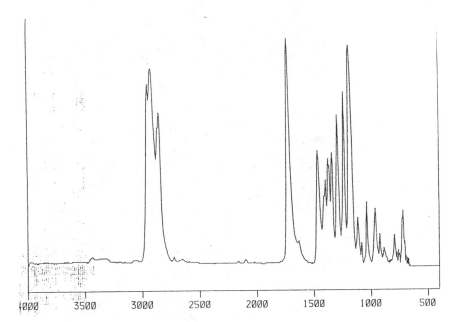

172 Isobutyl heptanoate

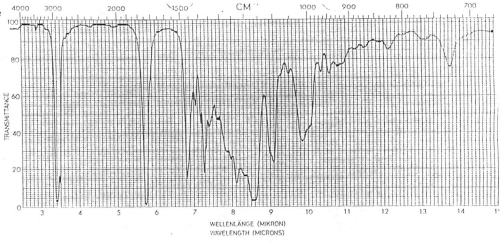

WELLENLÄNGE (MIKRON)
WAVELENGTH (MICRONS)

173 Methyl octanoate

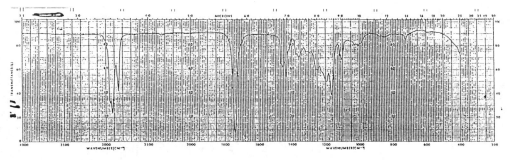

174 n-Amyl octanoate

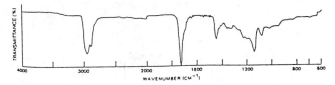

175 Hexyl octanoate

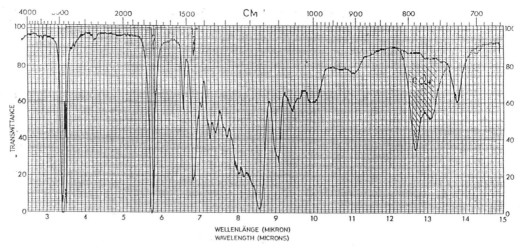

176 Heptyl octanoate

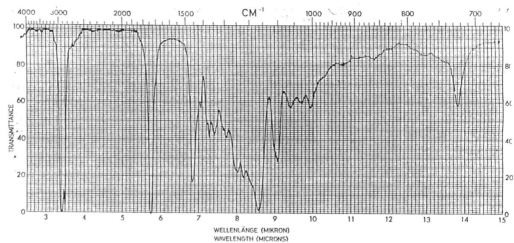

177 Octyl octanoate

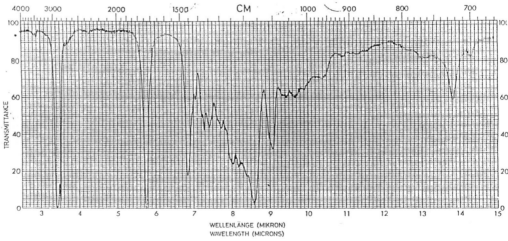

178 Nonyl octanoate

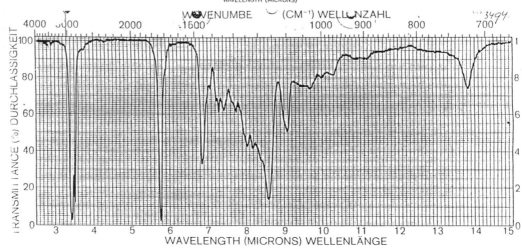

179   Methyl nonanoate

180   Methyl laurate

181   Butyl laurate

183   Methyl myristate

184   Butyl stearate

185   Methyl isobutyrate

186   Ethyl isobutyrate

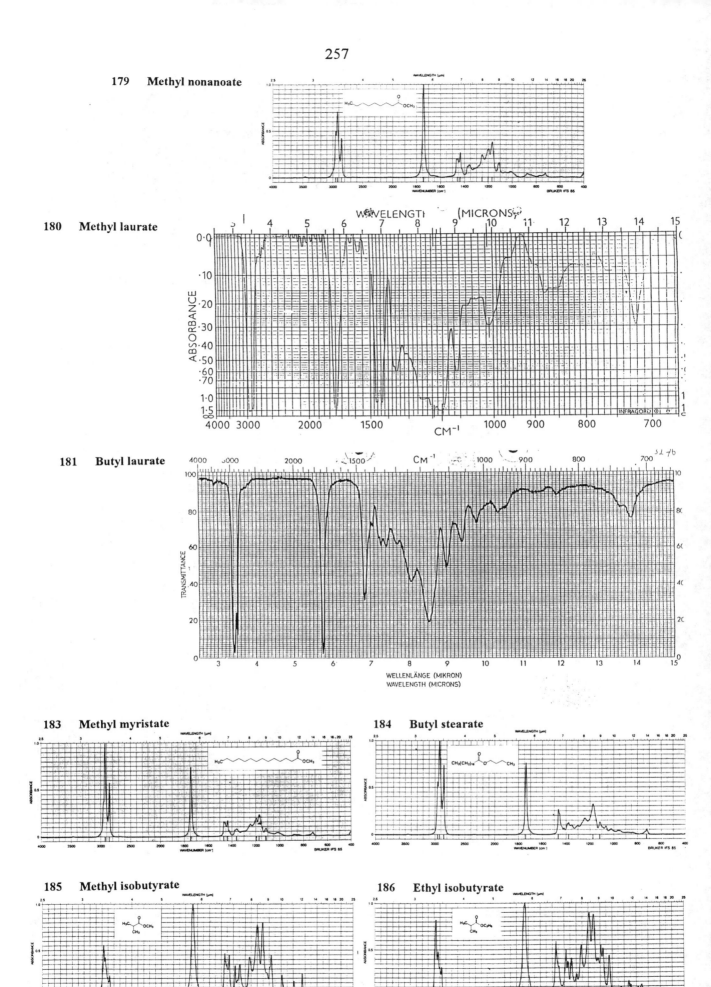

258

187   Propyl isobutyrate

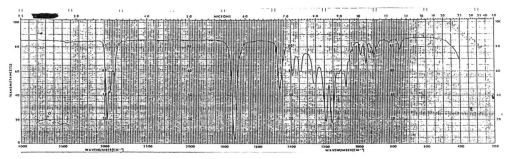

188   Butyl isobutyrate

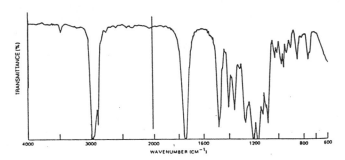

189   Hexyl isobutyrate

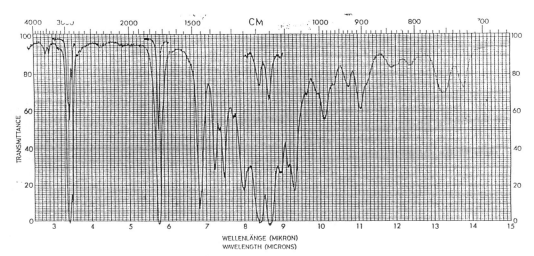

190   Heptyl isobutyrate

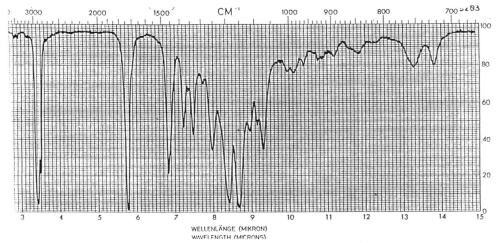

191   *trans-3*-Heptenyl 2-methylpropanoate

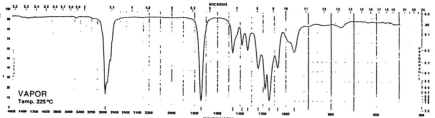

VAPOR
Temp. 225 °C

192 **Octyl isobutyrate**

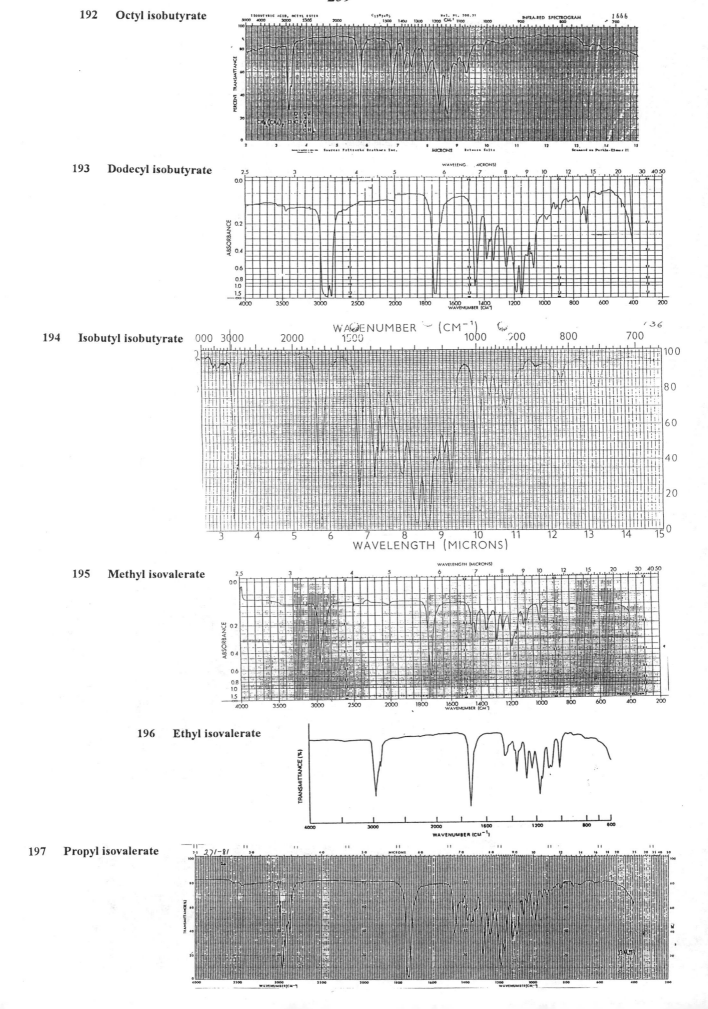

193 **Dodecyl isobutyrate**

194 **Isobutyl isobutyrate**

195 **Methyl isovalerate**

196 **Ethyl isovalerate**

197 **Propyl isovalerate**

198 Butyl isovalerate

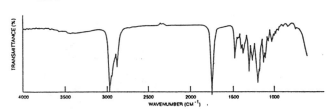

199 Hexyl 3-methylbutanoate

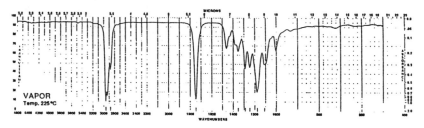

VAPOR
Temp. 225°C

200 Octyl isovalerate

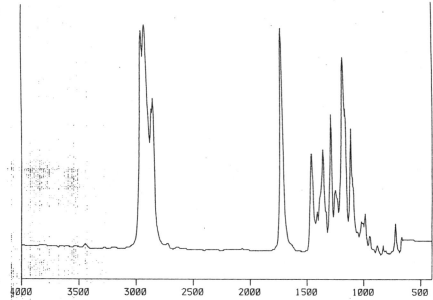

201 Nonyl isovalerate

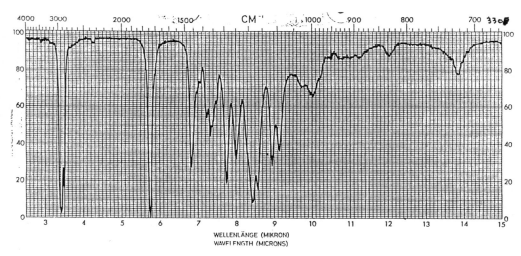

WELLENLÄNGE (MIKRON)
WAVELENGTH (MICRONS)

202 3-Hexenyl 3-methylbutanoate

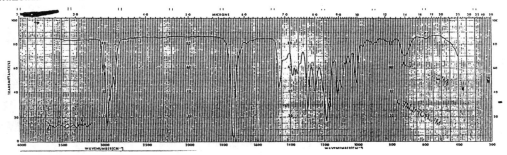

203   2-Methylpropyl 3-methylbutyrate

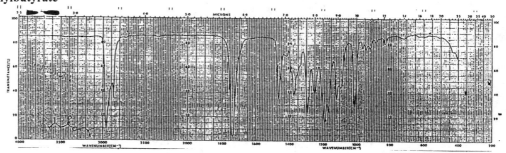

204   2-Methylbutyl 3-methylbutanoate

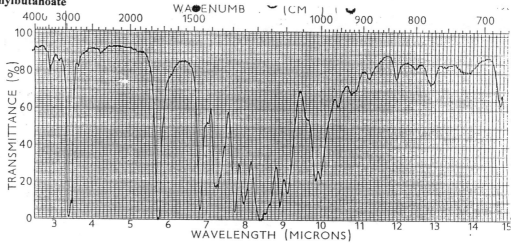

205   Methyl 2-methylbutyrate

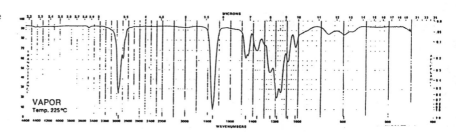

VAPOR
Temp. 225°C

206   Ethyl 2-methylbutyrate

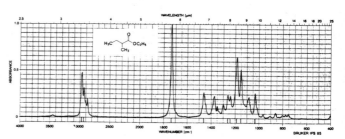

207   n-Butyl 2-methylbutyrate

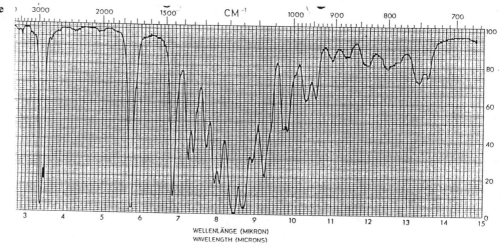

WELLENLÄNGE (MIKRON)
WAVELENGTH (MICRONS)

208   Hexyl 2-methylbutanoate

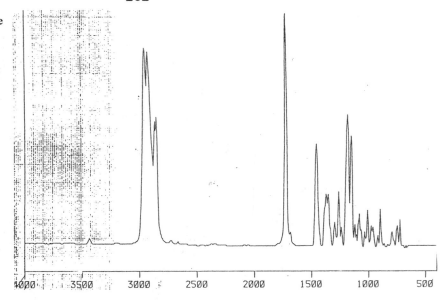

209   Octyl 2-methylbutyrate

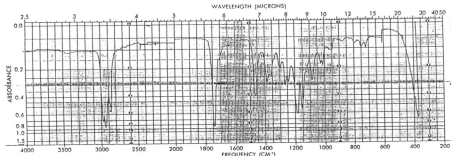

211   3-Hexenyl 2-methylbutanoate

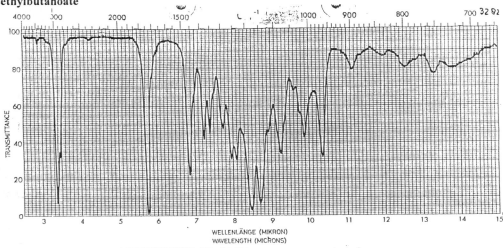

212   2-Methylbutyl 2-methylbutyrate

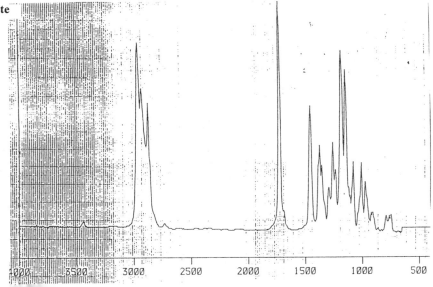

213   Methyl 2-methylpentanoate

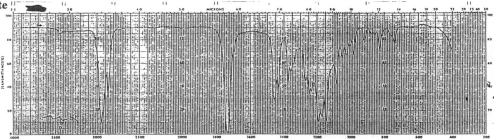

214   Ethyl 2-methylpentanoate

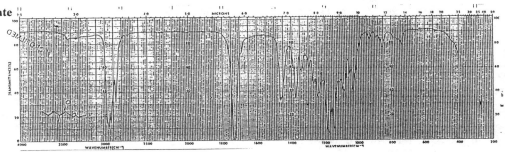

215   Ethyl 3-methylpentanoate

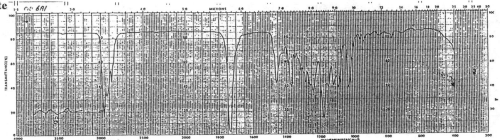

216   Methyl 4-methylvalerate

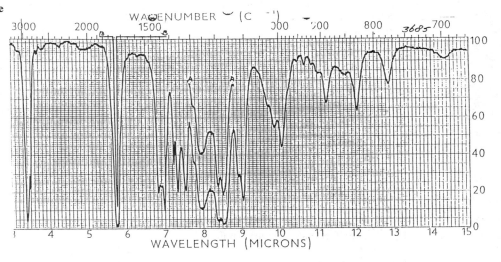

217   *trans*-Anethole

218   Citric acid

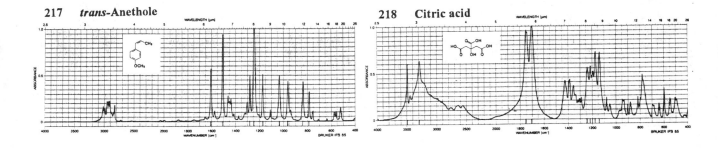

FAO TECHNICAL PAPERS

FAO FOOD AND NUTRITION PAPERS

Availability: November 1997

Ar – Arabic   Multil – Multilingual
C – Chinese   * Out of print
E – English   ** In preparation
F – French
P – Portuguese
S – Spanish

The FAO Technical Papers are available through the authorized FAO Sales Agents or directly from Sales and Marketing Group, FAO, Viale delle Terme di Caracalla, 00100 Rome, Italy.